SPC

Practical Understanding of Capability by Implementing Statistical Process Control,

third edition

By James C. Abbott

The *Walkabout*™ Series

Robert
Houston
Smith
Publishers

ROBERT HOUSTON SMITH PUBLISHERS
PO Box 2193
Easley, SC 29641-2193
888-747-6484 (telephone)
888-747-3291 (facsimile)
rhsp@mail.serve.com
www.bookzone.com/businessbooks

Cover design – Lightbourne Images
Content Advisor - Ron Parker
Production Manager - Kelly Boland
Graphic Design - Krista Spivey & Charles Hughey

Publisher's Cataloging-in-Publication
(Provided by Quality Books, Inc.)

Abbott, James C.
SPC : practical understanding of capability by implementing statistical process control / by James C. Abbott. -- 3rd ed.
p. cm. -- (Walkabout series)
Includes index.
LCCN: 98-89305
ISBN: 1-887355-03-0

1. Process control--Statistical methods. I. Title. II. Title: Statistical process control III. Title: Practical understanding of capability by implementing statistical process control IV. Series: Walkabout series (Easley, S.C.)

TS156.8.A22 1999 658.5'62'015195
QBI98-1660

Table Of Contents

This book is dedicated to the many outstanding teachers I have had over the years. Thanks goes to the faculties of Clarksville High School in Clarksville, Tennessee; Coffee High School in Florence, Alabama; and Auburn University in Auburn, Alabama.

I would especially like to thank Mr. Robert B. Sewell, my high school physics teacher at Coffee High School. Mr. Sewell instilled in me a lifelong desire to learn and use both science and mathematics in everyday practice.

Preface

This book is one part of the *Walkabout*™ series for managers of the future. The series is composed of:

- *Organize for the Ease of Doing Business*
- *Optimize your Operation: Stories, Tools, and Lessons for Using the Principles of Process Management to Improve Your Quality*
- *SPC: Practical Understanding of Capability by Implementing Statistical Process Control*

Organizations are changing dramatically; the last two decades has seen the pace of this change increase. Many companies are attempting to organize and run their business like it was three decades ago. New and more effective tools are required to keep up. These tools apply to both manufacturing and service organizations.

We view running a business, or an improvement process, like an expedition ascending a mountain to its summit. A mountain climbing expedition always meets roadblocks. The expedition requires certain essential elements to overcome these obstacles and so does the improvement process. The mountain climbing expedition's essentials include having the right equipment, access to the essentials of life (food, water, air), having a stable launch point, and properly trained team members. These essentials are referred to as the base-camp for a mountain climbing expedition and in our improvement process, a base-camp will also be required.

For improvement to occur, a base-camp of product and process knowledge must be built. This base-camp will include knowledge about each machine's strategic correctness -- its correct, consistent, and capable operation. A medium for communicating this knowledge is key. This medium must present the knowledge in a useable fashion -- one that is controllable and maintainable. The base-camp must be built in a predefined sequence. The first step is "correct," followed by "consistent," and finally "capable." These three functions must be done for every aspect of the business. This includes determining the correct, consistent, and capable running of each individual machine. Finally, the product and process knowledge must be used, and the brilliant execution of our knowledge base will lead to improvements.

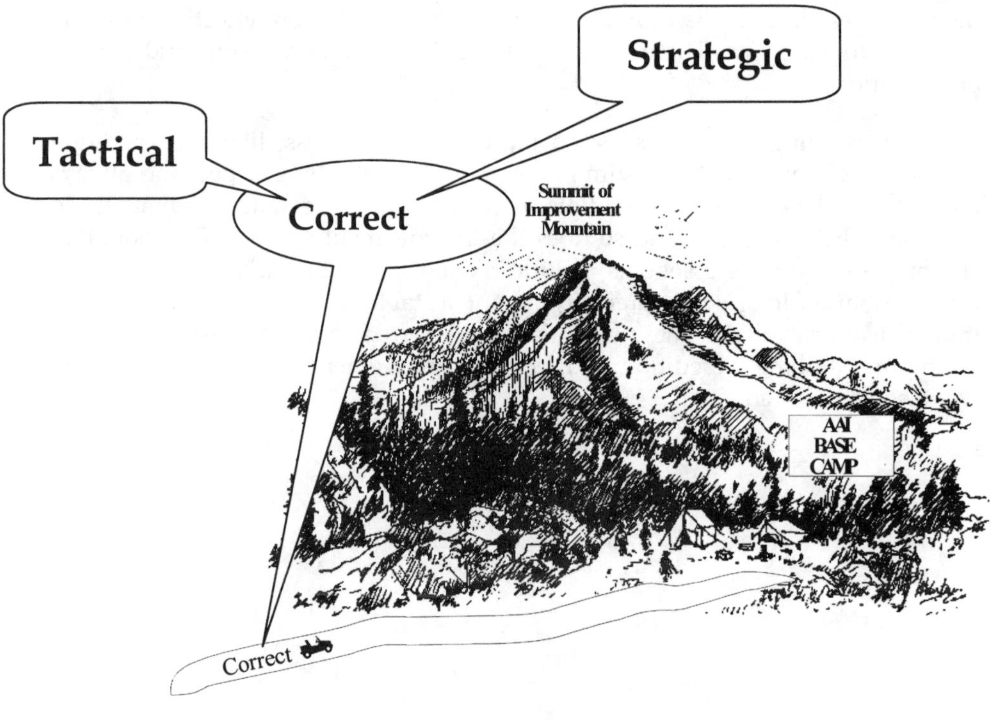

Now, let's look at each step in its prescribed order.

The first step in our journey to build the base-camp establishes correctness. This correctness is divided into strategic correctness and tactical correctness.

First the strategic correctness must be established. A correct, functional organization with clearly defined roles must be determined to cover marketing and sales, product design, process design, manufacturing, and quality assurance. The product and process factorial families must be correctly calculated. A clearly defined product and a detailed method must be created.

The tactical correctness is the optimization of the methods for each machine to run the product. This correct method must be communicated, and our tactical workforce must perfectly execute the plan.

Strategic Correctness

Organize for the Ease of Doing Business covers what functional roles are vital in every organization. A clear understanding of the product and process life cycle time reduction is fundamental. This cycle time reduction has impacted the speed at which we must learn how to make a product in order to remain competitive. Also, a clear understanding of the Division of Labor (strategies and tactics) is essential to organizational ease and the fundamental roles of all.

Tactical Correctness

Optimize Your Operation: explains the "what" and "how" of tactical correctness. This book explains the details and subtleties of the Principles of Process Management. For tactical execution and optimization the *Walkabout*™ Dependency Diagram and *Walkabout*™ Method are explained. These give a clear plan and structure for the optimization of your facility. This book explains the method for optimizing each machine to achieve tactical correctness.

The second step toward our base-camp is the monitoring of every metric for every machine to determine how consistent each product and process metric is. This consistency provides a way of predicting what will be produced time after time.

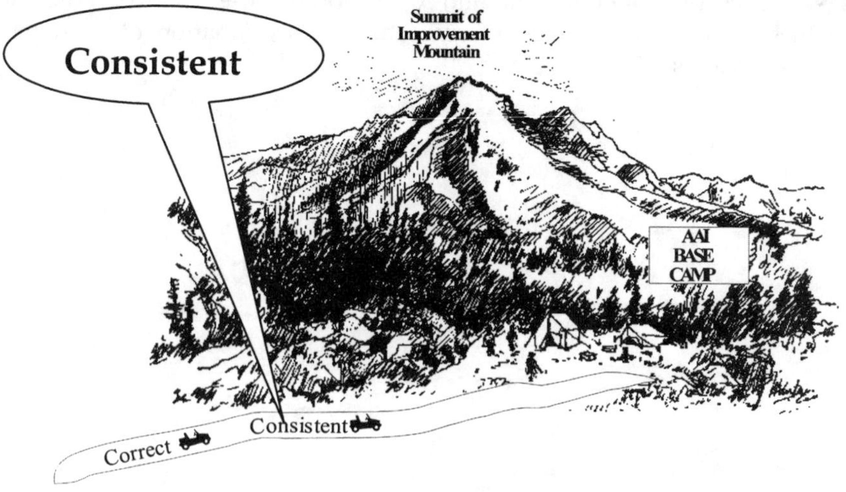

Finally, with the steps of correctly and consistently run machines or processes we are positioned to assess how well the product we make meets the customer's expectation.

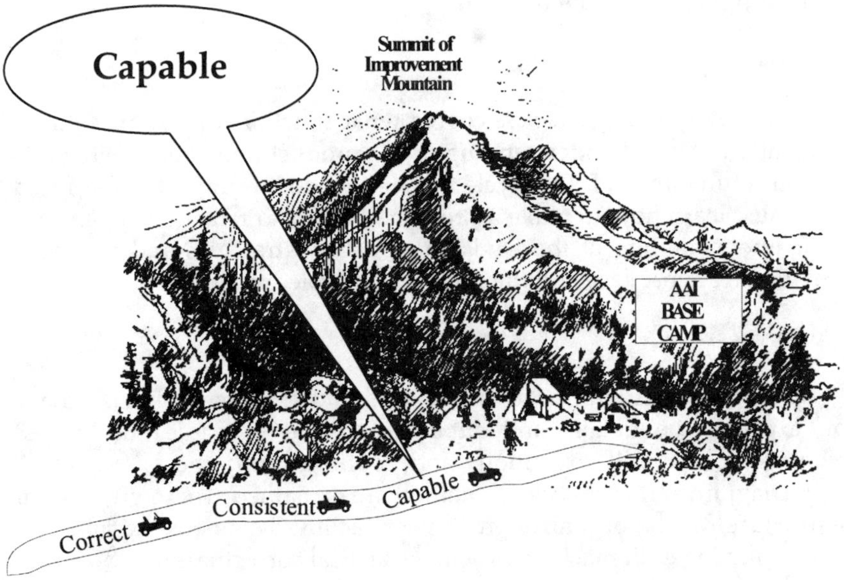

Consistency and Capability

The book *SPC: Practical Understanding of Capability by Implementing Statistical Process Control* deals with the latter two components of the base-camp: the consistent running of each machine, and an evaluation of the machine's capability. The correct organization and operation of the facility radically influence these topics. *SPC* gives a comprehensive explanation of both the theory and practical uses of SPC.

With a base-camp built our decision-makers are positioned in mass to make the ascension to the summit of Improvement Mountain. The *Walkabout*™ series explains the details of how we accomplish each step in our journey to build the base-camp.

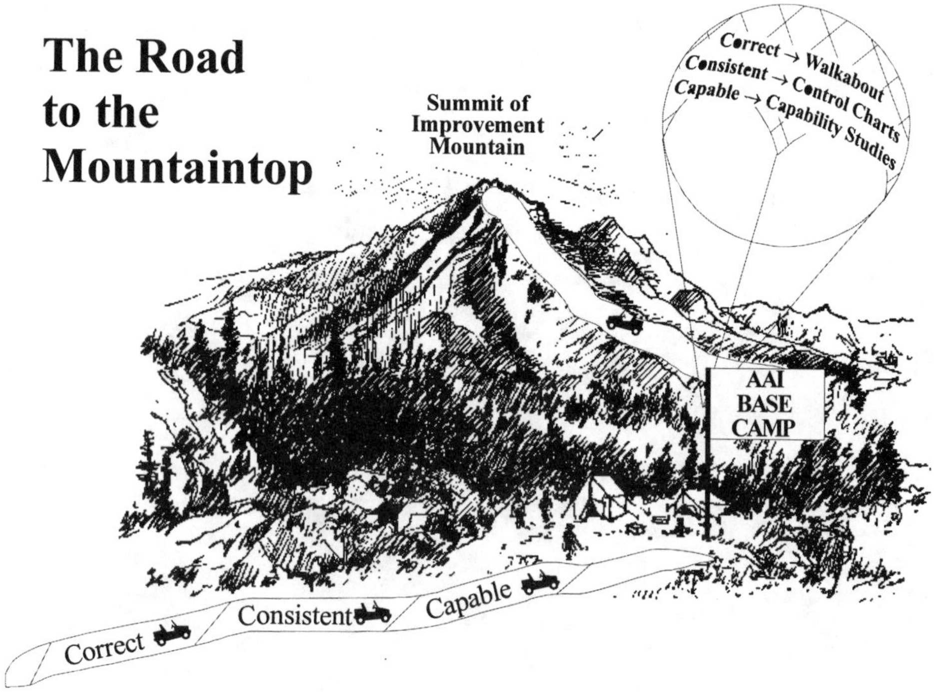

Introduction

In my business career, I have found many profound concepts, principles, techniques, and methods. This book, ***SPC: Practical Understanding of Capability by Implementing Statistical Process Control,*** includes all of these into one cohesive package.

SPC is much more than a simple mathematical tool. The math is intertwined with the concepts and principles. This book rigorously covers the math and as a bonus also covers the concepts, principles, techniques, and methods. Failure to have a complete grasp of all the components will lead to a deterioration of quality and cost, not just a stagnant situation.

SPC: Practical Understanding of Capability by Implementing Statistical Process Control is the most rigorous and thorough book on the topic of SPC. I have made the effort to be complete and thorough, but still understandable. Much time and effort has been expended to assure a book that will be helpful to everyone.

A key to understanding SPC is to understand both what to do and what not to do.

IDENTIFYING "GOOD INTENTIONS" ON THE ROAD TO QUALITY HELL

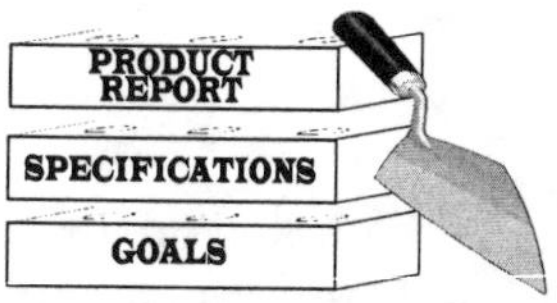

All stories and examples that are discussed in this book are true. Only the names, products, times, and places have been changed to protect the innocent. As we cover the material, I will show you that many of our well-intentioned efforts wind up causing exactly the reverse of the result we want. Often they not only stand in the way of improvement but also cause our efforts to deteriorate. These are like lead bricks covered with gold paint: the golden bricks of good intentions that we think are going to help but actually do the reverse.

In this book, we will discuss the idea of **good intentions**. Everyone has heard the saying *"the road to hell is paved with good intentions."* The golden bricks that I will describe in this book are paving a road that leads to a horrible, fiery place - a place called Quality Hell.

Many times throughout this book, we will be at a fork in the road. One path at this fork is paved with the golden bricks of good intentions leading to Quality Hell. The other road is paved with the bricks of the Principles of Process Management and leads to productivity and quality improvement. We must assure that we have a clear picture of the correct road so that we can plot a course to productivity and improvement.

Good intentions that put bricks on the road to Quality Hell (flawed logic and questionable input for decisions) will be indicated with the Quality Hell icon to the left. We will also provide practical examples of these good intentions, along with some common sense advice to avoid these mistakes. Be sure to pay special attention to the golden bricks of good intentions that we will be pointing out.

WHAT IS QUALITY?

The goal of this book is to provide usable capability knowledge to continually improve while at the same time making our customers happy. What is acceptable and terrific today will be considered terrible tomorrow. Many people use a one-dimensional definition of quality that leads to a trouble zone. For example, by focusing on performance and totally ignoring cost, we risk escalating our cost to an unreasonable level as we try to solve performance problems by simply throwing money at them. To help us avoid this kind of trouble zone, we will develop a definition of quality to use throughout this book as a means of describing our objective for product and process improvement.

One of the biggest problems facing the statistics, analysis, and quality professions is a poor understanding of terms, words, phrases, and concepts. One major purpose of this text is to clarify all the terminology. We will stay technically accurate throughout the book. Let's start this discussion of terms by clarifying the word **quality**.

Quality can have many definitions. In Webster's *New World Dictionary*, quality is defined as: **Any of the features that make something what it is; its characteristic elements; attribute.**

Quality must be put into perspective for use by all associates. Then quality can become an attitude that will flow throughout an organization in a positive way. A positive approach to quality must be used to get the desired results. Let's see how the definition of quality needs to be expressed.

WHAT DO WE MEAN BY QUALITY?

Write your definition of quality on a blank sheet of paper. This will give us a tool to compare your individual impression with my own definition of quality.

Our definition of quality is much broader in scope and more precise than the classic quality definition that states that we simply exceed our customer's expectations. I will show how our broadened definition will keep us out of trouble.

In this book I use the following questions to guide us in our definition of quality:

- Who is our customer?
- What is the customer's intended purpose?
- What are the customer's alternatives?

Quality means more than simply meeting the customer's stated requirements. It means meeting or exceeding the customer's implied or perceived expectations as well. Adding one more element, our objective of quality expands to understanding the customer's use of our product. Therefore, the first dimension of quality is exceeding the customer's perceived expectation of our product.

To summarize:

- ***Quality is meeting or exceeding the customer's perceived expectations and requirements.***

Our definition of quality is not complete yet. We must also reduce our cost. For our product to remain competitive, we must assure that the cost of our product is continually dropping. This gives us many options for directing our monetary savings. We could increase profits, reduce price, increase market share, and invest in the future, to name a few. The second dimension of quality is the continuous reduction of our cost.

Adding this next dimension:

- ***Quality is meeting or exceeding the customer's perceived expectations and requirements while reducing cost.***

Still more must be delivered to truly make the customer happy. We must deliver the product to the customer when he wants it. Having a product at a competitive price but which we cannot deliver is disastrous to our quality. Not having any product is just as bad as having a defective product. The third dimension of quality is being able to supply our product when the customer wants it.

Finally, our summary definition is:

- ***Quality is meeting or exceeding the customer's perceived expectations and requirements while reducing cost and providing the product to the customer when he wants it.***

The three components we've discussed - **Performance, Cost, and Time** - define quality. This gives us a total definition of quality. Our principle concern is to always strive to provide the best value to the customer. The key word to describe the three dimensions of quality is **VALUE**. A product that is perceived as quality or value by one customer may not be by another. This variation from customer to customer is caused by different uses of the same product.

Many have the mistaken impression that production and quality are conflicting objectives. Nothing could be further from the truth. For us to have production, we must have quality. For us to have quality, we must have production and quantity. To achieve production and quality, we must meet the three quality objectives:

- performance (specifications and requirements)
- time (schedule)
- cost (budget and production).

With these three criteria, we have a clear target. We must now marshal our efforts to achieve the goal.

Many times I hear this question: "Do you want quantity or quality?"

> **Production:** The act or process of producing. The creation of utility. The making of goods available for human wants.

Production is often mistakenly defined as activity, the keeping of machines running, movement of goods from area to area, or the number of goods produced. Goods sent to the warehouse are not counted as production. The **only** correct time to count production is when we ship the goods the customer wants, and he pays us. The only answer to the question above, "Do you want quality or quantity?" is that we want both **quantity and quality**.

Clearly, our definition of quality is extremely broad and encompassing. According to that definition, quality is comprised of three components: performance, cost, and time. Our research, analysis, and decisions must support our goal of delighting our customer (performance), while reducing our cost (cost), and providing our product to our customers the moment they want it (time). We must view this goal as a never-ending journey that continues to improve all three components because no one component is more important than the others. All three must be viewed with equal importance and balance. This balance requires the business genius of the manager of the future.

CONTINUOUS IMPROVEMENT

Improvement requires a clear understanding of the quality objective. All associates must understand that our objective is to continually strive for improvement. This improvement demands that three functions be in place. The first is the philosophy of quality and improvement. Secondly, an objective assessment system must be in place to assure that our course is always directed toward improvement. Finally, execution is key to assure that we actually implement changes and achieve improvement.

Each one of these must be expanded and clearly understood. This book focuses on the objective assessment of a continuous process through Statistical Process

Control (SPC). SPC must be in the context of an overall improvement model to function as it was intended. Let's now discuss the improvement model.

Improvement Model: Many techniques have been used over the years, with varying degrees of success. I will explain how to put them together to generate improvement.

TQM: What we call Total Quality Management (TQM) is called many other things by many other people. One name is "continuous improvement," which is defined as an ongoing effort for improvement. The Japanese refer to this effort as "Kaizen." For us to improve, we must have change, but all change is not improvement. Sometimes we change and unintentionally cause deterioration. The focus of continuous improvement is continuous change.

SOP: Standard Operating Procedure (SOP) is a management style that forces all procedures and activities to be the same for all machines. No matter what the machines' differences, the SOPs are the same across all machines. This allows management to have complete control of all activities.

SOPs have functioned as management's security blanket to assure that we are running the facility based on a set, standard procedure. Since all machines are somewhat different and the SOPs have remained the same, all machines are forced to run incorrectly. SOPs discourage change and creativity in order to achieve management simplicity. SOPs are designed to avoid deviation (change) and force the status quo. By following this SOP style, all machines are run inefficiently instead of at their optimum level.

The two modes of operation, TQM and SOP, are in conflict. SOP discourages change, while TQM encourages change. Since both modes have very positive aspects, a resolution to this conflict is required.

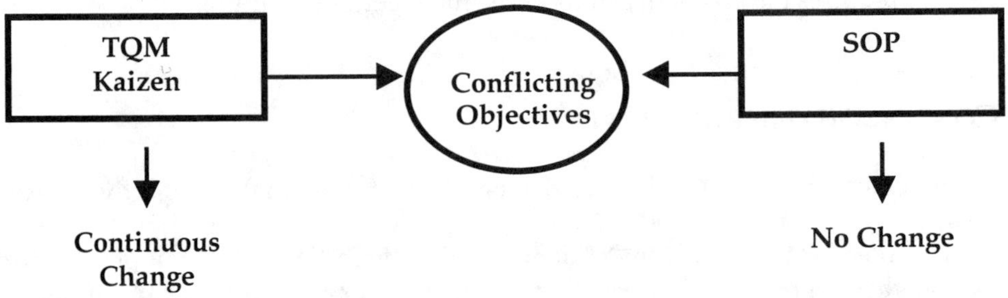

Conflict of TQM and SOP: TQM encourages change. SOPs detest change. TQM encourages the very thing SOPs detest. Therefore, TQM and SOPs are in direct conflict.

Monitoring a Continuous Process

Conflicting Objectives

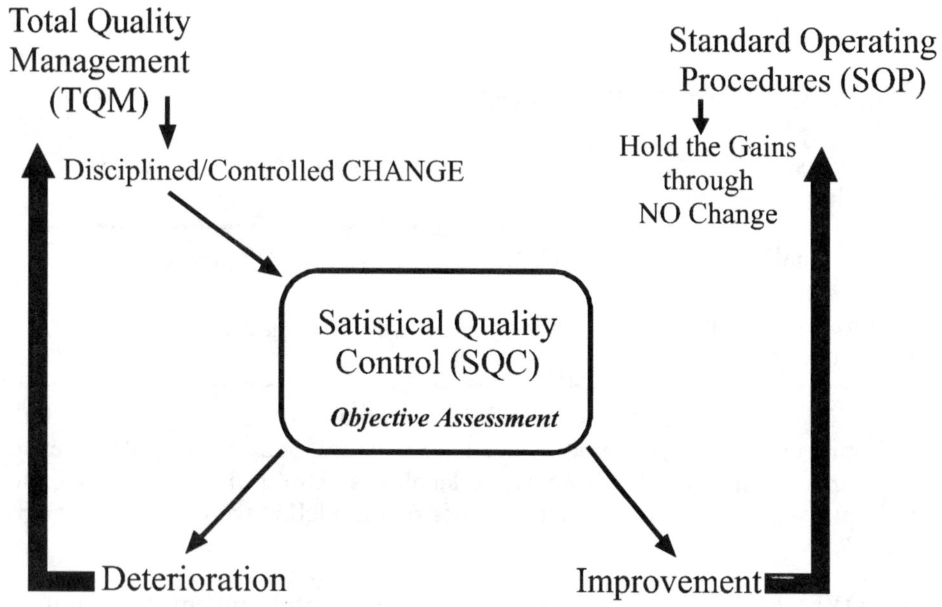

CONFLICT RESOLUTION

We must resolve the conflict between SOPs and TQM in an objective manner. What is required is an objective means of assessing all change. These assessments must be immediate and real-time. Changes that result in deterioration are stopped. Changes that bring improvements are incorporated into a revised SOP for a machine. The technique of systematically assessing and incorporating change is called Statistical Quality Control (SQC).

We all know that because people have individual personalities and differences, each person must be treated with his unique traits in mind in order for him to achieve the most he can be. Interestingly, machines are somewhat like people because each machine is different. Even machines that are produced by the same vendor on the same day will have differences. Because we do not expect all machines to be identical (just as all people are not the same), we need to have a distinct SOP for each individual machine and process. SOPs must be targeted to each individual machine.

The previous illustration shows how a TQM or continuous improvement model must be constructed. For TQM to perform correctly, we must incorporate the idea of Standard Operating Procedures (SOPs). The classic SOP is a static tool that is seldom used and infrequently updated. To be effective, SOPs must be used on the shop floor and continually updated to reflect our changing world.

In **Chapter Four**, we will explain the SPC structure required to make the improvement model work.

IMPROVEMENT MODEL SUMMARY:

When we seek to improve our business, we are presented with two basic approaches:

Total Quality Management (TQM), often referred to as continuous improvement, or KAIZEN, is always striving for change.	**Standard Operating Procedure (SOP)** in the classic sense is always attempting to never have change.

As we discussed earlier, the TQM and SOP approaches are always in conflict. The improvement model component called Statistical Quality Control strives to resolve this conflict. Use of this new model allows us to dramatically accelerate our improvement process. We will discuss this model as we progress through the book.

IMPROVEMENT is the watchword of the day, but for improvement to occur, a clear understanding of our product and process capability is essential. The tool to study and assess the capability of a continuous process is Statistical Process Control (SPC). This book will show all the subtleties, pitfalls, and benefits associated with using SPC in capability studies.

CONTROL

The word control is often misused and confused, so clarifying this term is critical to understanding our objectives.

Control: A mechanism used to regulate or guide the operation of a machine, apparatus, or system.

The words **consistency** and **predictability** are synonyms for the word **control**. Consistent means "repeatable and about the same." Predictable means "expected; able to be foretold." Keep these words close at hand for use in explaining the word control because when we can repeat an action and know what to expect, we can run (control) a machine better.

The traditional quality assurance department's role is to guarantee that only good product is received by the customer. The purpose of quality assurance is to ensure that the manufactured lots containing excessive defective items are not shipped to the customer.

Quality control has a much broader role in avoiding deterioration in the product and also continually searching for improvements to the product. Quality control's role thus is a preventive effort.

Quality professionals have taken the lead in pushing the use of the analysis tool called Statistical Process Control. The lead is positive and good, but SPC has received an image of being only the quality control department's tool. Actually, SPC was designed for use by both operations and management.

A clear understanding of the Principles of Process Management is mandatory to everything we will do. The first Principle of Process Management plays a crucial role in product improvement.

FIRST PRINCIPLE OF PROCESS MANAGEMENT

A fundamental understanding of BOTH the product and process is essential to improvement. Both the product and the process must be described and understood individually and separately. The underlying component for improving the product is the process.

There are two broad areas in which we should collect data. These areas are product and process. In general, it helps to have data from each area.

A product is...

- **Noun**
- **Result**

When we are discussing products, we are focusing on the result of our activities. The product is always a noun.

Product

A process is...

- **Verb**
- **Activity**
- **Something that builds the product**

Process discussions are focused on the activities that build the product. The process is always a verb.

Process

THE IMPORTANCE OF PROCESS DATA

When we just monitor the product, we are only aware of its deterioration or improvement. This awareness of the change in the product does not give us a reason for the change. Thus, product monitoring is important, but it:

- Is reactionary.
- Tolerates waste with no understanding of why.
- Accepts improvement with no understanding of why.

In my book *Optimize Your Operation,* I told the story of my mother learning the art of biscuit-making from my grandmother. Since Grandma was an accomplished biscuit chef but my mother was not, the knowledge transfer was very difficult. Without the proper analysis tools used in the correct areas, Mama burned many biscuits and the baking knowledge was never transferred. My story showed how improper focus keeps us from making improvement.

WITHOUT KNOWLEDGE OF "WHY," WE CANNOT IMPROVE

For us to make Grandma's biscuits, we must understand why things occur the way they do. Product information gives no insight into why we made some good biscuits or why we burnt other biscuits. Since we don't know why we are making good biscuits, we cannot repeat the activities that produced them. **This loss of knowledge is tragic.**

When we monitor the process and the product, the process parameters allow us to know the conditions that caused the change. Monitoring both product and process is essential for:

- Proactive decision-making
- Improvements
- Elimination of waste
- Understanding the "why's" of change

THE KNOWLEDGE OF "WHY" ALLOWS US TO IMPROVE CONTINUOUSLY

By adding knowledge about the activities required to make a biscuit (process or oven), we begin to learn what is required to make good biscuits. The additional information about the different processes that were used for good biscuits and defective biscuits allows us to continue to repeat the improvements and to discontinue the defects.

In the perfect world of my grandmother and her biscuits, I never saw her check the biscuits when she removed them from the oven. Instead, she kept her focus on the process. Since she knew all the subtleties of baking, she would take corrective action as the oven was cooking the biscuits so that, in a proactive manner, she avoided ever making any burnt biscuits. She was a perfect chef; unfortunately, most of us are not perfect chefs of our processes.

Since we live in a not-so-perfect world, and our knowledge of our process is not nearly as complete as my grandmother's was about her oven, we must continue to monitor both our biscuits and our oven with equal intensity. More precisely, we must monitor **both** process and product.

Our goal is to use Statistical Process Control to make economical decisions about actions on the process in order to improve the product.

WHAT IS STATISTICAL QUALITY CONTROL?

We need to understand that Statistical Quality Control (SQC) is the major umbrella that all the statistical tools fall under. Statistical Quality Control is really the toolbox of all our analytical tools.

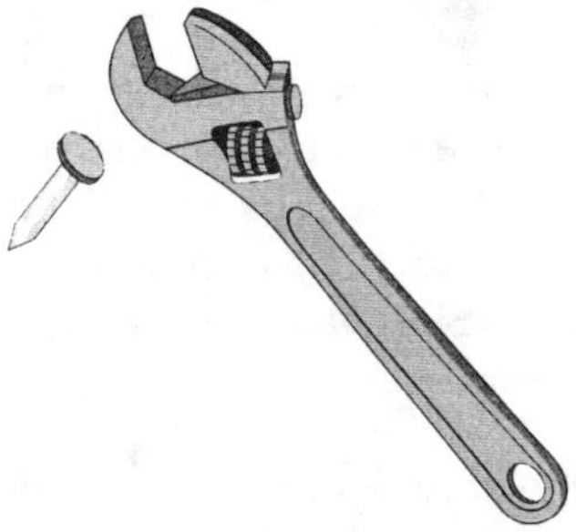

A toolbox that we use in our home holds a variety of tools. A hammer is intended to put nails in a wall. A saw is intended to cut wood. A wrench will tighten and loosen nuts from bolts. We could use a hammer to attempt to remove a bolt, but how effective would this tool (the hammer) be at this job? You can easily see how foolish it is to use the wrong tool for the job. Each tool is intended for a particular function and a particular set of problems. As we understand the problems, we will learn which tools are appropriate and how each works. Then we will see how to apply the appropriate tool to each problem. The chart below shows the many tools found in the SQC toolbox.

OBJECTIVE ASSESSMENT

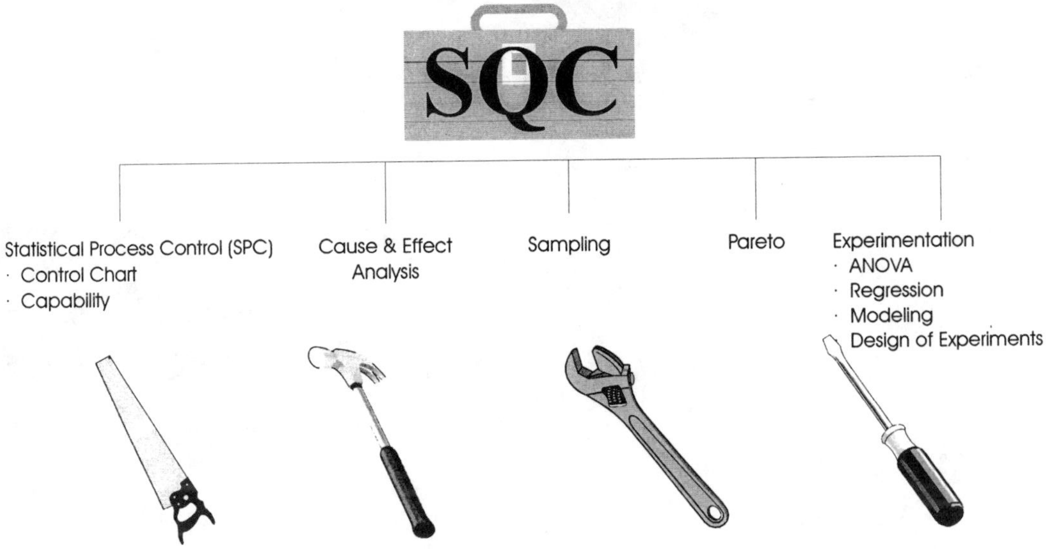

SQC AS THE ASSESSMENT TOOL

Many books on preparing information, reports, or statistics focus all of their attention on the analytical tools. Our purpose here is to preserve the classic approach while adding focus on the specific situations we will encounter. For each situation, we will examine the specific tools that can be used. Once the appropriate tool has been identified for each situation, we can begin to learn about the tool. Each analytical tool was devised for a particular situation or problem. The following is a quick overview of those situations:

Monitoring of a Continuous Process • Machines • Product or Process Consistency • Noting Changes • Assessing Capability	**Process and Product Optimization** • R & D • Ongoing Facility • Minimum Tests • Optimum Parameter Settings
Snapshots of a Moment of Knowledge • Receipt of Shipment • Shipping of Product • Determining Appropriate Test or Sample Sizes • Polling • Surveys	**Analysis of Continuous Data** • Process Parameter Optimization • Relationships
Comparative Group Analysis • Groups • Machines or Machine types • Departments or Divisions • Laboratories • Vendors • Management Reports	**Focusing Your Staff's Time and Tasks** • Task Dependency • Critical Task • Task Priorities • Critical Resources

This book will focus on **monitoring a continuous process** through the use of Statistical Process Control. The next section begins our effort to select the correct analytical tool. We will discuss the situation, describe the analytical tool for the situation, and suggest study areas. This book's objective is to explain the SQC component called Statistical Process Control (SPC - control charts and capability studies). The Statistical Process Control tools will focus on the quality dimensions of performance and cost.

Looking back at the many situations described above, SPC is a razor sharp tool to monitor:

A Continuous Process - Machines, systems, operations
- Product or Process Consistency
- Detection and Notation of Changes
- Assessment of Capability

BALANCED RISKS

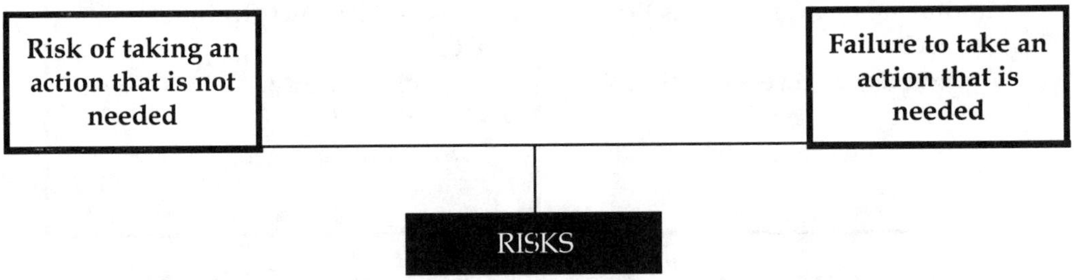

All decisions have risk. Statistical Process Control provides a means of reducing the unknown so as to minimize that risk. The focus of SPC is to provide the base-camp components of consistency and capability knowledge for each product and process.

STATISTICAL PROCESS CONTROL IS A SPECIALIZED TOOL

Just as a saw from our household toolbox has specific uses, the SPC components (control charts and capability studies) are the objective assessment tools for a continuous operation. The control chart detects any changes in the continuous process. Once a change is detected, the capability study is used to assess the impact to the customer.

We must make sure SPC is used for the right situation. Using a great tool for the wrong job can lead to terrible results. If a saw is used to put a nail in the wall, the saw will become dull and the nail will not be solidly in the wall. SPC, in like manner, must be used in the correct situation to get proper results.

Since change can be either an improvement or deterioration, capability studies and control charts must work as a team. The details and subtleties of SPC and the relation of control charts and capability studies to one another will be explained later. The control chart is our detection tool for change while the capability study assesses the impact of the change.

Monitoring a Continuous Process

Conflicting Objectives

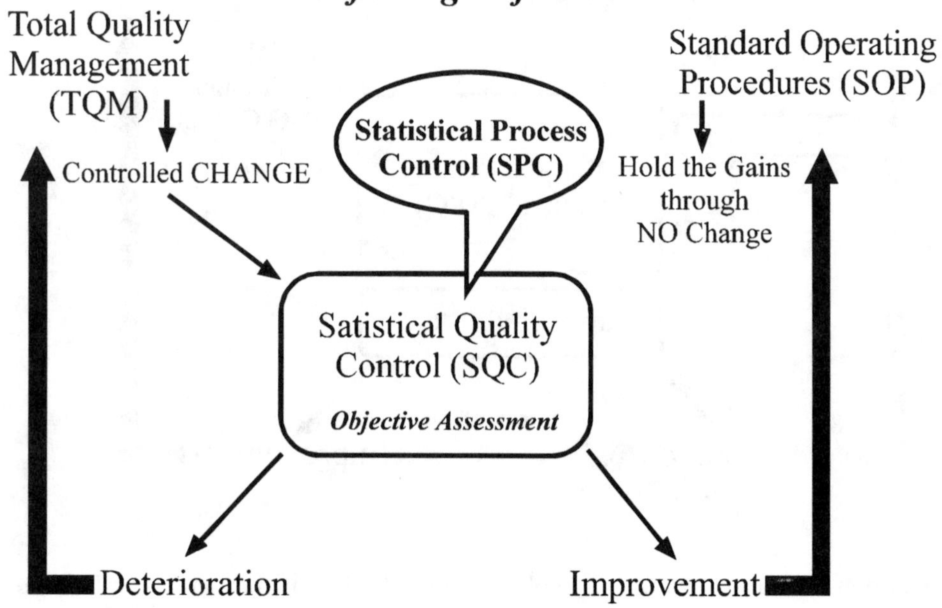

Monitoring a Continuous Process

Conflicting Objectives

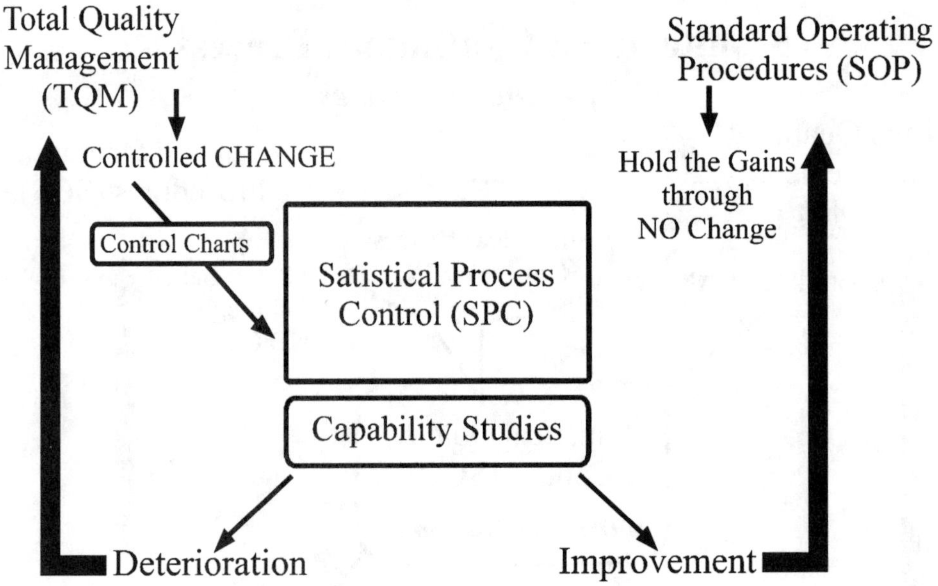

Chapter One and **Two** of this book will cover basic statistics. The third chapter covers proper grouping of our data to arrive at good information. The fourth chapter explains the general SPC components of control charts and capability studies. **Chapter Five** explains where we get started, **Chapter Six** through **Chapter Nine** explains the construction, use, and interpretation of control charts, and **Chapter Ten** explains capability studies.

Let's start our journey into SPC by now learning basic statistics.

Chapter One:
Basic Statistics

What is STATISTICS? The dictionary states that statistics are 1) facts or data of a numerical kind, assembled, classified, and tabulated so as to present significant information about a given subject. 2) The science of assembling, classifying, tabulating, and analyzing such facts or data.

Researchers, analysts, and anyone studying numbers require a common communication language. Statistics is that common language.

Statistics is comprised of a set of tools used to prepare meaningful information. The purpose of this chapter is to present some statistical tools of practical value. Our first look at statistics will help us to understand the tools called point estimates. Statistics is the informational eyes of the decision-maker. Since we must make decisions in the face of uncertainty, statistics offers the tools to assist in these situations.

Our objective must always be to provide as clear a picture of the data as possible while also keeping our volume of numbers as low as possible. To assure that we never present improper information, we must identify the proper statistical procedures and the areas that will cause our information to be flawed.

REPORT AND ANALYSIS FLAWS

The objective of analysis is an increased knowledge base. The analysis of our data provides the cohesion to build the strategies and tactics that will drive our improvement. It must always be done with clear guidelines so that we will avoid any tainted results. The product of our analysis is a knowledge base.

It is not enough to simply trace the history of events. Our analysis also must uncover the causes of the effects. Since an effect is not caused by simply one item, our analysis must continuously strive to uncover more and more of the causes and how much of the effect can be assigned to one cause.

The analysis must endeavor to uncover the who, what, where, and when of the cause that is driving the effect. This is not a one time effort but a continuing and on going search to increase our knowledge base. We must clearly understand and adhere to the science of how to analyze the who, what, where, and when so that we avoid any improper or inappropriate information that might drive us to make improper decisions.

MANAGEMENT REPORTING FLAWS

Our objective is to assure that we understand the potential flaws of improperly prepared data. In order to avoid these costly mistakes, we must have a clear set of guidelines so that we can prepare information that allows us to make accurate and intelligent decisions. The following are the two major statistical reporting flaws:

Flaw 1 - Improper Technique
We must understand and use proper techniques while we avoid the mistakes that can be caused by using improper techniques.

Technique: The systematic procedure by which a complex or scientific task is accomplished.

Statistics brings to us the consistent and common language of correctly preparing our numbers with proper technique.

Flaw 2 – Improper Grouping
Grouping can lead to a different set of problems. These problems must be clearly understood so that all of our studies will use the proper groups.

Grouping: 1. A number of individuals or things considered together because of similarities. 2. A class or collection of related objects or entities

The efforts involved in the assurance that we are properly grouping are an integral part of statistical analysis.

Reports are used often to show when things are bad. Being a child of the 50s, I grew up watching TV. One of my favorite programs was "Dragnet." The main character was Joe Friday played by Jack Webb. His watchword and the theme of the program were always "Just the Facts Ma'am." We need to pattern ourselves after Joe Friday, neither looking for Good nor Bad, but always looking for the facts.

This chapter will explain proper statistical technique while **Chapter Three** will clarify the need for and types of grouping required for proper information to be presented.

Our first analytical study will revolve around a common problem. We will analyze the electricity usage for my household. The table below shows the household kilowatt consumption of my house for the years 1980, 1981, 1982, and part of the year 1983.

For statistics to work effectively, a clear objective must be stated. Therefore, the information gained from this study will be used to plan a household budget so that enough funds may be set aside to pay for the electricity consumed.

ELECTRICITY USAGE

	1980	1981	1982	1983
JANUARY	2749	4081	4982	3936
FEBRUARY	5405	5004	4299	5024
MARCH	3936	2708	3793	3239
APRIL	2232	2423	1870	
MAY	1079	1493	1514	
JUNE	1330	2197	1713	
JULY	2616	2918	1890	
AUGUST	2820	2041	1897	
SEPTEMBER	2321	2041	1923	
OCTOBER	1583	1494	1316	
NOVEMBER	1877	1859	1843	
DECEMBER	3439	3936	2919	

These values represent the kilowatt consumption for our house.

FORMULAS

In mathematics, a clear way to communicate our calculations is required, and this communication is achieved through the use of formulas. A formula calculates a value based on numbers mathematically computed. In this book, all formulas will contain variables to compute the value. The symbols for the mathematical operations that will be used in this book are listed below:

( ) order of operations

*** multiplication**

/ division

+ addition

- subtraction

Raising to a power means multiplying the number by itself a given number of times.

$$X * X = X^2$$

Taking a root is the reverse of the power-raising process.

$$\sqrt{X^2} = X \qquad \sqrt[3]{X^3} = X$$

The square root of 4 is 2, or $\sqrt{4}$, while the cube root of 8 is also 2, or $\sqrt[3]{8}$.

Summation of a set of numbers can be expressed several ways. The simplest is to write the complete expression. For our example we will total the 1980 kilowatt consumption. Each month - January through December - will be represented using the summation symbol. The use of three dots indicates the repeating of the pattern until the signified value is reached.

$$\text{Total KWH consumption} = X_{Jan} + X_{Feb} + X_{Mar} + \ldots + X_{Dec}$$

This expression can be rewritten as a more general equation:

$$\text{Total KWH consumption} = X_1 + X_2 + X_3 + \ldots + X_N$$

where N equals the last data point.

The Greek symbol sigma, shown below, is the symbol used to identify the summation of a series of numbers. The formula below is the same equation as the simpler version above. This i=1 identifies the starting point while N denotes the ending point. The X_i is the equation to be totaled.

$$\sum_{i=1}^{N} X_i$$

where N is the last data point.

The above equation can be used rather than writing out the complete expression like the first method.

Let's see how to put our math to use in statistics. Proper statistical technique requires the monitoring of three components: central tendency, variability, and distribution. Each component must be understood and used correctly. Our first tool will monitor the data's central tendency or balance point.

WHAT IS BALANCE?

When we were children, we used to play on a seesaw or teeter-totter. One of the main things we tried to do was get the seesaw to balance two people on opposite ends of a board. The spot the board rests on is called the fulcrum.

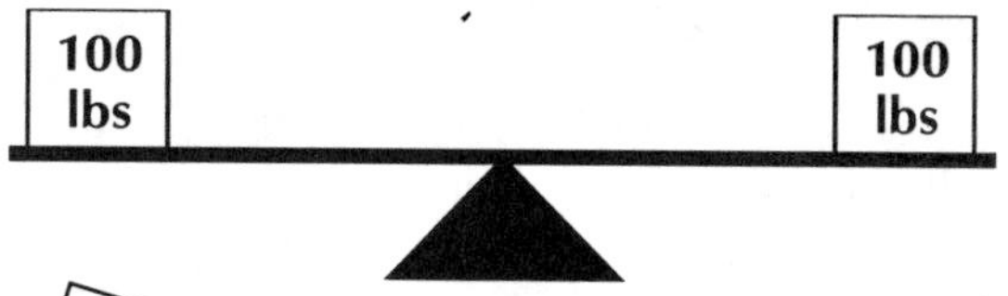

When both sides weigh equal amounts, the fulcrum is positioned in the center.

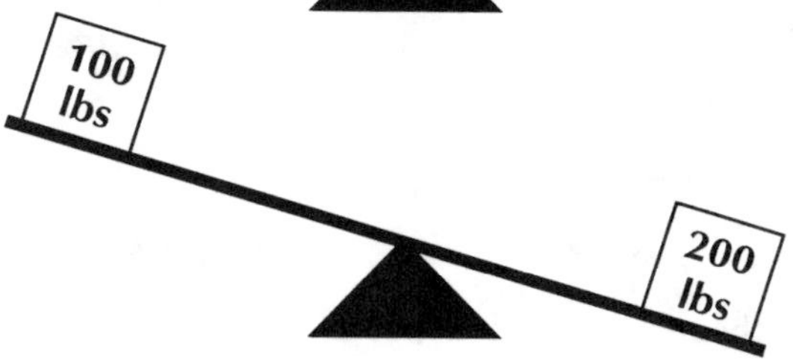

When one side weighs more than the other, the board will tilt toward the side of the heavier weight.

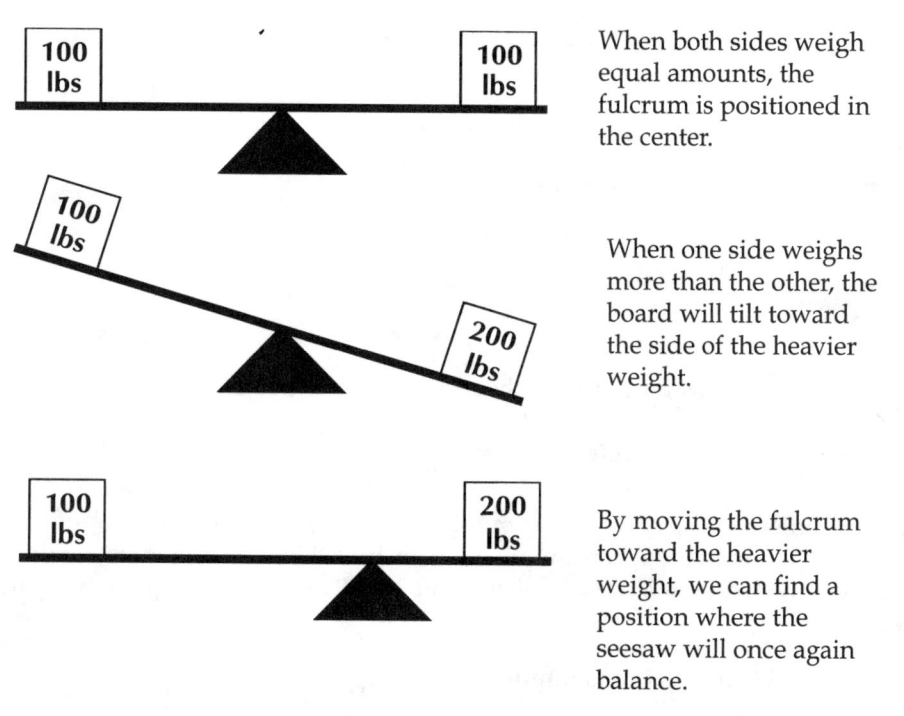

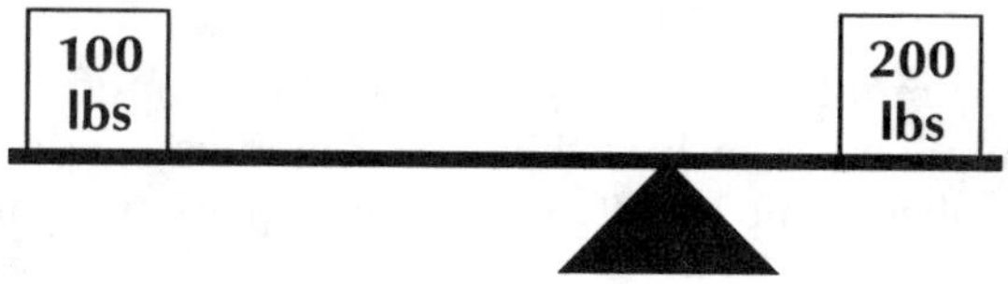

By moving the fulcrum toward the heavier weight, we can find a position where the seesaw will once again balance.

This balance point is critical information in many fields like physics and mechanical engineering. Knowledge about balance associated with numeric measurements is essential to statistics. The balance point of is called central tendency.

CENTRAL TENDENCY

Since central tendency is critical to understanding our numeric measurements, monitors of it must be established. Our first monitor of central tendency is average. Average is a point estimate of the measurement of the central tendency of our data. Average is a statistical tool to monitor the central tendency and is referred to as mean, arithmetic mean, and simply - average. All the different names are describing the same monitor. Average is the balance point of all the data points giving equal weight to each value.

AVERAGE

Average divides the sum of the measurements by the number of measurements. The average monitors central tendency.

The algebraic expression for average is shown next:

$$\frac{X_1 + X_2 + X_3 + \ldots X_N}{N}$$

where N equals the number of data points.

The equation can also be written as follows:

$$\frac{\sum_{i=1}^{N} X_i}{N}$$

where N equals the number of data points.

The average may also be referred to as: X_{Ave} **or** $\overline{X}$.

For our earlier electricity data, to compute the average kilowatt consumption for the year 1980, individual consumption for each of the twelve months is added and then divided by the total number of months (twelve). The equation would read:

$$\textbf{Total KWH consumption} = X_{Jan} + X_{Feb} + X_{Mar} + \ldots + X_{Dec}$$

$$= 2{,}749 + 5{,}405 + 3{,}936 + \ldots + 3{,}439$$

$$= 31{,}387$$

The 1980 total KWH consumed is 31,387 which is then divided by 12 to arrive at the average which is 2616 Kilowatt hours.

$$= \frac{X_{Jan} + X_{Feb} + X_{Mar} + \ldots + X_{Dec}}{12}$$

$$= \frac{2{,}749 + 5{,}405 + 3{,}934 + \ldots + 3{,}439}{12}$$

$$= \frac{31{,}387}{12}$$

$$= 2{,}616$$

The following chart shows how the average is representing the central tendency of our household power data for 1980.

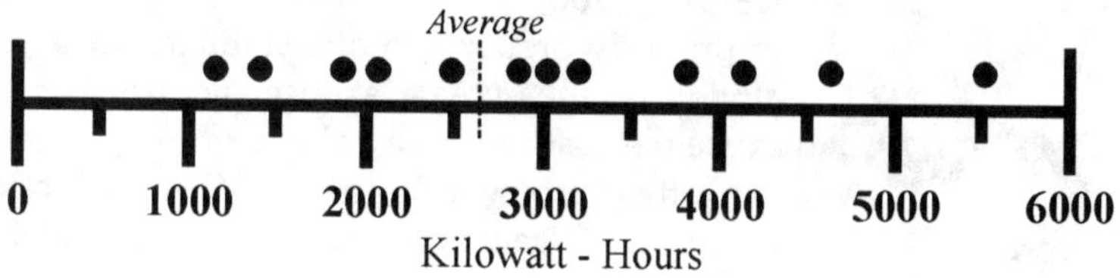

Note how clearly the average shows the center point of our electricity consumption.

Never use average as a stand alone measure of a set of values!! Central tendency should not be discussed without a companion monitor of variability.

MISLEADING AVERAGES

Motel Location	A	B	C
Greenville, SC	25	25	10
Charlotte, NC	27	25	15
Atlanta, GA	24	25	20
Birmingham, AL	25	25	25
Nashville, TN	26	25	20
Indianapolis, IN	26	25	15
Louisville, KY	24	25	10
Lexington, KY	23	2	25
Cincinnati, OH	24	25	35
Columbus, OH	26	25	15
Denver, CO	27	25	40
Las Vegas, NV	23	25	35
Dallas, TX	25	25	30
Los Angeles, Ca	25	25	25
San Francisco, CA	24	56	30
Newark, NJ	26	25	35
Toledo, OH	25	25	40
Average	$25	$25	$25

The three sets of data to the left are intended to demonstrate that simply looking at an average can give an erroneous impression.

Suppose we are trying to compare the price point of three motel chains. Notice that all three of the motel chains wind up with exactly the same average of $25 per night, but all the values of the data set are radically different. The first set of values is relatively close to the average. The second set has two values extremely removed from all the other values. The third set has a widely dispersed set of values. The only common link between values is that they all have an average of $25.00

My family has convinced me that vacations can be a wonderful experience. We have planned and been on several vacations over the last several years. Imagine planning a vacation's sleeping room cost based on the previous improperly prepared motel statistics. The stand-alone averages create a false picture that could cause the cost to be way above our expected cost. An otherwise wonderful vacation is destroyed when our vacation money is exhausted. Statistics must provide a clear summary picture of our numbers. Improperly prepared statistical technique must be avoided to assure that these kinds of prediction mistakes are avoided.

We must always get a complete picture of our data. Nothing is wrong with the average - it simply shows only part of the picture.

ELECTRICITY USAGE

	1980	1981	1982	1983
JANUARY	2749	4081	4982	3936
FEBRUARY	5405	5004	4299	5024
MARCH	3936	2708	3793	3239
APRIL	2232	2423	1870	
MAY	1079	1493	1514	
JUNE	1330	2197	1713	
JULY	2616	2918	1890	
AUGUST	2820	2041	1897	
SEPTEMBER	2321	2041	1923	
OCTOBER	1583	1494	1316	
NOVEMBER	1877	1859	1843	
DECEMBER	3439	3936	2919	
Average	**2616**	**2???**	**????**	

2683 2497

Returning to our household kilowatt hour (KWH) consumption, the average is 2,616 KWH for the year of 1980.

SAMPLE PROBLEM

Compute the remaining yearly averages and make an interpretation of the results. The answer can be found in the "**Problem Solutions**" section of the **Appendix**.

Now let's expand our knowledge and add another statistical component that is needed to complement the average. This component is the amount or magnitude of spread associated with our measurements.

MAGNITUDE OF SPREAD

We have seen from the motel example that an average by itself can be very misleading. This would be like saying that all people who weigh the same amount look the same. As our illustration shows, the two individuals above are very different. One area of their difference is that one person has a spread and the other does not. If we were analyzing people's weights, we would want to make sure that we had an additional technique to monitor this spread. The magnitude of this spread can be crucial to our view of a person.

When we are doing statistical analysis, a technique for monitoring spread is required just as it is with a person's weight. The magnitude of this spread is vital just like it is in monitoring a person. The name for the magnitude of the spread is called variability. Next we will begin to discuss a series of techniques for monitoring variability or the magnitude of the spread.

VARIABILITY

We need to have a way of distinguishing the difference between the three sets of motels from the prior discussion. The means of doing this is called monitoring the variability. Our first technique for monitoring the variability of the measurements is by viewing the highest and lowest values of the data.

When using minimum and maximum, two values are always required. This can be reduced by using the distance between the maximum and minimum values.

This distance is called the range value. Sometimes the range is abbreviated and called the R value.

Range is a measure of the variability of a set of numbers. The smaller the range, the lower the variability, or the amount of spread.

Using the electricity data to compute the kilowatt consumption range for the year 1980, the high value of each month's consumption is 5,405 and the low value 1,079. The range for 1980 KWH consumption equals X_{Max} - X_{Min}. The values can then can be placed in the equation to compute the range, as shown below:

$$\text{Range} = X_{Max} - X_{Min}$$

$$= 5{,}405 - 1{,}079$$

$$= 4{,}326$$

Finally, the 1980 range KWH consumed of 4,326 kilowatts is computed. The chart below shows our monthly kilowatt hour consumption on a graph along with the average, maximum, minimum, and range values.

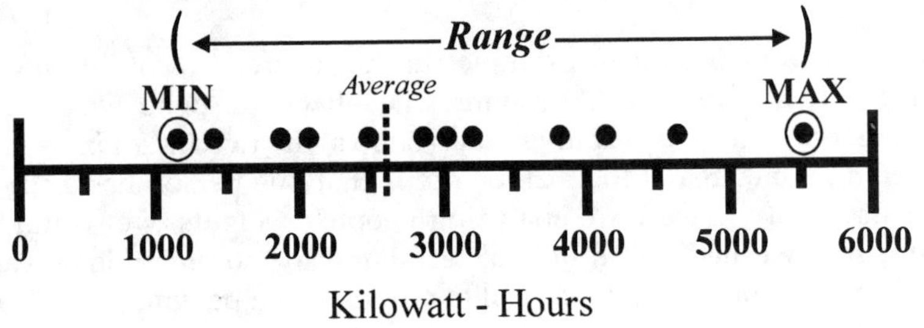

THE INTERPRETATION AND USE OF RANGE

As the range increases, the magnitude of the variability (spread) increases. Should the range be zero, all values are the same and the average is a perfect indicator of each data point. The larger the range, the more variable the data. As the range increases, the average becomes a less precise indicator of the actual values.

INTERPRETING RANGE

The three sets of data in the next chart demand some monitor of variability to clearly depict the different hotel chains.

Motel Location	A	B	C
Greenville, SC	25	25	10
Charlotte, NC	27	25	15
Atlanta, GA	24	25	20
Birmingham, AL	25	25	25
Nashville, TN	26	25	20
Indianapolis, IN	26	25	15
Louisville, KY	24	25	10
Lexington, KY	23	2	25
Cincinnati, OH	24	25	35
Columbus, OH	26	25	15
Denver, CO	27	25	40
Las Vegas, NV	23	25	35
Dallas, TX	25	25	30
Los Angeles, CA	25	25	25
San Francisco, CA	24	56	30
Newark, NJ	26	25	35
Toledo, OH	25	25	40
average	**$25**	**$25**	**$25**
Maximum	**$27**	**$56**	**$40**
Minimum	**$23**	**$2**	**$10**
Range	**$4**	**$54**	**$30**

By using range and average together, we can begin to understand the differences in the three sets of data. Chain A has a mean cost of $25 and a range of $4. This drives us to the conclusion that Chain A's rates are all close to the mean. Chain B has a mean cost of $25 and a range of $54. We would conclude that Chain B's rates are very widely spread. Chain C has a mean cost of $25 and a range of $30. We would conclude that Chain C's rates are also widely spread.

Since the range values for both Chain B and Chain C are both high values, we might conclude that both chains charge similar rates. We can see by analyzing the data, however, that the costs of both B and C are very different. Chain B has two very extreme values with the remaining rates all being equal to $25. All of Chain C's rates are extremely different. Therefore, the range value fails us in differentiating between these two motel chains.

We must always get a complete picture of our data. Nothing is wrong with the average, but it simply shows only part of the picture. To add more precision to our study, we must monitor both central tendency and variability together. Neither one can be used without the other.

Properly prepared statistical information can be a wonderful tool for estimates and predictions for all decision-making, including our vacation plans.

Now our family can anticipate a pleasant vacation because our statistics have been prepared with a more vivid picture that now includes both central tendency and variability. We must always be careful to follow proper statistical technique. Our plans now can be made with reliable and predictable results. Using this proper statistical technique, fun filled future vacations can be assured while avoiding the disaster of exceeding our planned vacation budget.

ELECTRICITY USAGE

	1980	1981	1982	1983
JANUARY	2749	4081	4982	3936
FEBRUARY	5405	5004	4299	5024
MARCH	3936	2708	3793	3239
APRIL	2232	2423	1870	
MAY	1079	1493	1514	
JUNE	1330	2197	1713	
JULY	2616	2918	1890	
AUGUST	2820	2041	1897	
SEPTEMBER	2321	2041	1923	
OCTOBER	1583	1494	1316	
NOVEMBER	1877	1859	1843	
DECEMBER	3439	3936	2919	
Average	**2,616**	**2,683**	**2,497**	**4,066**
Range	**4,326**	**3,511**	**3,666**	**1,785**

The kilowatt average and range now work together to allow us to begin to plan our future electricity needs.

The average for 1980 is 2,616 KWH with a range of 4,326 KWH. A range of this magnitude in relation to its average is quite large. Our conclusion would indicate that large swings from month to month should be anticipated if 1980 is representative of the future.

The year 1981 also has a large range of 3,511 KWH in relation to its average of 2,683 KWH; this reinforces our conclusion from the analysis of 1980. Similarly, 1982 has a large range of 3,666 KWH in relation to the average of 2,497.

Since 1983's KWH consumption is incomplete, no conclusion should be made from this year's data.

To increase our information about the spread of our data, a more advanced method of monitoring variability is required. This improved method should include all of our data.

AVERAGE RANGE

ELECTRICITY USAGE

	1980	Range
JANUARY	2749	133
FEBRUARY	5405	2789
MARCH	3936	1320
APRIL	2232	-384
MAY	1079	-1537
JUNE	1330	-1286
JULY	2616	0
AUGUST	2820	204
SEPTEMBER	2321	-295
OCTOBER	1583	-1033
NOVEMBER	1877	-739
DECEMBER	3439	823
SUM	31387	
AVG	2616	
Max	5405	
Min	1079	
Range	4326	

As an alternative to a simple range, we could possibly develop a range value for each data point. This could be accomplished by comparing each data point to the monitor of central tendency called average.

Range = Data Point - Average

$= X_i - X_{Ave}$

For the electricity used in 1980, we compute the range for January by taking the January value of 2,749 KWH and subtracting the 1980 average of 2,616 KWH. The result yields a positive 133 as in the table above.

The February range requires subtracting February's value of 5,405 KWH by the average of 2,616 KWH. The February range is a positive 2,789 KWH. This process is continued for each month. The shaded column in the table above shows the range value for each month. The March range is 1,320 and the April range is a negative 384. Each month's range is shown in this column. Some month's ranges are positive while others are negative.

The problem with a range for every data point is that as we increase our number of tests or samples, the number of range values becomes unmanageable. Computing an average of the ranges becomes an optional solution.

ELECTRICITY USAGE

	1980	Range
JANUARY	2749	133
FEBRUARY	5405	2789
MARCH	3936	1320
APRIL	2232	-384
MAY	1079	-1537
JUNE	1330	-1286
JULY	2616	0
AUGUST	2820	204
SEPTEMBER	2321	-295
OCTOBER	1583	-1033
NOVEMBER	1877	-739
DECEMBER	3439	823
SUM	31387	**-0**
AVG	2616	
Max	5405	
Min	1079	
Range	4326	

$$R_{Ave} = \frac{\sum_{i=1}^{N}(X_i - X_{Ave})}{N}$$

To solve the problem of an unmanageable number of range values, we could try to calculate an average range. This idea is great. It allows us to take into account all the data points and give them equal weight. The problem we encounter is that some of the values are above the mean and some are below the mean. This is because the mean, or average, is a monitor of central tendency. This is exactly what we expected to see! Since the average is equidistant from all the data points, when we compute an average range, the pluses and minuses offset and result in a zero (0).

The resulting zero creates a problem for our use as a monitor of variability. So, for averaging range, a method that compensates for the minus signs must be found.

STANDARD DEVIATION AND THE RESULTS OF SQUARING

ELECTRICITY USAGE

	1980	Range	Range Squared
JANUARY	2749	133	17689
FEBRUARY	5405	2789	7778521
MARCH	3936	1320	1742400
APRIL	2232	-384	147456
MAY	1079	-1537	2362369
JUNE	1330	-1286	1653796
JULY	2616	0	0
AUGUST	2820	204	41616
SEPTEMBER	2321	-295	87025
OCTOBER	1583	-1033	1067089
NOVEMBER	1877	-739	546121
DECEMBER	3439	823	677329

To remove the sign for each range, we can square each range value. The squaring effort, shown in the last column above, always returns a positive sign. For the January usage of 2,749, a range of 133 is computed. This January 133 KWH range is squared. The squared range is 17,800. For the February usage of 5,405 a range of 2,789 is computed. This February 2,789 KWH is squared. The squared February range is 7,780,845. Note how large the squaring process makes this value. For every data point this squared range is computed. We repeat this squaring process for each data point. The last column of the chart shows our squared ranges. The equation for the process is:

$$R_i^2 = (X_i - X_{Ave})^2$$

Each of the range squares must now be included in a range square average. The formula is shown below and is referred to as the sum of squares method:

$$R_{Ave} = \frac{\sum_{i=1}^{N}(X_i - X_{Ave})^2}{N}$$

$$= \frac{17{,}800 + 7{,}780{,}845 ... + 678{,}015}{12}$$

$$= \frac{16{,}121{,}409}{12}$$

$$= 1{,}343{,}451$$

The formal name for this value is the variance. The variance is simply our range average. The variance for the 1980 power usage is 1,343,451. The variance is overstated relative to the average because of our squaring process that solved the problems of negatives.

ELECTRICITY USAGE

	1980	Range	Range Squared
JANUARY	2749	133	17800
FEBRUARY	5405	2789	7780845
MARCH	3936	1320	1743500
APRIL	2232	-384	147136
MAY	1079	-1537	2361088
JUNE	1330	-1286	1652725
JULY	2616	0	0
AUGUST	2820	204	41786
SEPTEMBER	2321	-295	86779
OCTOBER	1583	-1033	1066228
NOVEMBER	1877	-739	545505
DECEMBER	3439	823	678015
Sum	31387		
Avg	2616	Sum of Squares =	16121409
Max	5405	Number of Data =	12
Min	1079	SS/n =	1343451
Range	4326	Standard Deviation =	1159
Std	1159		

To get our unit of measure back to its original state, we take the square root of the above value giving the following equation:

$$\text{Standard Deviation} = \sqrt{\frac{\sum_{i=1}^{N}(X_i - X_{Ave})^2}{N}}$$

The resulting equation is called standard deviation. The square root of the variance also yields the standard deviation.

Since we are squaring the range component of this equation, we may reverse the values to give the following formula:

$$\text{Standard Deviation} = \sqrt{\frac{\sum_{i=1}^{N} (X_{Ave} - X_i)^2}{N}}$$

The standard deviation is abbreviated as S or Std while variance uses S^2. In many respects, standard deviation is simply a more elaborate range calculation. Thus the method for interpreting standard deviation is similar to the method for interpreting range.

Standard Deviation Interpretation: As the magnitude of the standard deviation increases, the variability increases. Should the standard deviation be zero, all values are the same. Thus average becomes a perfect indicator of all the data with a standard deviation equal to zero. Standard deviations are all positive numbers.

In the statistical community the term sigma, shown as σ, is used to signify the population's variability. In addition the term mu, shown as μ, is used to signify the population's central tendency.

SMALL SAMPLE CORRECTION OF STANDARD DEVIATION

The equation below uses sample size (N) as the divisor. Averages of samples are imperfect estimates of population central tendency. Repeated samples produce a range of averages. Standard deviations of samples are also imperfect estimates of the population variability. Repeated samples produce a range of standard deviations. Unlike sample averages, standard deviations of samples tend to underestimate the variation of the population. When the sample size falls below thirty, this difference becomes significant. Below thirty samples, the formula provides poor results in tracking the variability of the measurements for the population.

$$\text{Population Standard Deviation} = \sqrt{\frac{\sum_{i=1}^{N} (X_{Ave} - X_i)^2}{N}}$$

The solution to this problem is to subtract one from the sample size or N. This tracks the true variability of the population measurements. This function is called the small sample correction factor.

$$\text{Small Sample Standard Devation} = \sqrt{\frac{\sum_{i=1}^{N}(X_{Ave} - X_i)^2}{N-1}}$$

Many times we see the average or X_{Ave} written as $\overline{X}$. When $\overline{X}$ is used as the symbol for average, the equation reads as follows:

$$\text{Small Sample Standard Deviation} = \sqrt{\frac{\sum_{i=1}^{N}(\overline{X} - X_i)^2}{N-1}}$$

The only difference in the two standard deviation equations is the minus one (-1) in the divisor. When the sample size is large, the population formula should be used, but the difference is so small that generally the small sample correction formula for standard deviation is used. The N-1 is referred to as degrees of freedom.

INTERPRETING STANDARD DEVIATION

Motel Location	A	B	C
Greenville, SC	25	25	10
Charlotte, NC	27	25	15
Atlanta, GA	24	25	20
Birmingham, AL	25	25	25
Nashville, TN	26	25	20
Indianapolis, IN	26	25	15
Louisville, KY	24	25	10
Lexington, KY	23	2	25
Cincinnati, OH	24	25	35
Columbus, OH	26	25	15
Denver, CO	27	25	40
Las Vegas, NV	23	25	35
Dallas, TX	25	25	30
Los Angeles, CA	25	25	25
San Francisco, CA	24	56	30
Newark, NJ	26	25	35
Toledo, OH	25	25	40
Average	**$25**	**$25**	**$25**
Maximum	**$27**	**$56**	**$40**
Minimum	**$23**	**$2**	**$10**
Range	**$4**	**$54**	**$30**
Standard Deviation	**$1**	**$9**	**$10**

Now our additional monitor of variability, standard deviation, should be used. Remember, this value must be used in conjunction with average.

For the three motel chains on the previous page, we would draw the following conclusions. Chain A's having an average of $25 and a standard deviation of $1

indicates that the rates in this chain are very tightly clustered. Chain B's having the same average of $25 but a standard deviation of $9 indicates that the rates in this chain are widely spread. Chain C's having an average of $25 and a standard deviation of $10 indicates that the rates in this chain are also very widely spread.

For this example, using monitors of central tendency and variability, Motel A is clearly different from Motels B and C. By viewing the actual rates of Motels B and C, we see that additional techniques may be required for analysis of these motels. We will discuss these techniques later in this chapter.

Now with our new variability knowledge, let's revisit our kilowatt hours problem.

ELECTRICITY USAGE

	1980	1981	1982	1983
JANUARY	2749	4081	4982	3936
FEBRUARY	5405	5004	4299	5024
MARCH	3936	2708	3793	3239
APRIL	2232	2423	1870	
MAY	1079	1493	1514	
JUNE	1330	2197	1713	
JULY	2616	2918	1890	
AUGUST	2820	2041	1897	
SEPTEMBER	2321	2041	1923	
OCTOBER	1583	1494	1316	
NOVEMBER	1877	1859	1843	
DECEMBER	3439	3936	2919	
Average	**2,616**	**2,683**	**2,497**	**4,066**
Range	**4,326**	**3,511**	**3,666**	**1,785**
Std	**1,211**	**1,112**	**1,211**	**900**

The kilowatt average, range, and standard deviation work together to allow us to plan our future electricity needs even better. The standard deviation for the three years of 1980, 1981, and 1982 are very similar: 1,211; 1,112; and 1,211 respectively. This will allow us to conclude that our monitor of variability is a good measure. The magnitude of the standard deviation is still very high in relation to the averages, thus forcing us to plan for large swings in the amount of electricity that will be consumed each month.

WHERE THE SPREAD IS LOCATED

From our prior discussion, Motels B and C both have averages and standard deviations that are relatively similar. A new technique is required to show the difference for examples like this. The problem is that the magnitude of the central tendency and variability are similar. This new technique needs to show a different dimension. This dimension needs to represent, not the magnitude of the spread, but the location of the spread. Notice the three drawings below of people who weigh the same amount.

The first example (the person to the left) is a person whose shape is that of a body builder. His largest mass is located at the top of his body.

The second example is someone who weighs the same as the first person. The difference between these two people is that the second person's mass is located in the center of his body.

The third person is a person weighing about the same as the first two individuals. This person's mass is located at the bottom of his body.

All three drawings are similar but all three are different. The technique we need to differentiate between the three people needs to show the location of their spread. The drawings above do an excellent job of presenting this information. Let's discuss how we can prepare a picture of data that will present the location of the spread just like the pictures above present the people's location of their spread.

Now let's begin to analyze a new set of data which we want to convert into significant information. We'll begin with a set of data about the presidents of the United States from the first president to the fortieth president. Our information includes the term number of each president, his first and last names, the state and year of his birth, and his age at his inauguration. We want to prepare a report based on this data.

The particular aspect we will analyze is the age of each president at inauguration. We have already calculated the average age of the presidents at inauguration to be 55.55 years of age. The standard deviation is 6.07 years. In other words, the balance point of the presidents is 55 years of age with the amount of spread being 6 years of age. Let's now begin to analyze the location of the spread or distribution of the presidents' ages.

Term	First Name	Last Name	Home State	Birth year	Inauguration Age
1	George	Washington	Virginia	1732	57
2	John	Adams	Massachusetts	1735	62
3	Thomas	Jefferson	Virginia	1743	58
4	James	Madison	Virginia	1751	58
5	James	Monroe	Virginia	1758	59
6	John	Adams	Massachusetts	1767	58
7	Andrew	Jackson	South Carolina	1767	62
8	Martin	Van Buren	New York	1782	55
9	William	Harrison	Virginia	1773	68
10	John	Tyler	Virginia	1790	51
11	James	Polk	North Carolina	1795	50
12	Zachary	Taylor	Virginia	1784	65
13	Millard	Fillmore	New York	1800	50
14	Franklin	Pierce	New Hampshire	1804	49
15	James	Buchanan	Pennsylvania	1791	66
16	Abraham	Lincoln	Kentucky	1809	52
17	Andrew	Johnson	North Carolina	1808	57
18	Ulysses	Grant	Ohio	1822	47
19	Rutherford	Hayes	Ohio	1822	55
20	James	Garfield	Ohio	1831	50
21	Chester	Arthur	Vermont	1830	51
22	Grover	Cleveland	New Jersey	1837	48
23	Benjamin	Harrison	Ohio	1833	56
24	Grover	Cleveland	New Jersey	1837	56
25	William	McKinley	Ohio	1843	54
26	Theodore	Roosevelt	New York	1858	43
27	William	Taft	Ohio	1857	52
28	Woodrow	Wilson	Virginia	1856	57
29	Warren	Harding	Ohio	1865	56
30	Calvin	Coolidge	Vermont	1872	51
31	Herbert	Hoover	Iowa	1874	55
32	Franklin	Roosevelt	New York	1882	51
33	Harry	Truman	Missouri	1884	61
34	Dwight	Eisenhower	Texas	1890	63
35	John	Kennedy	Massachusetts	1917	44
36	Lyndon	Johnson	Texas	1908	55
37	Richard	Nixon	California	1913	56
38	Gerald	Ford	Nebraska	1913	61
39	James	Carter	Georgia	1924	53
40	Ronald	Reagan	Illinois	1911	70
			Average Age At Inauguration		**55.55**
			Std Dev At Inauguration		**6.066094**

To keep our following examples simple we will use rounded averages of 55 and a rounded standard deviation of 6.

DISTRIBUTION

Not only do we need to know the center point and the magnitude of the spread, we also need to know where the spread is occurring.

The distribution answers the question, "Where Is The Spread?". From what we saw of the spread of the people's weights, the best way to analyze the distribution is through pictures. This is accomplished through either a frequency table or a histogram. The frequency table is the tabular means for analyzing where the data is distributed. The histogram is the pictorial technique for analyzing the distribution.

The frequency table counts the items in the data that fall into a series of intervals. The example shown below includes the age at election of the first 40 presidents of the United States. The histogram then shows them in a pictorial manner.

The frequency table and histogram show where the occurrences are spread.

The Age Groups	The Number of Presidents
40	0
45	2
50	6
55	12
60	11
65	6
70	3
75	0

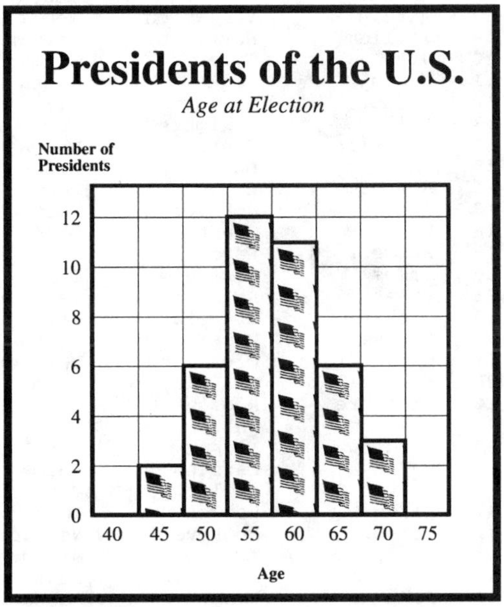

The frequency table and histogram are constructed by determining the following items:

- X axis range
- Number of bins
- Width of each bin
- Number of data points in each bin

Now let's break down each step and explain it in detail.

FREQUENCY TABLE CONSTRUCTION

The steps below show us how to prepare a frequency table. The frequency table uses cells to count the number of occurrences for each group. These groups may be referred to as classes, groups, or bins.

Determine the Range of the X axis

We must determine and record the lowest actual value. For our example, the youngest president is Theodore Roosevelt whose age was 43 at inauguration. Next, we determine and record the highest actual value. For our example, the oldest president is Ronald Reagan whose age was 70 at inauguration. The table below shows the results of the analysis of the presidents of the United States ages at inauguration:

	Actual
Minimum	43
Maximum	70

To add more information to determine the X axis, we now determine and record the lowest contract or specification value. For our example, the United States Constitution states no one shall be elected to the office of president younger than 35 years of age. Now we determine and record the highest contract or specification value. For our example, there is no upper end to the age of a president.

	Actual	Specification
Minimum	43	35
Maximum	70	None

Now, compute the low end of the X axis by taking the lowest actual value or specification. Should no low specification be available, then provide some space on the low axis for any future values outside our current values. The lowest of the actual (43 years of age) for our presidents and the low specification from the Constitution (35 years of age) is now found. This value of 35 years of age becomes the low end of the X axis.

Now, compute the high end of the X axis by taking the highest actual value or specification. Should no upper specification be available, then provide some space on the high axis for any future values outside our current values. The highest of the actual ages (70 years of age) for our presidents and the high specification is not specified in the Constitution. The extra space for future high values is 75 years of age and now becomes the high end of the X axis. The table below shows the selected X axis for the presidents' ages:

	Actual	**Specification**	**X axis Boundary**
Minimum	43	35	35
Maximum	70	None	75

Finally, the range of the X axis is computed and saved for the next step. This X axis range is shown below:

	Actual	**Specification**	**X axis Boundary**
Minimum	43	35	35
Maximum	70	None	75
		X axis Range	**40**

Number of Classes

Classes for a frequency table are the number of bins in the chart. The bins are equivalent to the bars on a histogram. Classes can be referred to using several different names such as bars, bins, or groups.

First, we must determine the number of classes. A good rule of thumb is approximately seven to ten classes. Too few or too many bins will cause the distribution to have an inappropriate appearance. For this example, we will select eight classes because the range of 40 is evenly divisible by eight.

Class Size

The size of each class is the key to forming the frequency table. The size defines what data points fall in each group.

We determine the class size for the frequency table by dividing the X axis range by the number of classes as selected from above. For the presidents, the range of 40 years is divided by the number of classes which is eight. Each bin will encompass five years.

Prepare the frequency table

In a column, enter the series of values defining the lower limits of the classes. The first class will start at 35 years of age for a length of five years. The second class will start at just above 40 for a range of five years. Leave a blank column to the right of the bin values, including one blank cell below the largest value. This column will contain the frequency distribution. The table below shows how the list bins would look for the presidents of the United States:

The Age Groups	The Number of Presidents
35-40	
40^{+}-45	
45^{+}-50	
50^{+}-55	
55^{+}-60	
60^{+}-65	
65^{+}-70	
70^{+}-75	

The above table shows how the presidents' ages will be grouped.

Count the number of occurrences for each bin. For example, George Washington's age of 57 when inaugurated into office falls in the 55-60 class, John Adams' age of 62 falls in the 60-65 range, and Thomas Jefferson's age of 58 would add a second value in the 55-60 age class. The counting would continue through our list up to Ronald Reagan. This frequency table is the forty presidents of the United States grouped in five year increments:

The Age Groups	**The Number of Presidents**
35-40	0
40^+-45	2
45^+-50	6
50^+-55	12
55^+-60	11
60^+-65	6
65^+-70	3
70^+-75	0

This frequency table shows the shape of the distribution of our data. An even better way to observe the distribution is with a picture or graph called a histogram. The next section explains the histogram.

HISTOGRAM

The histogram displays in pictorial form the measurement distribution and explains where the spread or concentration of values is occurring. The horizontal axis shows how the measurement groups were formed. The vertical axis depicts the number of occurrences for each group.

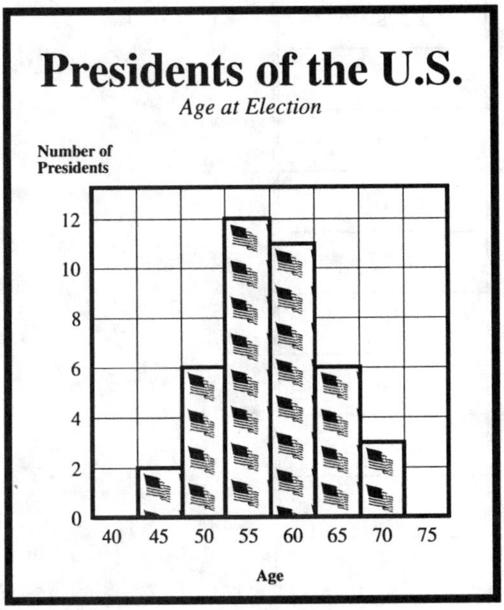

The vertical or Y axis shows the number of events that occurred for this group. The age group from 35 years to 40 years has no presidents, 40 years to 45 years has two presidents, while 45 years to 50 years has six presidents. This chart continues for all of the presidential age groups. The horizontal or X axis shows how the groups are formed in five year increments. The first group is the 35 to 40 age range; 40 is the upper limit. The second group is the 40+ to 45 age range, with 45 as the upper limit. The groups continue, and end with the 70+ to 75 year group with 75 as the upper limit.

This chart is used to assess how well the distribution is fitted to a normal curve. The location of the spread of the United States presidents' ages is shown in the histogram above. From our prior statistics, we know the average age of a president is 55 years. The bars that form the histogram are the tallest closest to this average. As the ages become older and younger (farther from the average), the number of occurrences drops rapidly on both sides of the average. The bars above the average and below the average are symmetric to each other. From this analysis, we can conclude that presidents' ages are normally distributed and thus we can use the probabilities of the normal to make predictions. Now we need to learn the normal probabilities so that we can use them for predictions.

NORMAL DISTRIBUTION

Everyone has been graded on a bell shaped curve at some point in school. This bell curve is another name for our friend, the normal distribution or Gaussian distribution. The normal distribution is used to convert the actual grades or test scores to a letter grade.

Normal distribution is described with the average as the central point of the measurements and the standard deviation as the variability of the measurements.

The normal distribution is symmetric around its average. Fifty percent of the data points are above the average and fifty percent of the measurements are below the average. The frequency of occurrence (or the number of occurrences) drops rapidly as we move further and further away from the center. This characteristic is true both above and below the average. The frequencies of occurrences above and below the average are symmetric.

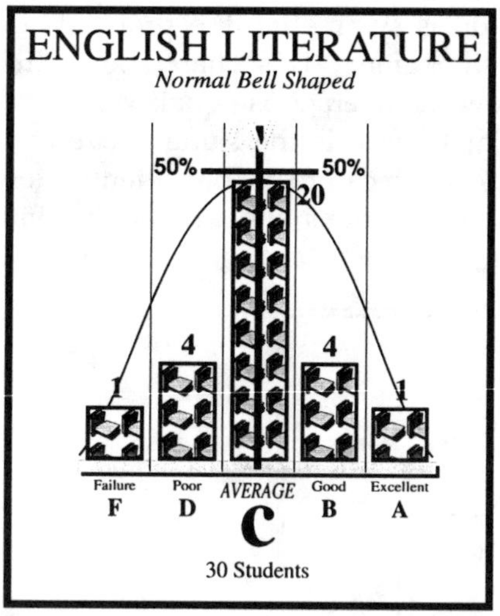

The chart to the left is used to depict a picture of how a process with its measurements will look. The chart shows the spread of grades from an English literature class of thirty students. When the score measurements are converted to grades and look like the diagram, the process is well represented by a normal distribution. The perfect normal does not have the steps of a histogram but is a smooth curve.

WHY IS THE NORMAL DISTRIBUTION IMPORTANT?

Having data that is well represented by a normal distribution allows us to predict using the probabilities of the normal. Because a good understanding of these probabilities is essential, let's now look at them in more detail.

This chart shows how a typical class in English literature could have been graded using a bell shaped curve. Out of a class of thirty students twenty would receive a "C", four would receive a "B", another four would receive a "D", one would receive an "A", and one would receive an "F".

HOW DO WE DETERMINE THE NORMAL PROBABILITY?

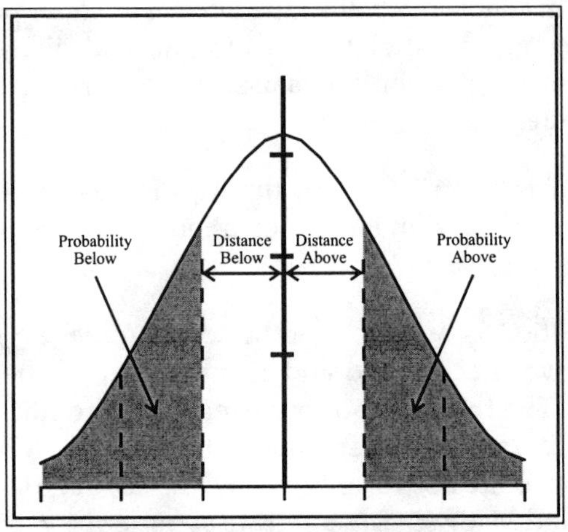

All measurements that track like a normal distribution have a very definitive set of probabilities. Since the normal distribution is symmetric, the probabilities above and below the average are exactly the same. This chart shows the symmetry when the distance above and below the average is equal. When the distances are equal, the area under the normal curve is the same above and below the average. Since the bell is symmetrical, we can focus our attention on the "distance above" side, because the same calculations and probability will apply for the "distance below" side.

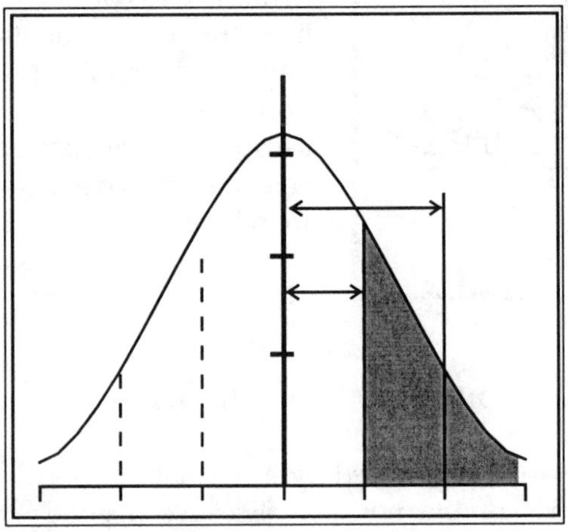

As the distance away from the mean, or center, of a normal distribution gets bigger, the probability gets smaller. . Due to the normal distribution's symmetry, only one formula is required and the sign is always positive.

This distance can be calculated with the following formula.

$$\text{Distance from the average} = X_i - X_{Ave}$$

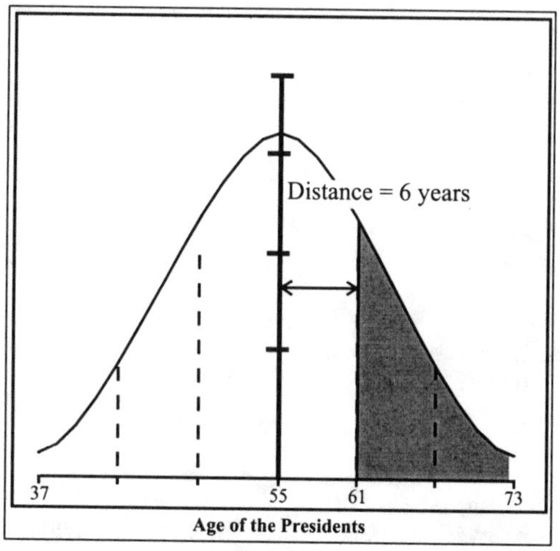

Should we desire to compute the probability of a person's presidential election based on age, this formula is used. For a person 61 years of age or older, we can compute this distance by subtracting the average of the presidents' ages (55) from the age (61). Now we can build the equation that follows.

61 years:

Distance from the average $= X_i - X_{Ave}$

$= 61-55$

$= 6$ years

Now to make a general rule for all measurements we must convert this distance to a ratio. The ratio will be the distance as a function of variability. This ratio will remove units of measure such as the president's age and will give us a conversion factor that all measurements can use. The ratio's formula is calculated below. The ratio of the distance from the average divided by the standard deviation is called Z.

$$Z = \left| \frac{X_{Ave} - X_i}{Std} \right|$$

We use the absolute value in the equation because of the symmetry of the normal distribution. This symmetry allows the same equation to be used both above and below the average.

To compute the Z value for our example of 61 years and older, the following must be computed.

We insert the president's age of 55 and standard deviation of 6 (see the chart on page 43) into the Z calculation.

$$Z = \left| \frac{55 - X_i}{6} \right|$$

Now we insert the age of 61 into the equation and solve for Z.

$$Z_{61} = \frac{55-61}{6}$$

$$= \frac{6}{6}$$

$$= 1$$

Once again, Z is the ratio of the distance away from the average as a function of variability measured by standard deviation. This Z value, which is a ratio, allows the use of one probability table for any measurement. Now this table is used to locate the probability for the particular Z value that has been computed. For our example, the Z value is one.

Z	Probability
4	.00003
3	.00135
2	.0228
1	**.1587**
0	.500

This table shows us the relationship of distances away from the average. The ratio of the distances away from the average, or Z, allows us to determine the probability from the point out.

In the table above, a Z value of four gives a probability of .00003, or three out of 100,000 occurrences. A Z value of three yields a probability of .00135 or 1.35 out of 1,000 occurrences. A Z value of two yields a probability of 2.28 out of 100. A Z value of one gives a probability of .1587 or 15.87 out of 100 occurrences, while a Z value of zero yields a 50 times out of 100 occurrence rate.

The Z ratio of one for our age of 61 can be used with the above tables to determine a probability. For our example, a person of 61 years of age and older has a probability of 15.87 chance out of 100 to become president based on past history. Now let's expand our understanding of the Z value with a second example.

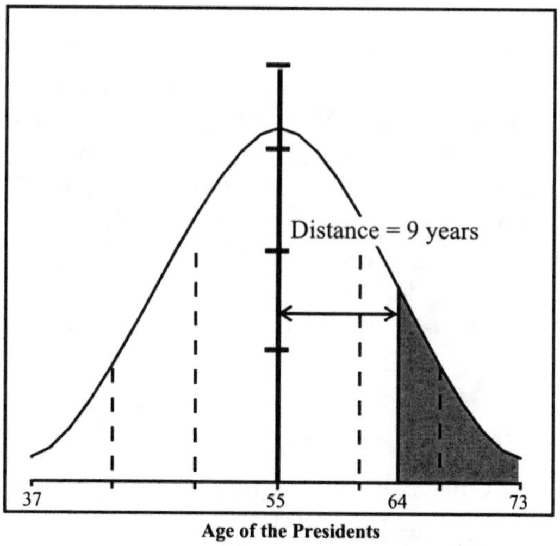

For a person 64 years of age or older, we can compute this distance by subtracting the average (55 years) from the age (64 years).

64 years:

Distance from the average = $X_i - X_{Ave}$

= 64-55

= 9 years

This ratio once again will remove all the units of measure such as the president's age. This ratio will give us a conversion factor for 64 years that we can use to arrive at the probability. The ratio for 64 years is calculated below:

$$Z = \left| \frac{X_{Ave} - X_i}{Std} \right|$$

To compute the Z value for this example of 64 years and older, the following must be computed.

$$Z_{64} = \frac{55 - 64}{6}$$

$$= \frac{9}{6}$$

$$= 1.5$$

This example forces us to increase our Z table precision to the first decimal place.

Once again, Z is the ratio of the distance away from the average as a function of variability measured by standard deviation. This Z value, which is a ratio, allows the use of one probability table for any measurement. Now the table is expanded to include more detail with Z values to one decimal place. We look down the Z value column until we find the value of 1.5. The probability for the particular Z value that has been computed; for our example it is immediately to the right. The probability for a Z of 1.5 is .0668. In other words, 6.68% of the presidents would be 64 and older.

Z	Probability
4.0	.00003
3.5	.00023
3.0	.00135
2.5	.0062
2.0	.0228
1.9	.0287
1.8	.0359
1.7	.0446
1.6	.0548
1.5	.0668
1.4	.0808
1.3	.0968
1.2	.1151
1.1	.1357
1.0	.1587
.9	.1841
.8	.2119

With this example, we have added more precision to our normal distribution Z table. Our Z table now has to include the whole number and the first decimal place.

Now we can use a third example to add even more detail to the same table.

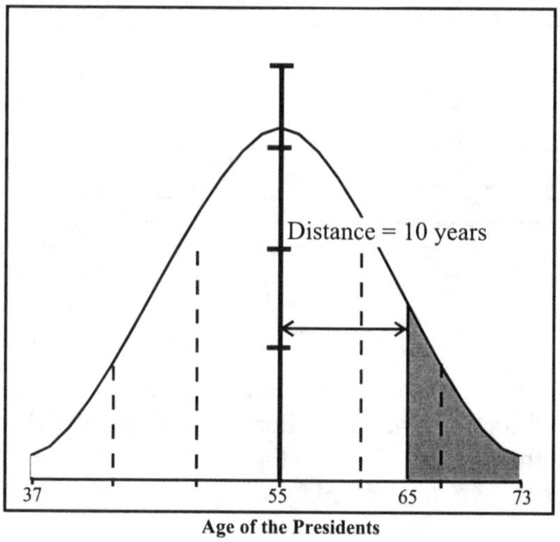

For a person 65 years of age or older, we can compute this distance by subtracting the average age (55 years) from the age of 65 years.

65 years:

Distance from the average $= X_i - X_{Ave}$

$= 65-55$

$= 10$ years

To remove the age units of measure, the Z ratio will once again be used. The Z ratio will give us a conversion factor for 65 years that we can use to arrive at the probability. The ratio for 65 years is calculated below.

$$Z = \left| \frac{X_{Ave} - X_i}{Std} \right|$$

To compute the Z value for this example of 65 years and older, the following must be computed:

$$Z_{65} = \frac{55-65}{6}$$

$$= \frac{10}{6}$$

$$= 1.67$$

This example forces the Z table precision to a second decimal place. To take the Z value to a second decimal place, the normal table must be revised. Now a series of columns are used to identify the second decimal place. The following shows the look of the table. The first column identifies the Z value whole and first decimal place and the remaining columns identify the second decimal place. For

a Z value of 2.93, the row would be 2.9 and the column would X.X3 with the resulting probability being .0017.

Z	x.x0	x.x1	x.x2	x.x3	x.x4	x.x5	x.x6
3.0	.00135	.00131	.00126	.00122	.00118	.00114	.00111
2.9	**.0019**	**.0018**	**.0018**	**.0017**	.0016	.0016	.0015
2.8	.0026	.0025	.0024	.0023	.0023	.0022	.0021

Now turn to the next page and look up the Z_{65} of 1.67. Find row 1.6 and column X.X7; that should give you a probability value of .0475. Thus we would expect 4.75% of the presidents to be 65 and older. The reverse of 65 and younger yields 95.25% of the presidents falling in this range. The next page provides a full normal distribution table for Z values to two decimal places.

Remember, the first column and top row are the Z values. The remaining body of the table is composed of probabilities for the corresponding Z values.

Normal Distribution Table

The table on the next page allows you to look up the area (percent) of the normal distribution probability based on the distance away from the center of the distribution monitored by the average. This distance away from the average as a function of the variability monitored by standard deviation is a ratio called the Z value. This Z value can then be used to look up the probability of occurrence outside the point. The table is a tail-oriented probability table with the values representing one of the shaded areas in the bell curve diagram. This probability is the same for both upper and lower tails because of the symmetry of the normal distribution. The first column represents the Z value to the whole number and one decimal place while the top row represents the second decimal place for the Z value.

NORMAL DISTRIBUTION TABLE

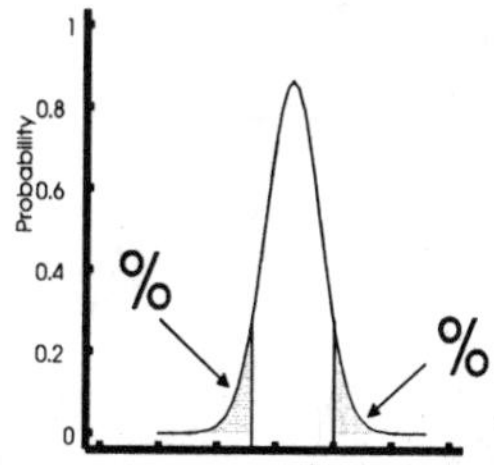

$$Z = \left| \frac{X_{Ave} - X_i}{Std} \right|$$

Z	X.X0	X.X1	X.X2	X.X3	X.X4	X.X5	X.X6	X.X7	X.X8	X.X9
4.5	0.000003	0.000003	0.000003	0.000003	0.000003	0.000003	0.000003	0.000002	0.000002	0.000002
4.0	0.000032	0.000030	0.000029	0.000028	0.000027	0.000026	0.000025	0.000024	0.000023	0.000022
3.5	0.000233	0.000224	0.000216	0.000208	0.000200	0.000193	0.000185	0.000179	0.000172	0.000165
3.0	0.001350	0.001306	0.001264	0.001223	0.001183	0.001144	0.001107	0.001070	0.001035	0.001001
2.9	0.001866	0.001807	0.001750	0.001695	0.001641	0.001589	0.001538	0.001489	0.001441	0.001395
2.8	0.002555	0.002477	0.002401	0.002327	0.002256	0.002186	0.002118	0.002052	0.001988	0.001926
2.7	0.003467	0.003364	0.003264	0.003167	0.003072	0.002980	0.002890	0.002803	0.002718	0.002635
2.6	0.004661	0.004527	0.004397	0.004269	0.004145	0.004025	0.003907	0.003793	0.003681	0.003573
2.5	0.006210	0.006037	0.005868	0.005703	0.005543	0.005386	0.005234	0.005085	0.004940	0.004799
2.4	0.008198	0.007976	0.007760	0.007549	0.007344	0.007143	0.006947	0.006756	0.006569	0.006387
2.3	0.010724	0.010444	0.010170	0.009903	0.009642	0.009387	0.009137	0.008894	0.008656	0.008424
2.2	0.013903	0.013553	0.013209	0.012874	0.012545	0.012224	0.011911	0.011604	0.011304	0.011011
2.1	0.017864	0.017429	0.017003	0.016586	0.016177	0.015778	0.015386	0.015003	0.014629	0.014262
2.0	0.022750	0.022216	0.021692	0.021178	0.020675	0.020182	0.019699	0.019226	0.018763	0.018309
1.9	0.028716	0.028067	0.027429	0.026803	0.026190	0.025588	0.024998	0.024419	0.023852	0.023295
1.8	0.035930	0.035148	0.034379	0.033625	0.032884	0.032157	0.031443	0.030742	0.030054	0.029379
1.7	0.044565	0.043633	0.042716	0.041815	0.040929	0.040059	0.039204	0.038364	0.037538	0.036727
1.6	0.054799	0.053699	0.052616	0.051551	0.050503	0.049471	0.048457	0.047460	0.046479	0.045514
1.5	0.066807	0.065522	0.064256	0.063008	0.061780	0.060571	0.059380	0.058208	0.057053	0.055917
1.4	0.080757	0.079270	0.077804	0.076359	0.074934	0.073529	0.072145	0.070781	0.069437	0.068112
1.3	0.096801	0.095098	0.093418	0.091759	0.090123	0.088508	0.086915	0.085344	0.083793	0.082264
1.2	0.115070	0.113140	0.111233	0.109349	0.107488	0.105650	0.103835	0.102042	0.100273	0.098525
1.1	0.135666	0.133500	0.131357	0.129238	0.127143	0.125072	0.123024	0.121001	0.119000	0.117023
1.0	0.158655	0.156248	0.153864	0.151505	0.149170	0.146859	0.144572	0.142310	0.140071	0.137857
0.9	0.184060	0.181411	0.178786	0.176186	0.173609	0.171056	0.168528	0.166023	0.163543	0.161087
0.8	0.211855	0.208970	0.206108	0.203269	0.200454	0.197662	0.194894	0.192150	0.189430	0.186733
0.7	0.241964	0.238852	0.235762	0.232695	0.229650	0.226627	0.223627	0.220650	0.217695	0.214764
0.6	0.274253	0.270931	0.267629	0.264347	0.261086	0.257846	0.254627	0.251429	0.248252	0.245097
0.5	0.308538	0.305026	0.301532	0.298056	0.294598	0.291160	0.287740	0.284339	0.280957	0.277595
0.4	0.344578	0.340903	0.337243	0.333598	0.329969	0.326355	0.322758	0.319178	0.315614	0.312067
0.3	0.382089	0.378281	0.374484	0.370700	0.366928	0.363169	0.359424	0.355691	0.351973	0.348268
0.2	0.420740	0.416834	0.412936	0.409046	0.405165	0.401294	0.397432	0.393580	0.389739	0.385908
0.1	0.460172	0.456205	0.452242	0.448283	0.444330	0.440382	0.436441	0.432505	0.428576	0.424655
0.0	0.500000	0.496011	0.492022	0.488033	0.484047	0.480061	0.476078	0.472097	0.468119	0.464144

NORMAL CURVE PROBABILITIES REVIEW

The area under the curve represents the probability of occurrence.

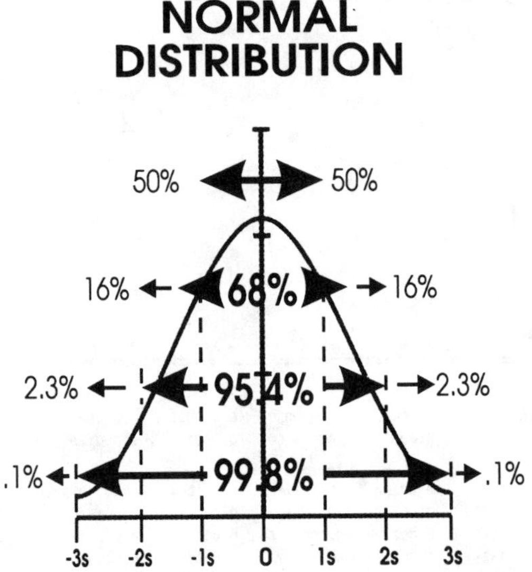

An occurrence outside plus or minus one standard deviation (one is the Z value) equates to a probability of 16% above or 16% below or 68% inside. An occurrence outside plus or minus two standard deviation (two is the Z value) equates to a probability of 2.3% above or 2.3% below or 95.4% inside. An occurrence outside plus or minus three standard deviation (three is the Z value) equates to a probability of .1% above or .1% below or 99.8% inside.

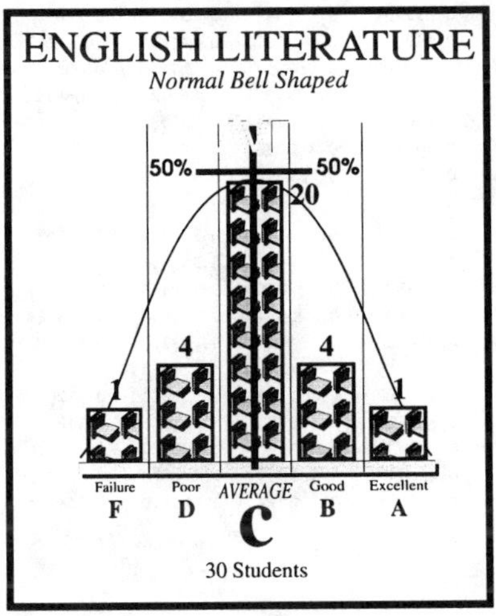

Returning to the English literature class, how were the different letter grades determined? First the "C" grades were inside the range of plus or minus one standard deviation. In this range, the probability is 68%. Thus, the 20 students receiving a C grade are 68% of the total 30.

Notice that 95.4% of the grades fall in the plus or minus two standard deviations. Of these, 68% have already received their C grade leaving a total of 27% receiving a B or a D. Since the normal distribution is symmetric, half of the students and those above the average will receive a B; that is 13% or four B grades. The remaining four students in the low end of this range will receive a D grade.

Now 99.8% of the grades fall in plus or minus three standard deviations. Similarly, 95.4% have already received a B, C, or D. The remaining 4.4%, or two students, will receive an F or A grade. The student on the low side of the average will receive the F while the student on the high side of the average will receive the A.

USING THE NORMAL TABLE FOR INFORMATION RISK MANAGEMENT

Not only can the normal table be used to compute probability, but this process can be reversed to have a probability of risk and arrive at the spots where this amount of risk would occur. The English literature class is an example of having known probabilities and arriving at the number of occurrences or the particular spot. The Z value formula below remains true.

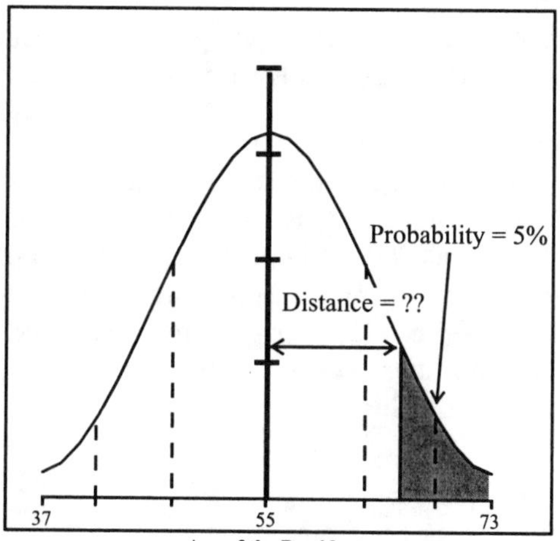

$$Z = \left| \frac{X_{Ave} - X_i}{Std} \right|$$

Now the equation is simply rearranged using algebra to solve for X_i. The resulting equation becomes:

$$X_i = X_{Ave} \pm Z * Std$$

Z	X.X0	X.X1	X.X2	X.X3	X.X4	X.X5
1.6	0.054799	0.053699	0.052616	0.051551	0.050503	0.049471
1.5	0.066807	0.065522	0.064256	0.063008	0.061780	0.060571
1.4	0.080757	0.079270	0.077804	0.076359	0.074934	0.073529
1.3	0.096801	0.095098	0.093418	0.091759	0.090123	0.088508
1.2	0.115070	0.113140	0.111233	0.109349	0.107488	0.105650
1.1	0.135666	0.133500	0.131357	0.129238	0.127143	0.125072
1.0	0.158655	0.156248	0.153864	0.151505	0.149170	0.146859
0.9	0.184060	0.181411	0.178786	0.176186	0.173609	0.171056
0.8	0.211855	0.208970	0.206108	0.203269	0.200454	0.197662
0.7	0.241964	0.238852	0.235762	0.232695	0.229650	0.226627
0.6	0.274253	0.270931	0.267629	0.264347	0.261086	0.257846
0.5	0.308538	0.305026	0.301532	0.298056	0.294598	0.291160
0.4	0.344578	0.340903	0.337243	0.333598	0.329969	0.326355
0.3	0.382089	0.378281	0.374484	0.370700	0.366928	0.363169
0.2	0.420740	0.416834	0.412936	0.409046	0.405165	0.401294
0.1	0.460172	0.456205	0.452242	0.448283	0.444330	0.440382
0.0	0.500000	0.496011	0.492022	0.488033	0.484047	0.480061

With intervals, we reverse the process of using the Z table starting at the bottom of the second column to find a probability and to obtain a Z value.

In our example, the five percent is converted to .05. The Z value to correspond with the percentage is the reverse of the process that we have been using. When converting from a percentage to a Z, we start at the bottom of the table in the second column. The value .500000 is the percentage at the bottom of this column. Our search continues up the column until our value (.5) is bigger than the values in the table. Then we move from left to right on the selected row until our value is bigger than the table's number. At this point, we have selected the column and row for our corresponding Z value.

Z	X.X0	X.X1	X.X2	X.X3	X.X4	X.X5
1.6	0.054799	0.053699	0.052616	0.051551	0.050503	0.049471
1.5	0.066807	0.065522	0.064256	0.063008	0.061780	0.060571
1.4	0.080757	0.079270	0.077804	0.076359	0.074934	0.073529
1.3	0.096801	0.095098	0.093418	0.091759	0.090123	0.088508
1.2	0.115070	0.113140	0.111233	0.109349	0.107488	0.105650
1.1	0.135666	0.133500	0.131357	0.129238	0.127143	0.125072
1.0	0.158655	0.156248	0.153864	0.151505	0.149170	0.146859
0.9	0.184060	0.181411	0.178786	0.176186	0.173609	0.171056
0.8	0.211855	0.208970	0.206108	0.203269	0.200454	0.197662
0.7	0.241964	0.238852	0.235762	0.232695	0.229650	0.226627
0.6	0.274253	0.270931	0.267629	0.264347	0.261086	0.257846
0.5	0.308538	0.305026	0.301532	0.298056	0.294598	0.291160
0.4	0.344578	0.340903	0.337243	0.333598	0.329969	0.326355
0.3	0.382089	0.378281	0.374484	0.370700	0.366928	0.363169
0.2	0.420740	0.416834	0.412936	0.409046	0.405165	0.401294
0.1	0.460172	0.456205	0.452242	0.448283	0.444330	0.440382
0.0	0.500000	0.496011	0.492022	0.488033	0.484047	0.480061

For example, compute the age of presidents where the risk above average is five percent and the risk below the average is five percent. First the Z associated with five percent risk must be determined. Five percent equates to .05. Now we go to the normal table and look in the body for the value closest to .05. On the row 1.6, the values of .0505 and .0495 are found. The probability of .0505 has a Z

of 1.64 while the probability of .0495 has a Z of 1.65. Since .05 is in the center of the two probabilities, the Z in the center of 1.64 and 1.65 or 1.645 is selected.

Now the average age of the presidents (55 years) and the standard deviation of the presidents' ages (6 years) are both used in conjunction with the selected Z of 1.645 to compute the selected spots. We use the following equation to compute X_i

$$X_i = X_{Ave} \pm Z * Std$$

In this equation we insert the president's average age of 55 and the president's standard deviation of 6.

$$X_i = 55 \pm Z * 6$$

Now we insert the Z of five percent into the equation. The equation now has a $Z_{5\%}$ of 1.645 inserted.

$$X_i = 55 \pm 1.645 * 6$$

Solving the multiplication, the equation now reads:

$$X_i = 55 \pm 9.87$$

Finally,

$$X_i = 45.13 \longleftrightarrow 64.87$$

Thus, five percent of the presidents should be over 64.87 years of age and five percent of the presidents should be under 45.13 years of age. Ninety percent of the presidents should be in the range of 45.13 to 64.87 years of age.

CHAPTER SUMMARY

For proper numerical analysis technique, we must monitor each of the following:

- **Central Tendency**
- **Variability**
- **Distribution**

Failure to monitor all three will lead to catastrophic mistakes. The following briefly recaps the monitor of each area:

MONITOR	FORMULA
Central Tendency or balance point of the data:	
Average	$\frac{\sum_{i=1}^{N} X_i}{N}$
Variability or amount or magnitude of the data's spread:	
Range	Maximum-Minimum
Standard Deviation	$\sqrt{\frac{\sum_{i=1}^{N} (X_{Ave} - X_i)^2}{N-1}}$
Distribution or location of the data's spread:	
Frequency Table	
Histogram	

If the data that we are analyzing is normally distributed, then the probabilities associated with the normal curve can be used to make predictions. These predictions use a normal table. This normal table is comprised of two values: the Z value and the probability.

If the probability is to be determined, then the Z value formula below must be used. Our knowns must be the average of the data, the standard deviation of the data, and the point for which we desire to know the probability.

$$Z = \left| \frac{X_{Ave} - X_i}{Std} \right|$$

If the probability is known, then the equation is simply rearranged using algebra to solve for X_i. The resulting equation is shown below. The knowns of the average of the data, the standard deviation of the data, and the risk that we are prepared to take must be determined.

$$X_i = X_{Ave} \pm Z * Std$$

We have discussed the first major flaw associated with statistical analysis: improper technique. An understanding of the importance of proper technique and how to do a proper study should now be in place. Before we go to the other major flaw - improper grouping - a clear explanation of some math tricks to make SPC work will be covered in the next chapter.

SAMPLE PROBLEM

From our analysis of the electricity usage, compute the amount of funds that must be on reserve to pay the maximum kilowatt usage for any one month. This study will assume that the distribution of the kilowatts is normal, the cost of a kilowatt is $.10, and that we are prepared to take a five percent risk of not having enough funds available to cover the usage. Use a blank sheet of paper to show all your work and the amount of money that you must keep in reserve. The solution to this problem is found in the **Appendix**.

Chapter Two:
Math Tricks to Make SPC Work

STATISTICAL PROCESS CONTROL FLOW

Statistical Process Control (SPC) is used to analyze and monitor a continuous process. SPC should be used to monitor both product and process characteristics of all continuous operations.

SPC is comprised of a tactical tool called a control chart and a strategic tool called the capability study. Control charts are the operator's tool to run the machine while the capability study is management's tool to assess the impact on the customer.

Later in this book we will discuss the SPC flow pictured to the left. For now we must focus on the math that supports SPC.

CONTROL CHARTS

A control chart is the alarm system that notes changes in a continuous operation. A control chart is a pictorial alarm system to detect any change in the consistency of the machine's operation. Any deviations from the consistent operation are a change and must be investigated. Remember, change can be either an improvement or deterioration. Another way of describing a control chart is to call it a change alarm system. The objective of a control chart is to provide a tool that helps the operator run the process to its optimum.

CAPABILITY STUDIES

A capability study is the tool to assess the impact of all changes detected by a control chart. The capability study is the management tool to analyze the change and determine whether it is an improvement or deterioration.

Since control charts only detect changes and capability studies only assess the impact, then specialized mathematics can be used for each purpose. In the studies of process management, a few basic principles must be clearly understood. The second Principle allows all the mathematics in SPC to work. The second Principle is stated below.

The second Principle of Process Management (Division of Labor) drives the decision-making process. It dictates who will be in charge of the different kinds of decisions (strategic or tactical). We are doomed to a state of Quality Hell if the managers of the future fail to fully grasp Division of Labor.

SECOND PRINCIPLE OF PROCESS MANAGEMENT

Division of Labor is the framework for all aspects of decision-making. It must be clearly understood to separate the strategic and tactical decisions. Operations makes the tactical decisions of running the facility. Management makes the strategic decisions of assessing the facility's suitability for the job.

Control is a major tactical issue associated with operational duties. Capability is a major strategic issue associated with management, customer, and sales concerns.

If we have a clear understanding of the Second Principle of Process Management, or this "Division of Labor", we will possess the key to appreciating the difference between tactical and strategic decisions.

Division of Labor requires a clear understanding of the difference between management, customer, and sales issues, and operational issues.

Tactical: The art or skill of employing available means to accomplish an end.

Operational decisions are tactical and detect change. Operations or tactics use the available means. All tactical analysis must support this mission.

Strategic: The art of devising or employing plans or stratagems toward a goal.

Management decisions are strategic and assess impact. Management or strategy selects, assesses, and provides the means. All strategic analysis must support this mission.

Both decision types are crucially important. The two types of decisions have a very specific set of mathematical principles that work only for tactics or strategy but never for both. Very specialized tools must be provided to support each decision type specifically.

These mathematical tools will provide a common language for discussing process deviations, performance, and change. The tools must be used following the classic definition to avoid confusion.

CAUTION! Do not confuse control charts with strategic management reports that use customer specifications.

Division of Labor allows us to have two sets of books for very precise objectives and to serve very different audiences. In the accounting community, the same set of numbers may be manipulated several different ways to accomplish differing needs. The financial information that is required to support a cash flow projection is completely different from the needs of a profit and loss statement sent to the government for tax purposes. Both tax numbers and cash flow numbers are equally important but they require very different preparation. These different numbers support very precise and but very different needs. Our tactical and strategic objectives require different information, thus our need to discuss the two statistical sets of books.

Let's use our new statistical skills to analyze the randomly derived numbers shown on the next page. In **Chapter One**, you learned about the normal distribution. The normal distribution allows us to use a probability table to make projections. These projections are valid only if the data conforms to a normal distribution.

The chart on the next page shows a set of evenly distributed numbers that range from zero to one hundred. Each number in the range has an equal chance of occurring for each value. The chart shows one set of numbers and each set

contains five columns. (Space constraints have forced us to split the set of numbers into two groups. The group of five columns to the right is a continuation of each column in the left-most group.)

***** Random Numbers ***** | **Random Numbers, Cont.**

31	94	7	0	1	87	95	63	84	93
78	86	5	51	15	90	5	5	75	96
74	76	65	88	52	95	44	75	69	77
62	49	87	46	89	68	44	54	37	15
11	3	92	91	79	71	12	92	1	36
76	23	36	1	83	36	79	51	38	42
31	64	93	30	87	13	90	58	97	93
93	39	65	20	63	33	59	18	45	49
40	54	85	11	71	18	63	50	99	70
78	81	11	7	27	75	8	72	85	80
90	21	10	21	43	3	68	12	26	97
6	90	78	52	48	93	83	20	62	80
97	94	50	56	91	18	17	15	45	21
26	23	25	95	83	37	41	34	26	41
52	27	52	64	65	91	34	44	82	99
17	8	5	86	93	40	27	5	78	14
18	12	39	49	36	27	77	49	71	47
8	23	94	32	13	56	38	71	90	42
78	44	60	27	10	53	24	55	60	98
0	59	100	38	66	10	48	77	5	89
60	97	85	82	42	100	42	95	51	98
3	30	64	56	18	8	83	19	92	78
79	85	95	29	38	1	28	26	77	95
30	98	84	92	15	13	98	44	27	3
15	83	12	57	63	57	99	92	99	83
64	59	25	40	58	24	10	73	24	70
47	12	7	35	89	78	27	69	72	80
12	26	68	38	99	93	82	34	88	67
30	80	91	16	60	41	28	10	2	42
55	26	48	85	36	1	57	14	69	96
81	30	8	31	12	47	58	40	29	61
98	9	99	64	11	98	71	74	20	71

We must compute a monitor of central tendency, variability, and the data distribution. The monitor of central tendency that I want you to compute is the average. The monitor of variability is standard deviation. The monitor of the data distribution is a histogram.

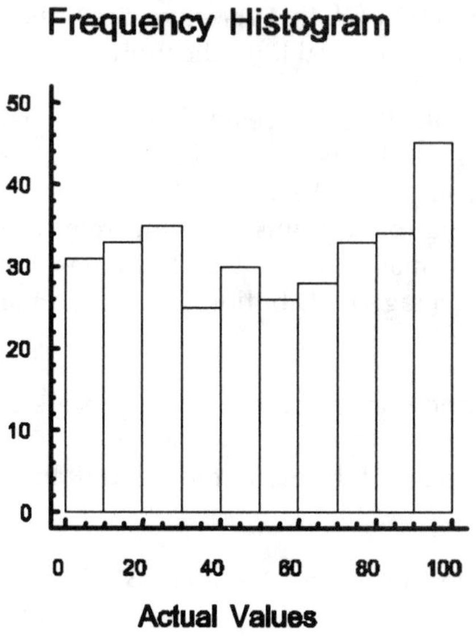

The average of the data (Ave_{Ind}) is 52.

The standard deviation is 30. The distribution of the data is a very flat distribution and is not even near a normal distribution. Thus we must conclude that this set of values is non-normal.

This table summarizes the results of our analyses:

		Individual
Central Tendency	Average	**52**
Variability	Standard Deviation of the Individuals	**30**
Distribution	Histogram	**Non-normal**

In the real world, processes, products, or data sets may not always be well represented by a normal distribution.

The above must be used by management for strategic calculations. Since the distribution is not bell shaped, a more sophisticated analysis must be used. This analysis must include the computing of the probabilities for this one particular set of numbers. Remember, this analysis will compare the product that we are making to the product the customer desires. In this analysis, customer specifications will be included. This analysis will be covered in **Chapter Ten**.

TACTICAL SUPPORT

To support operations, clarity of Division of Labor is required. The operator's role is to correctly and consistently run the machine. The operator must run the machine to its optimum. Customer specifications cannot be used to run a machine let alone get the machine to its optimum. With this objective clear, then we can introduce a natural phenomenon known as central limit theorem.

There is a natural set of factors that tend to make these processes have a normal distribution. This is explained by the central limit theorem. This theorem implies that the sum of a large number of data points will be normally distributed regardless of the distribution of the individual data points. The theorem also states that the mean of the samples will be normally distributed. The larger the number of samples, the closer the sum or average distribution is to a normal distribution.

This process is a means of normalizing a non-normal process. The process is accomplished by averaging subgroups of data points. The following shows how our original random numbers can be normalized through the central limit theorem.

We compute the average of our first set of five values from the table; 31, 94, 7, 0, and 1, as shown below:

$$\text{Average} = \frac{31+94+7+0+1}{5}$$

$$= 26.6$$

Similarly, we compute the average of our second set of five values from the table; 78, 86, 5, 51, and 15, as shown below:

$$\text{Average} = \frac{78+86+5+51+15}{5}$$

$$= 47.0$$

Again, we compute the average below of our third set of five values from the table; 74, 76, 65, 88, and 52, as shown next:

$$\text{Average} = \frac{74+76+65+88+52}{5}$$

$$= 71.0$$

Once more, we compute the average of our fourth set of five values from the table; 62, 49, 87, 46, and 89, as shown below:

$$\text{Average} = \frac{62+49+87+46+89}{5}$$

$$= 66.6$$

Still again, we compute the average of our fifth set of five values from the table; 11, 3, 92, 91, and 79, as shown below:

$$\text{Average} = \frac{11+3+92+91+79}{5}$$

$$= 55.2$$

Finally, we compute the average of our sixth set of five values from the table; 76, 23, 36, 1, and 83, as shown below:

$$\text{Average} = \frac{76+23+36+1+83}{5}$$

$$= 43.8$$

These computations are continued for every set of values. Each set of five values is called a subgroup.

Random Numbers					Row Average
31	94	7	0	1	**26.6**
78	86	5	51	15	**47.0**
74	76	65	88	52	**71.0**
62	49	87	46	89	**66.6**
11	3	92	91	79	**55.2**
76	23	36	1	83	**43.8**

The table to the left shows the results of the normalizing of the first six subgroups with their normalized averages. This table can be simplified to include only the average of each row's group of five data points.

The values below are the resultant normalized averages for every one of the subgroups of five. The first value of 26.6 in the table is the average of five individual values in the first group. Each value in the table is its corresponding subgroup's average.

*****Average of the Random Numbers *****

26.6	84.4
47.0	54.2
71.0	72.0
66.6	43.6
55.2	42.4
43.8	49.2
61.0	70.2
56.0	40.8
52.2	60.0
40.8	64.0
37.0	41.2
54.8	67.6
77.6	23.2
50.4	35.8
52.0	70.0
41.8	32.8
30.8	54.2
34.0	59.4
43.8	58.0
52.6	45.8
73.2	77.2
34.2	56.0
65.2	45.4
63.8	37.0
46.0	86.0
49.2	40.2
38.0	65.2
48.6	72.8
55.4	24.6
50.0	47.4
32.4	47.0
56.2	66.8

Now what can these numbers do for us? First let's analyze the subgroup averages using the proper techniques that we learned in **Chapter One**.

NORMALIZED DATA

This process is a means of normalizing a non-normal process. The process is accomplished by averaging subgroups of data points. Then the averages for each subgroup must be analyzed. This set of tools is specifically a tactical tool to

detect change. The subgroup averages from our example are now ready for analysis. Note the results of the simple statistics we learned in **Chapter One**.

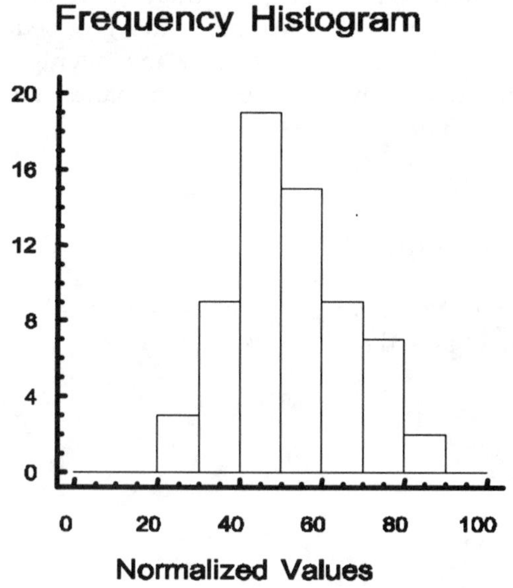

The average of the subgroup averages is 52.2 with a standard deviation of 14.7. The histogram depicting the distribution of the subgroup averages shows a very well formed normal distribution.

The following table shows the results of our normalizing process:

		Average
Central Tendency	Average	**52.2**
Variability	Standard Deviation of the subgroup average	**14.7**
Distribution	Histogram	**Normal**

As a special note, the average of the individual values (our original random numbers) was 52 and the average of the subgroup averages (Ave_{Ave}) is also 52. The fact that both sets of numbers result in the same answer gives us a tool to tactically detect a change.

Also the standard deviation of the individuals (Std_{Ind}) is 30 and the standard deviation of the averages (Std_{Ave}) is 14.7. Std_{Ind} is always bigger than Std_{Ave}. The technical name for the standard deviation of the averages (Std_{Ave}) is standard error.

The number of values that we are averaging is the subgroup size. The size of subgroup N depends on the original distribution and how much averaging is required to force the original distribution to normality. As the number of values grouped together increases, the closer to a normal distribution the grouped averages become. Generally, when the subgroup size is five, the average distribution becomes normal. Having more than five in a subgroup makes the average distribution a better normal distribution.

WHAT THE NORMALIZED NUMBERS CAN DO FOR US

We can place both the individual results and the averaging results on one chart, as seen below. Note that the center point of both distributions is the same.

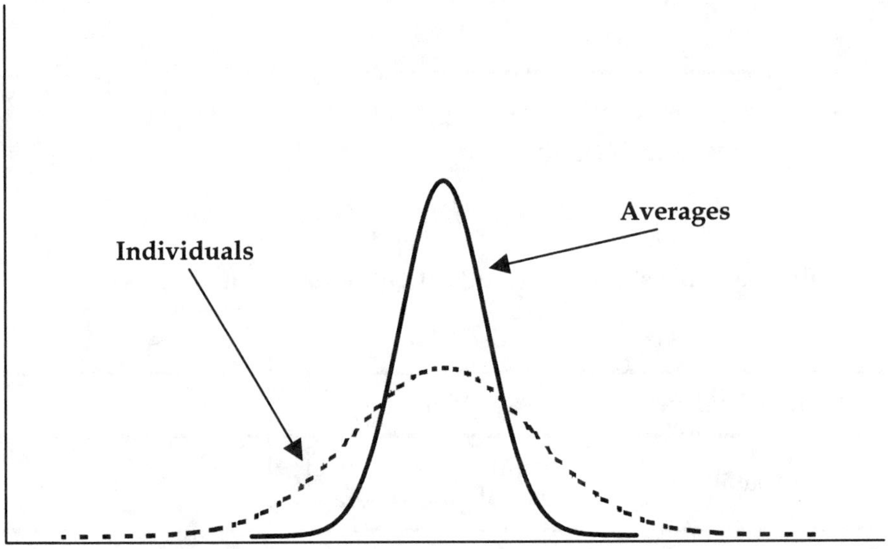

Since both the average of the individuals and the average of the averages are the same, we can use the subgroup distribution with its monitors of central tendency and variability to track and detect any changes in the true or individual distribution's center point. As the individual distribution shifts, so does the distribution of the subgroups. Both distributions will track or move in the same direction.

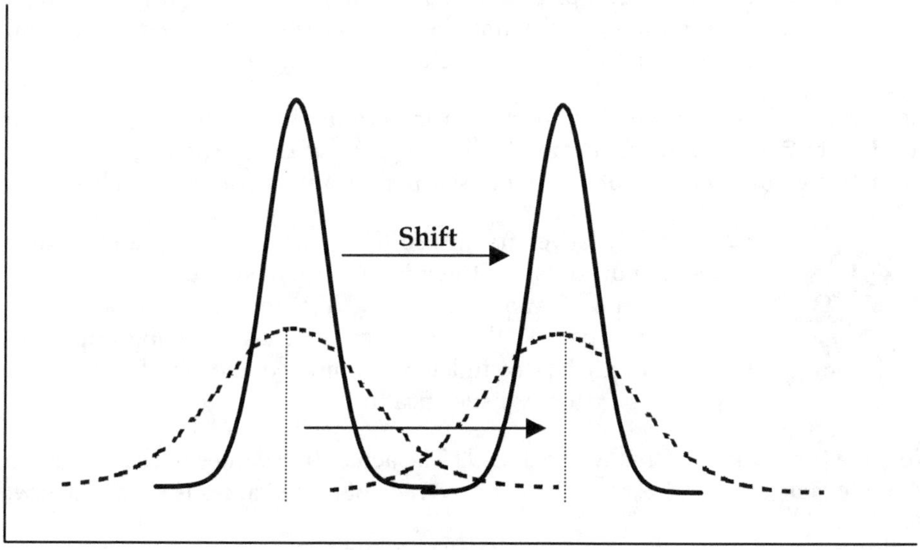

The graph shows that the individual and average distributions will track together. By tracking in the same direction, the distribution of the subgroups provides an indirect means of detecting a shift in the individual distribution. The advantage of using the subgroup distribution to detect change is that the subgroup's distribution is a normal distribution. This normality is a fact of nature and a guaranteed benefit. The assurance of the normal eliminates the need for testing the distribution. The subgroup assurance of normality allows us to always use the probabilities of the normal in our change detection system.

This detection of change is only a tactical tool to give quick and easy feedback of change. It cannot provide any strategic impact. This distinction is critical to assure that the correct set of books is always being used for the particular situation that is under analysis.

WHY USE SUBGROUP SAMPLES OF 5

Since the increasing number of values in the subgroup simply normalizes the data, there is a point of diminishing returns, where more values clustered together does not improve the subgroup or average distribution's normality. As a general rule of thumb, samples of five in a subgroup will normalize most distributions. In our example the flat distribution (nowhere near a normal) becomes normalized when five values are clustered together.

More values clustered together forming a larger subgroup will simply tighten the distribution around the mean. The subgroup size is strictly a means of normalizing our data and not a tool for assuring the accuracy of our analysis.

CAUTION! Never try to use the tactical tools or numbers for strategic purposes. Strategic management reports that use customer specifications must use the individual readings to assess the impact to the customer. The use of subgroups and their averages has completely eliminated the ability to assess impact to a customer's specification.

Note the first subgroup that we analyzed. The actual five values in the subgroup from the table are 31, 94, 7, 0, and 1. The average of these values is shown below:

$$\text{Average} = \frac{31+94+7+0+1}{5}$$

$$= 26.6$$

The average of 26.6 is a radical departure from the high value of 94 and low value of 0 in the group. To assess how well the values meet a customer's specification, we must look at the individual values.

Remember!! Analysis of the individual readings is used for strategic and management reporting. Analysis of the averages is used for tactical and operational reporting. Standard deviation is used for strategic reports while standard error is used for tactical reports.

Another advantage of using the analysis of the averages is that we have eliminated the need for a decision assessing the normality of the distribution. Our tactical or operational workforce may not have the statistical expertise that would be required if we only used the original or individual distribution.

The use of averages by the tactician focuses their attention on their role - the correct and consistent running of the machine or process. Many times a tactician, in their zeal to help, will over adjust when they see an individual reading that is

not within customer specifications. Averaging the numbers removes that temptation.

WHAT IF THE ORIGINAL DISTRIBUTION IS NORMAL?

The figure below shows a distribution of individuals that is normal. The subgroup average distribution is also shown in the same chart, and this distribution is much tighter around the center point.

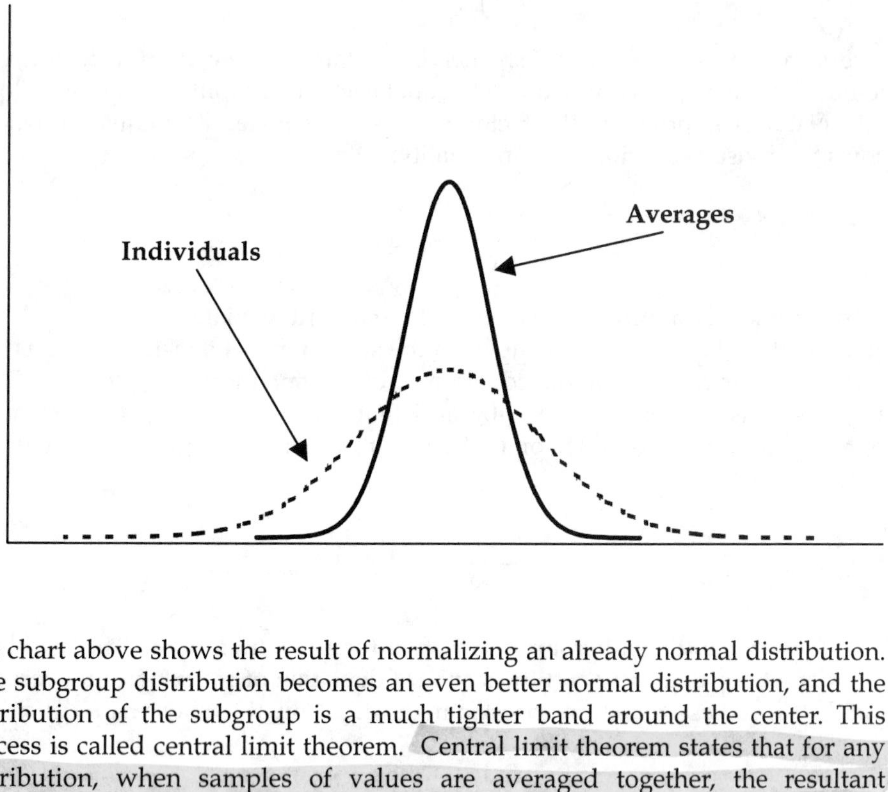

The chart above shows the result of normalizing an already normal distribution. The subgroup distribution becomes an even better normal distribution, and the distribution of the subgroup is a much tighter band around the center. This process is called central limit theorem. Central limit theorem states that for any distribution, when samples of values are averaged together, the resultant distribution of the averages will be approximately normal. The larger the number of values averaged together, the closer to a normal distribution. This theorem works no matter how far away the original distribution is from a normal distribution. Normalizing our data simply tightens our curve around the average. This does not have any sort of detrimental impact when the averages are used for tactical purposes. Thus, the tactical uses do not have to test for normality because of the central limit theorem guarantee.

RELATIONSHIP OF STANDARD ERROR AND STANDARD DEVIATION

Standard deviation of the individuals is the monitor of the variability of the actual distribution and individual readings. Standard error or the standard deviation of the averages is the monitor of the variability of the subgroup averages. In this text, standard deviation of the individual will be symbolized as Std_{Ind} and standard error or standard deviation of the averages will be noted as Std_{Ave}. Standard deviation is greater than the standard error. In mathematics this would be written as follows:

$$Std_{Ind} > Std_{Ave}$$

Since standard error is always smaller than standard deviation, a factor that would allow the two to approximately equal each other would be a tremendous tool. Nature has provided the factor, so let's investigate. The equation below shows the revised equation with an equality:

$$\frac{Std_{Ind}}{Factor} = Std_{Ave}$$

Standard error is approximately equal to standard deviation divided by the square root of the number of samples in the subgroup. The factor that must be replaced in our equation is the square root of the subgroup sample size. This sample size is the size of the subgroup that we have averaged. The most appropriate name for this factor is the subgroup size. Subgroup size will be referenced as N.

$$\frac{Std_{Ind}}{\sqrt{N}} = Std_{Ave}$$

For our example, the subgroup size is five for each subgroup. The standard deviation of our data is 30 and the standard deviation of the subgroup averages is 14.7. When these values are inserted in the equation, the following results:

$$\frac{Std_{Ind}}{\sqrt{N}} = Std_{Ave}$$

The square root of five is roughly 2.2.

$$\frac{30}{2.2} = 13.6$$

The standard deviation of 30 divided by the square root of a subgroup size of five is 13.6 and happens in this case to be a little under the calculated standard deviation of the average of 14.7. The knowledge of the relationship of standard

error and standard deviation allows us to build two sets of formulas for intervals.

As the number of subgroups increases, the standard error and standard deviation divided by the square root of N will get closer and closer. The more samples in the subgroup that are analyzed, the stronger the relationship between the standard error and standard deviation. Now, let's incorporate standard deviation and standard error into intervals. The interval formula from **Chapter One** is:

$$X_i = X_{Ave} \pm Z * Std$$

In **Chapter One**, we discussed the use of average, standard deviation, and the Z value to build an interval. This basic idea of intervals will be used for two sets of analytical books to support Division of Labor.

STATISTICAL SUPPORT FOR STRATEGIC DECISIONS AND GOALS

Strategic: the art of devising or employing plans or stratagems toward a goal.

Management decisions are strategic and assess impact. Management or strategy selects, assesses, and provides the means. All strategic analysis must support this mission.

In a manufacturing quality setting, strategic issues deal with assuring that we have the correct facility to make what the customer wants. We must compare our data to the customer's specification. To accomplish the strategic mission, the individual values must be used. To make the objective a more general statement, the strategist is responsible for providing the correct facility and for assuring that if the facility is changed in any way, it will still be capable.

The statistical tool using the individual values is called a prediction interval. Prediction intervals are based on individuals and the use of standard deviation. All the statistical tools based on prediction intervals will be the strategist's tool kit. The formula for prediction intervals is:

$$X_i = X_{Ave} \pm Z * Std_{Ind}$$

Remember, for strategic purposes, prediction intervals do not guarantee a normal distribution.

For strategic analysis the following prediction interval is used:

$$\text{Prediction Interval} = X_{Ave} \pm Z * Std_{Ind}$$

STATISTICAL SUPPORT FOR TACTICAL DECISIONS AND GOALS

Tactical: The art or skill of employing available means to accomplish an end.

Operational decisions are tactical and detect change. Operations or tactics use the available means. All tactical analysis must support this mission.

In a manufacturing setting, the operator is our tactician. He must use the available means to its optimum while he runs the facility as correctly and consistently as possible. Therefore, a separate set of tools that alert the tactician to change is required to support the tactician's mission of consistently running the available facility. The statistical tools called confidence intervals will be the tactician's toolkit.

Confidence intervals are based on averages and the use of standard error. All the statistical tools based on confidence intervals will be the tactician's tool kit. The formula for confidence intervals is:

$$X_i = X_{Ave} \pm Z * Std_{Ave}$$

We can show the relationship between standard deviation and standard error in the formula:

$$\frac{Std_{Ind}}{\sqrt{N}} = Std_{Ave}$$

Then we can substitute standard error (Std_{Ave}) in the equation with its equivalent value of standard deviation divided by the square root of the number of samples in the subgroup (N):

$$X_i = X_{Ave} \pm Z * \frac{Std_{Ind}}{\sqrt{N}}$$

When using our tactical tool, confidence intervals, we are guaranteed a normal distribution. For tactical analysis the following equation is used:

$$\text{Confidence Interval} = X_{Ave} \pm Z * \frac{Std_{Ind}}{\sqrt{N}}$$

where N = subgroup size.

The two tools supporting Division of Labor must now work together.

THE ANALYSIS SUPPORT TEAM FOR DECISION-MAKING

Tactical execution is required for strategic decisions to be effective. If operations fails to correctly run the facility, no strategy will work. Our strategic decision-maker must count on our tactical decision-makers to do their job, for only then can the strategic decisions be effective. Many strategic options are available, but they will work only if the operation can run smoothly.

To repeat, management can make good decisions only when operations is correctly and consistently running the facility. When this is the case, many options are available to management. When the plant is run incorrectly, we have no way of making a strategic decision that is based on sound logic.

The prediction intervals and confidence intervals become the eyes and ears for effective decisions. The correct set of books must be selected to provide the appropriate information to support the type of decision being made. The correct presentation of information is essential to good sound decisions. Failure to provide or choose the correct set of books and the correct analysis tool will yield incorrect information.

When strategic and tactical personnel both do their jobs, they form a team. Operations is in deep trouble when management does not do its decision-making job of providing the facility. If the facility (available means) is not capable, we are doomed to having dissatisfied customers and stockholders. If operations does not perform its role of running the facility (available means) correctly and consistently, then how can management assess the impact to the customer?

The correct selection of the analytical tool is of paramount importance so that the tactician and the strategist can become a team. Just like strategic and tactical decisions form a team, confidence and prediction intervals form an essential team for properly prepared information. Both the decision-makers and the proper support information must come together to build a finely honed team that allows for good, effective, clear decisions.

The tactician uses averages and confidence intervals. The strategist uses individuals and prediction intervals. The chart below summarizes the key points of the two sets of books.

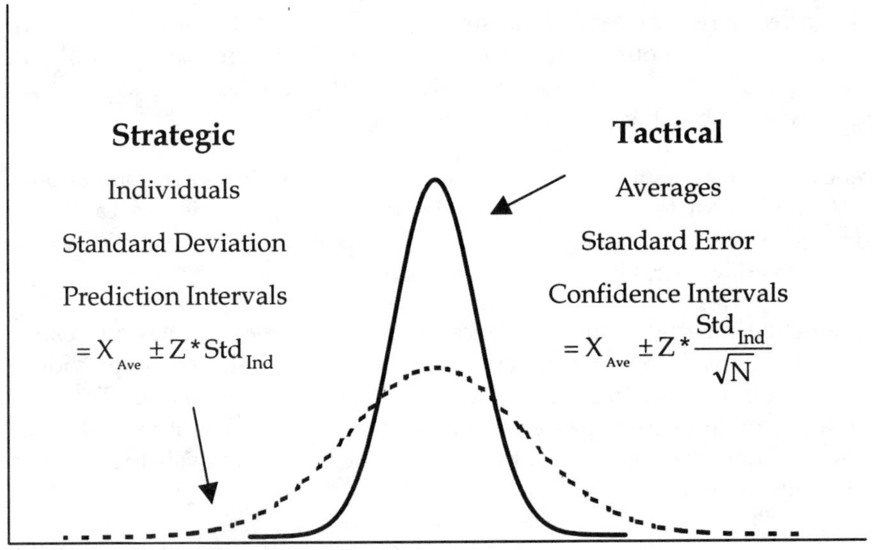

Clarity of the two sets of books and when to use them is the essence of effective analysis and decisions.

When operations (tacticians) and management (strategists) execute their jobs brilliantly, we can truly improve all three components of quality: performance, cost, and timeliness.

What are the appropriate decision-making tools for this team?

There are many tools to support both tactical and strategic decisions. Therefore, we must match the correct situation with the correct analytical tool. A few of the analytical tools are listed below:

Operational Tools for Tactical Decisions:

- Control charts
- *Walkabout* ™ diagrams
- Orthogonal Arrays
- Day planners
- Pert charts
- Gantt charts
- Resource charts
- Mean plots

Management, Customer, and Sales Tools for Strategic Decisions:

- Capability studies
- Box plots
- Feasibility studies
- Resourcing

CONTINUOUS OPERATION

We must understand Division of Labor in order to determine which analytical tools to use. The purpose of this book is to provide insight into the proper tools to run any continuous operation. The set of tools that must be used is called Statistical Process Control (SPC). This tool kit consists of a tactical tool (for operations) called control charts and a strategic tool (for management) called a capability study.

The control chart uses the set of books based on subgroup averages and the concept called confidence intervals. Control charts, which are based on confidence intervals, are the tools used by operations to detect change in the process. When a change is detected, the process is said to be "out of control." "Out of control" simply means something has changed.

The capability study uses the set of books based on individuals and the concept called prediction intervals. Capability studies, which are based on prediction intervals, are management's tool to assess any detected change in the process. When any change is detected in the process, management must assess the impact of the change in the product, and how this change will affect the customer's specification. Keep in mind we are assessing change, and change can be either an improvement or a deterioration. Thus both tools are essential, and nothing progresses if one is missing.

CHAPTER SUMMARY

In the first chapter, we discussed using good technique based on the concept of point estimates. The three areas that must be monitored are central tendency, variability, and distribution. Now we have added the concept of intervals and central limit theorem. Central limit theorem allows us to build specialized tools for monitoring both strategic and tactical situations.

Normal Distribution: Probability

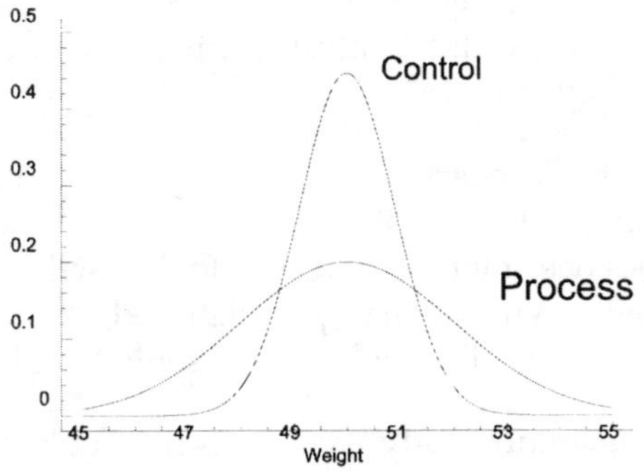

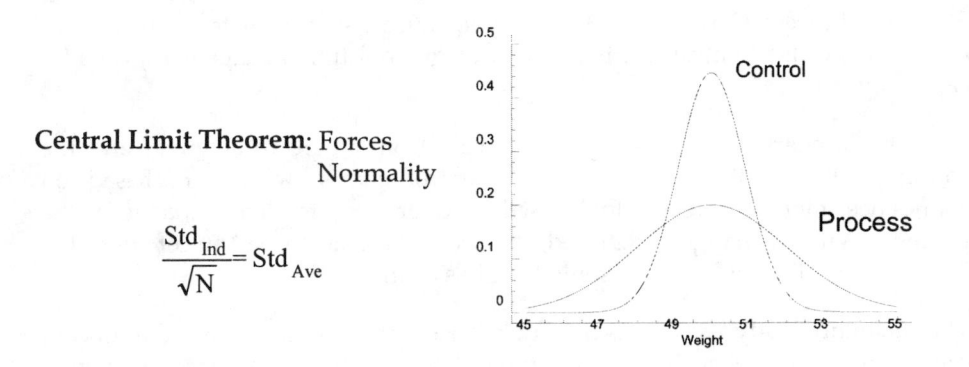

Central Limit Theorem: Forces Normality

$$\frac{Std_{Ind}}{\sqrt{N}} = Std_{Ave}$$

Statistical Support for the Second Principle Process Management

A clear understanding of Division of Labor is required to understand management and operational issues. Division of Labor is the driving force for all decisions and goals.

SECOND PRINCIPLE OF PROCESS MANAGEMENT

Division of Labor is the framework for all aspects of decision-making. It must be clearly understood to separate the strategic and tactical decisions. Operations makes the tactical decisions of running the facility. Management makes the strategic decisions of assessing the facility's suitability for the job.

Proper tools and tool selection are essential for the decision-making team and the analysis support team. Our understanding of Division of Labor must now be supported by proper analytical skills.

The following table summarizes the analytical tools to support tactical and strategic decision-making and goal setting:

	Tactical	Strategic
	Operations ↓ Detect Change ↓ Averages	Management/Customers/Sales ↓ Assess Capability ↓ Individuals
Central Tendency	$Ave_{Ave} = Ave_{Ind}$	
Variability	Std_{Ave}	Std_{Ind}
	$Std_{Ave} = \frac{Std_{Ind}}{\sqrt{N}}$ Where N = subgroup size	
Distribution	Central Limit Theorem ↑ Normalizes Data	Histogram
	Confidence Intervals $X_i = X_{Ave} \pm Z * \frac{Std_{Ind}}{\sqrt{N}}$	**Prediction Intervals** $X_i = X_{Ave} \pm Z * Std_{Ind}$

All reports must assure that the proper set of books matches the proper decision type - either strategic or tactical. No single analysis tool can support both types. Both sets of books must complement each other and work as a team.

Now we are ready to examine the reporting flaw of improper grouping in **Chapter Three**.

Chapter Three: Proper Grouping

We learned in **Chapter One** that two major analytical flaws stand in the way of providing proper information. The two flaws are 1) improper technique and 2) improper grouping. The focus of **Chapter One** was to clarify the first flaw of improper technique. For proper numerical analytical technique, we must monitor each of the following:

- Central tendency
- Variability
- Distribution

Failure to monitor all three technical characteristics will lead to catastrophic mistakes.

Now our attention must move to the second analysis flaw: improper grouping.

FLAW 2: THE GROUPING FLAW

After a commuter aircraft crash in 1994, newspapers had many articles about the safety of commuter airlines. In one article, the state of airline commuter aircraft safety was discussed. Graphs, charts, tables of statistics, and the body of the article focused on the unsafe nature of commuter aircraft. Deep in the body of the text the article stated that the FAA counts any aircraft with one to 30 seats as a commuter, including single-engine planes, bush planes flying in Alaska - even helicopters. The article continued that in 1991 and 1992, 22 of the 45 commuter accidents were in Alaska or dangerous off-shore locations. Since about 50% of the accidents were not typical of standard commercial commuter traffic, the article gave a false impression of the state of commuter traffic. This is a prime example of improper grouping.

The purpose of the article was to focus attention on the poor safety of commuters. However, by improper grouping, both the writer and the government have received bad information that caused major changes in airline regulations. Are the airline regulation changes necessary? In order to answer the question, proper grouping is essential. Using the counts from the FAA reports as published in the article would lead to a flawed base for any decision. Thus, any decision that is made based on this report is flawed. Money, resources, and time were expended simply because of bad information from poorly grouped data.

One of the most glaring problems with statistics and analysis is the improper grouping of our data. Just because we are using proper statistical technique does not mean that we are receiving accurate information. Grouping the ten machines below to report a one percent defect rate paints an incorrect picture of the overall performance. No machine is actually running at a one percent defect rate. Not only are none of the machines running at a one percent defect rate, no machine is even close to the one percent.

Machine	#1	#2	#3	#4	#5	#6	#7	#8	#9	#10
Percent Defective or Scrap	0%	0%	0%	0%	0%	0%	0%	0%	0%	10%

Using a one percent average might cause us to attempt to work on machines one through nine attempting to reduce the defect rate. Working on machines one through nine is going to cause an already good machine to change, potentially resulting in a problem.

The following are quotes from two of the masters of statistics--W. Edwards Deming and Eugene L. Grant. Their statements about the importance of proper grouping are clear and leave no room for ambiguity.

In his book *Out of the Crisis,* Deming says in the section called *"A first lesson in application of statistical theory"*, "Courses in statistics often commence with study of distributions and comparison of distributions. Students are not warned in classes nor in the books that for analytic purposes (such as to improve a process), distributions and calculations of mean, mode, standard deviation, chi-square, t-test, etc. serve no useful purpose for improvement of a process unless the data were produced in a state of statistical control."[1]

In *Statistical Quality Control,* Grant says, "The statistical tests discussed in this book begin with the presumption that samples are being drawn from a single universe. Until the control charts indicate that the presumption is true, estimates of the parameters of the distribution underlying the process are virtually meaningless. All the pitfalls regarding rational subgrouping apply, with special emphasis to capability studies."[2]

---

[1] Reprinted from ***Out of the Crisis*** by W. Edwards Deming by permission of MIT and the W. Edwards Deming Institute. Published by MIT, Center for Advanced Educational Services, Cambridge, MA 02139. Copyright 1986 by the W. Edwards Deming Institute.

[2] Eugene L. Grant and Richard S. Leavenworth, ***Statistical Quality Control***, 6th ed. (copyright 1988), pg. 167. Material is reproduced with the permission of the McGraw-Hill Companies.

There are three types of groups we must consider 1) Physical, 2) Associational, and 3) Time-series. We will discuss all three in the next section.

GROUP DEFINITION

In analysis and reporting, we must make certain assumptions and definitions. Therefore, all users must clearly understand the definition of the terms. A key assumption (both Deming and Grant understood and stated the importance of this assumption) is that all analysis is based on groups of like and homogeneous kind. Employing this definition, the term homogeneous is applied in the following ways:

Physical Groups are made of things that are materially the same. Members of physical groups are things having like kind such as type, size, color, same machine, or same operator.

Associational Groups are made of things that are similar but not necessarily exactly the same. Their members are also of like kind.

Time-Series Groups are composed of material that is similar over time. Members of a time-series group are manufactured at a time when consistency is demonstrated. This consistency is called "in control."

We must have an in-depth appreciation of why homogenous groups are critical. To more fully understand accurate analysis and reporting, the following example and scenarios will be used. A key ingredient is the assurance of homogeneous groups. The examples are to assure we can visualize and understand the concept.

Physical Groups - Certain aspects of homogeneous groups are obvious. We cannot mix size 12 and size 9 shoes together in a homogeneous group. Neither can we mix blue shirts with white shirts. An average of a size 10½ shoe or a pale blue shirt would be misleading. Instead, simple common sense is required to properly prepare homogeneous physical groups.

It appears to be obvious to keep physical groups separate, but as we saw from the excerpt in the newspaper article, this is not the case. The FAA data that the newspaper article referenced had grouped Alaskan bush planes and helicopters landing on dangerous offshore oil rigs with regular commuter traffic. This improper group caused panic in the regular commuter industry when most of the accidents had nothing to do with standard commuter traffic. Each day articles, radio and television newscasts, and daily conversation all make the grouping mistake.

Other grouping requirements are more difficult to conceptualize and even harder to assure. To pass the many difficult requirements for a homogeneous

group, we need tools like Statistical Process Control (SPC) for a time-series check, and Analysis of Variance (ANOVA) for an associational check.

Associational Grouping - Associational groups are things of like statistical kind. The machine that runs at ten percent defect versus a machine that runs at zero percent defect are associationally different. Analysis of Variance (ANOVA) is a tool that tests for grouping by association. Association is another way of saying that we only group those things of like kind. These groups are then called homogeneous. Non-homogeneous items must never be placed in the same group for analytical reports.

Time-series Group - Time-series groups are things that are similar over time. The machine that produces ten percent defective product for one hour out of 24 would require separate analysis of that one hour at ten percent defect versus the other 23 hours at zero percent defect. The control chart function of SPC provides the vehicle to assure a state of statistical control and validate the time oriented grouping. "In a state of Statistical Process Control" is another way of saying homogeneous or consistent over time.

The term homogeneous has the following requirements:

- Product having like kind, type, size, color, characteristics, etc.
- Product manufactured by the same machine and same operator.
- Product manufactured at the same time.
- Product manufactured using material from a common source.
- Product does not have to be exactly the same.

Homogeneous groups may seem obvious to one person and not to another. Thus clear guidelines are required. The control chart function of Statistical Process Control provides the vehicle to assure a state of statistical control. Statistical control is another way of saying homogeneous or consistent. We must never allow a mixture of non-homogeneous product groups.

WHY HOMOGENEOUS?

The "why" of homogeneous is critical. The following examples are designed to show us the advantages of correct group formations and the pitfalls of incorrect group formation. A key ingredient is the assurance of homogeneous products when grouping. The examples are exaggerated to assure we can visualize and understand the concept.

CANDY EXAMPLE

For our grouping example, we will use a facility that makes candy. Two types of candy are made in our facility. One contains peanuts while the other contains pecans. Our peanut product must fall inside a weight range of 45 grams to 55 grams to meet our customer's requirement. Any candy clusters that weigh less than the 45 grams are classified as defects.

Physical Grouping - For proper analysis, the pecan and peanut product should not be mixed into one group. In addition, the peanuts are denser than the pecans, thereby making the peanut product weigh about 50 grams while the pecan product weighs roughly 42 grams. Grouping an equal number of both products would yield an overall weight of 46 grams. The overall weight of 46 grams means absolutely nothing. Our customers always specify the specific product that they are interested in procuring.

Customer Order Background - We have a very demanding customer for our candies. He has just placed an order for 10,000 good peanut candy clusters. The customer wants 1000 candy clusters shipped in each of ten containers. This customer is willing to give us some room on performance since he understands the failings of humans. He has established that he will tolerate a small amount of defects. This customer expects and wants no defects, but he will not penalize us if we accidentally have no more than 500 defective units in his order. As stated in the contract, the defect rate cannot exceed five percent.

Our customer has also devised a method to assure enforcement of his requirements. Since we would destroy his product if we attempted to test all 10,000 clusters, he has devised a testing program that requires us to test 500 unbiased parts from each group of the order. The term for unbiased is random. If, of the 500 test products, more that 50 defective products are identified, then the order will be cancelled and all 10,000 parts returned.

Manufacturing Background - Our candy plant has ten identical machines working on the peanut candy clusters. Today, each machine is making the peanut candy product. This product is the same product the customer just ordered. At the end of the shift, each machine has manufactured 1000 units of clusters.

The scrap rate for each machine is listed in the table below. By reviewing data at a summary level, we run the risk of clouding or masking our problems. Take special note of machine ten and the scrap it produces.

	Mach 1	Mach 2	Mach 3	Mach 4	Mach 5	Mach 6	Mach 7	Mach 8	Mach 9	Mach 10	Tot.
Percent Defective or Scrap	0%	0%	0%	0%	0%	0%	0%	0%	0%	100%	
Product Produced	1000	1000	1000	1000	1000	1000	1000	1000	1000	1000	10000
Scrap	0	0	0	0	0	0	0	0	0	1000	1000

To calculate a summary plant percent, we divide the total scrap by the total production.

$$\textbf{Plant Percent Defective} = \left(\frac{\text{Total Scrap}}{\text{Total Production}}\right)100\%$$

$$= \left(\frac{1000\text{ parts}}{10{,}000\text{ parts}}\right)100\% = 10\%$$

Our plant percent defective is ten percent in the summary. By grouping these together, and simply looking at the summary information, we have the picture that we are running a fair to poor operation.

The product coming from each machine is put into a container holding the 1000 parts from only that one particular machine. Therefore, the containers for product from machines one through nine each contain 1000 good parts, but the container for machine ten contains 1000 bad parts.

Grouping For Shipping - For shipping, all the containers are grouped together. We have incorrectly called this a quality assurance group instead of a shipment. Let us discuss the ramifications and consequences of this incorrect definition.

We have now shipped the 10,000 parts to the customer. The customer's order specified that 500 candies would be tested to assure that the candies were good. To avoid a biased test, the customer develops a testing plan to test equal quantities from each container for the total of 500 test parts. The 500 piece test plan for the containers is shown below:

Container Machine No.	**1**	**2**	**3**	**4**	**5**	**6**	**7**	**8**	**9**	**10**
No. of parts Sampled	50	50	50	50	50	50	50	50	50	50

The customer pulls his test values from each container. Since only good product is in containers one through nine, we will obviously have only good test results. But in container ten, produced on machine ten, all the product is bad, so the test samples must all be bad. The test results are shown below:

Container Machine No.	**1**	**2**	**3**	**4**	**5**	**6**	**7**	**8**	**9**	**10**
No. of parts Sampled	50	50	50	50	50	50	50	50	50	50
Defective Parts	0	0	0	0	0	0	0	0	0	50

By incorrectly identifying the group as homogeneous, we have now put ourselves in the position of losing the complete order. No one should be surprised that the complete shipment of 10,000 candies is returned. The good product from machines one through nine is being lost because the bad product from the one bad machine – machine ten - is mixed in the shipment.

If we had tested true groups, we would have scrapped all products from machine ten. In doing this, we could ship our customer 9000 good parts. By correctly forming the group, we could increase our productivity or throughput because no product is returned. In other words, the 10,000 parts that include the scrap are returned, but the 9000 parts, if shipped separately, would be accepted. Generally, though, we do not have such an obvious situation. The next example is a more complex situation.

Mixing of Product - Imagine the same production schedule with an additional step to optimize the production system. This process allows us to thoroughly mix all machines' goods in a vat to form one large homogeneous group such that

no product can be identified with its producing machine. This group is now a true group.

Total Production	**10,000 parts**
Good candy	**9,000 parts**
Bad candy	**1,000 parts**

The product is gathered into one mixed group as shown to the left.

This chart shows the original production and product shipment containers:

Machine No.	1	2	3	4	5	6	7	8	9	10	TOTAL
Product Produced	1000	1000	1000	1000	1000	1000	1000	1000	1000	1000	10,000
Scrap	0	0	0	0	0	0	0	0	0	1000	1000
Percent Defective	0%	0%	0%	0%	0%	0%	0%	0%	0%	100%	10%

The problem with the mixed group is that we have contaminated good product with bad. Now the containers will have product that is like the example in the table below. As you can see, a few bad candies are in each container.

Container	A	B	C	D	E	F	G	H	I	J	TOTAL
Product Shipped	1000	1000	1000	1000	1000	1000	1000	1000	1000	1000	10,000
Good Parts	900	900	900	900	900	900	900	900	900	900	9000
Bad Parts	100	100	100	100	100	100	100	100	100	100	1000

The odds are very high that we will still lose the entire order in testing. However, the dilemma really occurs if we don't lose the group in testing, and we ship this order. We have shipped defective goods to the customer, and we should not be surprised to find the customer unhappy. We have shipped more bad product than the customer's order had stated would be acceptable. Remember, the customer stated that he wanted no bad parts at all and would tolerate no more than 500 bad parts in the order.

As is now obvious, proper group formation is vital to accurate reporting. Each machine's product is kept separate, and each homogeneous group can stand on its own. Once a group has been identified at the detailed level, these numbers can then be grouped into an aggregate report. Accurate and effective decisions can be made about each group when we avoid any contamination. By correctly forming groups, we are able to increase our throughput because we will not allow any bad product contamination.

Time-series Group - A more complex and less obvious example is a time-series production problem. We are working in the same plant but analyzing only one machine. Today this machine is making the customer's ordered product. Every hour of the shift the machine manufactures 1000 candies. The scrap rate for each hour is listed in the table below. Since a container holds 1000 parts, each hour's product is put into its own container.

	PRODUCTION TABLE									
	1:00	**2:00**	**3:00**	**4:00**	**5:00**	**6:00**	**7:00**	**8:00**	**9:00**	**10:00**
Parts Produced	1000	1000	1000	1000	1000	1000	1000	1000	1000	1000
Scrap Parts	0	0	0	0	1000	0	0	0	0	0
Percent Scrap or Defective	0%	0%	0%	0%	100%	0%	0%	0%	0%	0%

All of the machine's product from 1:00 through 10:00 is grouped together into one shipment as the product is produced. We are incorrectly calling this total production (all ten hours and 10,000 units) a group. We are taking an extremely big risk of having the complete shipment rejected.

We are filling the containers each hour as the goods are produced. The product in each container is shown below:

Container Hour	**1:00**	**2:00**	**3:00**	**4:00**	**5:00**	**6:00**	**7:00**	**8:00**	**9:00**	**10:00**
Container	A	B	C	D	E	F	G	H	I	J
Parts Produced	1000	1000	1000	1000	1000	1000	1000	1000	1000	1000
Bad Parts	0	0	0	0	1000	0	0	0	0	0
Good Parts	1000	1000	1000	1000	0	1000	1000	1000	1000	1000

The testing plan used by the customer will be similar to the prior plan and is shown below:

Container Hour	1:00	2:00	3:00	4:00	5:00	6:00	7:00	8:00	9:00	10:00
Container	A	B	C	D	E	F	G	H	I	J
No. of parts Sampled	50	50	50	50	50	50	50	50	50	50

We again see how the group will fail. Hours 1:00 - 4:00 and 6:00 - 10:00 have produced only good parts while the container for the 5:00 hour has only bad parts. We see in the table below that the 5:00 container sample will have 50 bad parts. Once again we should not be surprised to find that the customer will be unhappy, and the order will be returned and cancelled.

Container Hour	1:00	2:00	3:00	4:00	5:00	6:00	7:00	8:00	9:00	10:00
Container	A	B	C	D	E	F	G	H	I	J
No. of parts Sampled	50	50	50	50	50	50	50	50	50	50
Defective Parts	0	0	0	0	50	0	0	0	0	0

Production must be defined as only good product that the customer will accept. For us to maximize production, we must never allow bad parts to contaminate good parts. To maximize production, we must assure that no defective parts are knowingly mixed in good parts through combining of machines or hours. Once we have assured that all groups (i.e. machines, hours, etc.) are the same, then and only then, can we begin to mix.

Mixing of Hours - Imagine the same production schedule for one machine, with an additional step to optimize the production system. This process allows us to mix all the machine's goods for many hours into one vat. Each hour's product is mixed together to form one large homogeneous group called a true group. The production for all ten hours is mixed together as shown in the table below:

Total production	**10,000 parts**
Good candy	**9,000 parts**
Bad candy	**1,000 parts**

The machine's product is combined to form a mixture. This mixture is now a true group but has obvious problems because we have contaminated good product with bad. The odds are very high that we will lose the order in testing. However, again the real dilemma is that if we don't lose the group in testing and we ship this order, we have shipped defective goods to the customer. We should not be surprised to find the customer unhappy.

IMPROPER ASSOCIATIONAL GROUPS

We may never have a situation as obvious as the prior ones but imagine the following example for a machine. Each machine's production is lumped together forming inappropriate groups. Even when the differences are not so dramatic, the impact of bad reports is the same.

Machine	1	2	3	4	5	Total
Parts Produced	1000	1000	1000	1000	1000	5000
Parts Scrap	2	3	2	1	50	58
Percent Scrap	.2%	.3%	.2%	.1%	5%	1.2%

By mixing machines one through four with machine five, we have dramatically affected the defective percentage for machines one through four in a very detrimental way. We have the potential of contaminating good parts from machines one through four with the bad parts from machine five. An analysis of this incorrectly grouped example will generate a completely false impression. The 1.2% scrap rate represents absolutely nothing.

Chapter Two showed us the importance of intervals. For the previous example, the use of intervals provides a quantitative method for comparing machines one through five to identify which machines form an associational group. Intervals are an effective and appropriate mechanism to make associational groupings.

The chart below is called a mean plot. The mean plot is one of the tools for discrete group comparisons. The chart shows that machine five is distinctly different from machines one through four. These five machines are the same physically, but the defect rates are different enough to make two separate associational groups. One group contains machines one through four, while the second group contains only machine five.

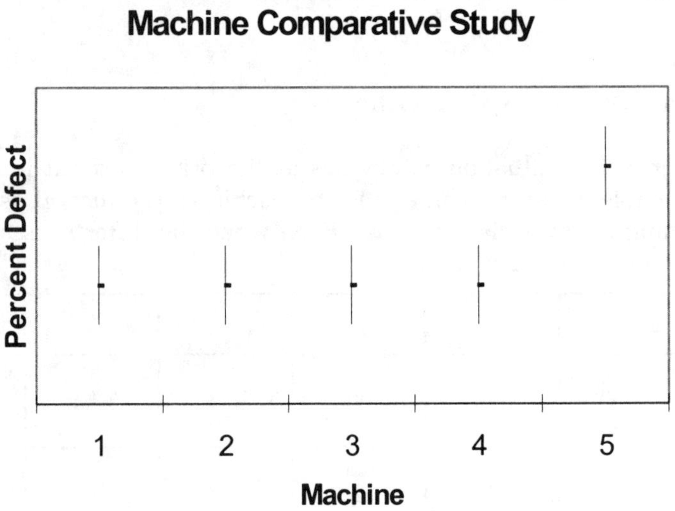

IMPROPER TIME-SERIES GROUPS

Imagine the time oriented production for a machine as shown below. Each hour is lumped together with no thought to proper grouping.

Time	1:00	2:00	3:00	4:00	5:00	6:00	7:00	8:00	Total
Parts Produced	1000	1000	1000	1000	1000	1000	1000	1000	8000
Parts Scrap	2	2	100	100	0	1	1	2	208
Percent Scrap	.2%	.2%	10%	10%	0%	.1	.1%	.2%	2.6%

The pocket of bad product produced from 3:00-4:00, if allowed to be mixed with that of the other hours, will contaminate the product of all other hours. A report stating that this machine ran a 2.6% scrap rate is just as incorrect as the improperly grouped machines.

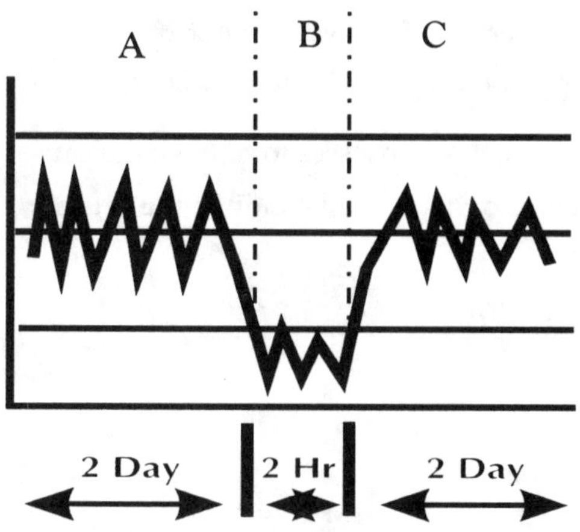

A + B + C = 1%
A = 0%
B = 6%
C = 0%

We would not be surprised if the customer and management complained about these mixed and contaminated goods.

The SPC tool called control charts is the tool to monitor any shift in the time-series groups. Any shifts from the usual running characteristics of the machine must be investigated.

The chart to the left shows the weight of peanut candy clusters when they are produced. The weight of the clusters has shifted from time period A to time period B. A second shift is shown from time period B to time period C.

The defective percentage for time period A is zero, for time period B is six, and time period C is zero. Two distinctly different groups can be seen, with A and C forming one group, and B forming a second group. If we attempted to group all the time periods together (A, B, and C), we would compute a one percent defect rate which would be completely misleading.

PROPER GROUP FORMATION SUMMARY

We can change the scenario by adjusting the percentages and the way in which the groups are formed, but correct formation of a group is critical to any report or analysis.

The product and process data must be kept separate by grouping so that we can identify homogeneous groups and be able to form an aggregate group. An aggregate group is composed of things of like kind.

In summary, we must group based on:

- Physical similarity
- Associational characteristics
- Time of manufacture

We can assure proper physical groups by employing common sense. The associational groups are identified by use of a technique called Analysis of Variance. The time-series groups are formed based on the analytical tool called control charts.

With proper group formation we can expect the following benefits:

- Avoiding the contamination of good product with bad product.
- Always taking action on bad product or processes to remove the cause.
- Always noticing an improvement so that we can continue the cause.
- Increased product throughput.
- Increased production and productivity.
- Improved processes.

...and the list of benefits just continues.

DATA COLLECTION

Our data collection objective is to provide information to support better decision-making. Each piece of data should have the clear purpose of supporting a specific decision, and this purpose should be clearly stated for all who are gathering the data. By having a clear purpose as the environment changes, the data gatherers can adjust the manner in which they collect the data. Should the specific decision no longer be needed, then the data collection can also be discontinued.

Management needs information to make intelligent decisions. This information must be prepared in a format that concisely and accurately presents factual data. The problem with a detailed analysis is that one can become overwhelmed with data. We can "lose the forest for the trees" if we don't condense. The trick is to condense without making grouping mistakes. An alternate plan is to aggregate the data (summarize the data of like kind) to carefully and logically create a series of homogeneous groups for summary.

For us to do the detailed analysis that will lead to accurate reporting, a great deal of data gathering will be required. To adequately handle the detailed reporting, all associates must participate in the data gathering effort. To support proper group formation, a bottom up strategy of data reporting is required. This bottom up group formation will test for both time-series and associational groups.

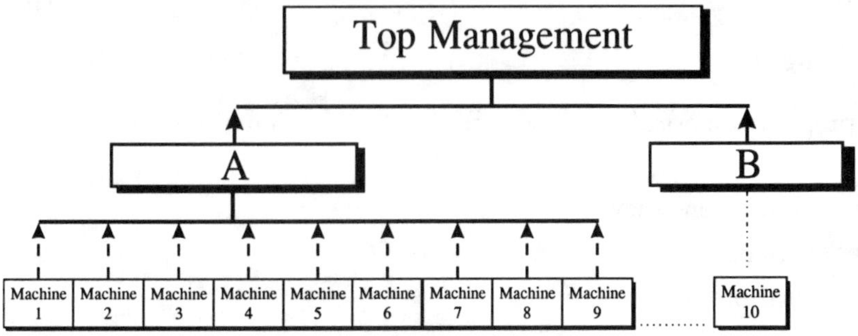

This bottom up strategy will clearly document the status of the area. The proper grouping will allow correct and accurate information to flow to top management. With better information in hand, better decision-making can be expected.

CHAPTER SUMMARY

For any analysis to be on solid ground, the following must be the centerpiece to any study.

Technique

For proper numerical analysis, our technique must monitor each of the following:

- Central tendency
- Variability
- Distribution

Failure to monitor any one of the three will have dire consequences.

Grouping

Our groups must form one (homogeneous) universe based on:

- Physical similarity
- Associational characteristics
- Time of manufacture

We can assure proper physical groups by employing common sense. The associational groups are identified by using a technique called Analysis of Variance. The time-series groups are formed based on the analytical tool called control charts.

Proper Analysis

All our analyses are based on the assurance that both proper technique and groupings have been used. This combination will allow us to provide good information. This analysis will require a bottom up strategy of data collection and analysis.

Chapter Four:
Statistical Process Control

Statistical Process Control (SPC) is used to analyze and monitor a continuous process. SPC should be used to monitor both product and process characteristics of all continuous operations.

Since SPC is designed to monitor a continuous process, an ongoing surveillance program is required. The flowchart to the left depicts the steps required for this monitoring system. First, we must gather data on a regular and consistent basis. Second, this data is measured for consistency with older data using a control chart. Once a state of statistical control is established, we must begin the third step of assessing how well the data meets the customer's needs using a tool called a capability study. The final step is maintaining control with a capable process.

Each one of these steps will be explained in this chapter and then later chapters will discuss all the details associated with each.

Statistical Process Control is comprised of two tools: 1) **control charts** and 2) **capability studies**.

A control chart is designed as an alarm system to detect change (both improvement and deterioration) in an operation. Because it is the operator's tool for monitoring a particular machine or system during its time of function, it includes an alarm system for detecting any type of shift or change. This alarm must be dynamically recalibrated to reflect the current status. The following are types of control charts:

- **P**
- **C**
- **U**
- $\bar{X}$ **and R**
- $\bar{X}$ **and S**
- **Individuals**

A capability study is the tool for management to assess how well the product being produced matches the product the customer desires.

The SPC team includes both control charts for tactical purposes and capability studies for strategic work. Therefore, both must work together to form a cohesive team. Let's first examine each tool independently. Then we will understand how the SPC team of control charts and capability studies works together.

MONITORING A CONTINUOUS PROCESS

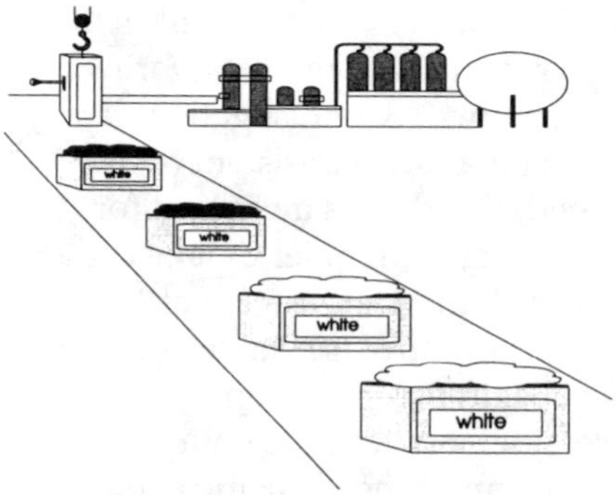

Monitoring the Candy Plant Packaging

Notice in the drawing to the left that we are packaging our candy in a white container. The third product shown is not white but has changed to black, and all subsequent product is black.

Analysis of a particular machine, process, product, system, or entity must be done in the chronological sequence. If we lose the integrity of the time of an event, we have lost a tremendous source of data.

This knowledge of when the candy package changed is critical to our analysis. The quicker change is detected, the better. The longer the package change goes undetected the more the bad product builds. We must not wait until many bad candy packages are produced. If we had lost the time of the product change, we might have mistakenly determined that the change was a random event rather than a systematic change. Instead, we must have a continuous surveillance to detect change as early as possible.

TIME SEQUENCE

In order to detect patterns, trends, and shifts, we must not only document the time of occurrence but also group the values in chronological sequence to detect the shifts. Chronological sequence is necessary for identifying causes.

If we lumped both the black and white containers together, we would have an incorrect impression of the quality level of the product. The result would be very camouflaged and confused. No decision from this kind of analysis would be valid. To get a complete production picture, any change must be separated and assessed.

Time-series

By maintaining the integrity of the time sequence, we also have the ability to take care of our time-series grouping. The time-series grouping is resolved by using control charts.

The SPC objective is much more than simply detecting a defect. Rather, the SPC objective is to monitor for both improvements and deterioration allowing us to get the most from our facilities. Like the United States army says, "Be all you can be." We want to use SPC to get all we can out of our facilities.

This objective uses the Second Principle of Process Management to make good decisions. The next section is a brief review of this principle.

The Second Principle of Process Management Summarized: Division of Labor drives the decision-making process. It dictates who will be in charge of the different kinds of decisions (strategic or tactical). We are doomed to a state of Quality Hell if the managers of the future fail to fully grasp Division of Labor.

SECOND PRINCIPLE OF PROCESS MANAGEMENT

Division of Labor is the framework for all aspects of decision making. It must be clearly understood to separate the strategic and tactical decisions. Operations makes the tactical decisions of running the facility. Management makes the strategic decisions of assessing the facility's suitability for the job.

Control is a major tactical issue associated with operational duties. Capability is a major strategic issue associated with management, customer, and sales concerns.

If we have a clear understanding of the second Principle of Process Management, or this "Division of Labor", we will possess the key to appreciating the difference between tactical and strategic decisions.

Division of Labor requires a clear understanding of the differences between management/customer/sales issues and operational issues.

Tactics: The art or skill of employing available means to accomplish an end.

Operational decisions are tactical and detect change.

Strategy: The art of devising or employing plans or stratagems toward a goal.

Management decisions are strategic and assess impact.

Division of Labor drives and controls goal setting and decision-making. Clarity of purpose is essential to effective goals and decisions. Operations must be tactically driven while management/sales/customer must be strategically driven.

The principle of Division of Labor will have a profound effect on decision-making. The concepts below must be clearly understood, for without them, no improvement is possible. These concepts are given in-depth coverage in my book *Optimize Your Operation*.

Second Principle of Process Management

Division of Labor

↓

Accountability

	Operations	**Management/Sales/Customer**
Accountability	The correct and consistent running of the facility.	Finding customers who will buy our products.
Responsibility	Running the provided facility correctly and consistently.	Providing the facility that will produce what the customer wants.
Missions	Control	Capability • Customer Specifications • Targets • Goals • Requirements
Decisions	Tactical	Strategic

For the most effective and efficient operations, we must understand our role according to Division of Labor and then execute brilliantly.

Strategy comes from the Greek word strategos, which means "the art of the general." Generals make several kinds of strategic decisions including which resources to use, when to use the resources, and where to use the resources in the conduct of battle. Strategy, for our context, is the planning and provision of the correct resources, at the correct time, at the correct place.

Tactics is the execution of the strategic plan that the general has developed. Our execution of the strategic plan must be the best and most effective use of the provided resources.

ACCOUNTABILITY

To be held accountable, we must first know whether we are in a tactical area or a strategic area. Tactical personnel should be held accountable for issues and decisions that deal with the execution of the plan. In a continuous operation, the plan deals with the facility that has been provided. The operator, who is the tactician, should be held accountable for the correct and consistent running of the facility. The operator is responsible for correctly and consistently running the machine he has been provided.

Strategic personnel should be held accountable for developing a plan and building a facility to meet the company's needs. This facility must produce the product that the customer wants.

For a complete and detailed explanation of Division of Labor, I suggest that you consult my book *Optimize Your Operation*.

Second principle violations must be understood and avoided in order to effectively make decisions. The kinds of situations that we will encounter if we violate the second principle are:

Division of Labor Violation 1 - No Thought to Capability

If we violate the second principle by confusing the responsibilities of management with those of operations, we have no basis for assessing the capability of the facility. We in management can only ask operations to do what the facility is capable of doing. In this way we can hold operations accountable for the correct and consistent running of the facility. Management must provide operations with a facility that is capable of producing the customer's product.

Division of Labor Violation 2 - Forced Capability

Good Trooper Award: If we violate the second principle by trying to place the responsibility for strategic decisions on operations, we will not be able to meet the customer's demands, and we also make a more defective product than was necessary in the first place. The harder a good associate works with improper instructions (violating the second principle), the poorer the quality. Quality will continue to degenerate.

Division of Labor Violation 3 - Poor Productivity

If we violate the second principle on an extremely capable process, we will make the machine appear less capable than it really is. Instead, we must run the machine to its own personality as correctly and consistently as possible. We must not be lulled into accepting products that are only as good as the customer wants and allow the process to float inside the customer's specification.

We must guard against any violation of the second principle – Division of Labor. A good associate who is put in the situation of having to run a facility with

improper directions that violate the second principle is doomed to disaster. The better and more conscientious the employee, the worse the situation will become because the person will go to any lengths to carry out those improper directions.

Because of Division of Labor, SPC is comprised of two tools specifically designed to support either tactical or strategic decisions. The tactical tool is called a control chart while the strategic tool is called a capability study. Let's now focus our attention on the operator's role, and provide him with analytical support to best run his machine. This effort is referred to as control. Later in this chapter, we will turn our attention to supporting the strategic role.

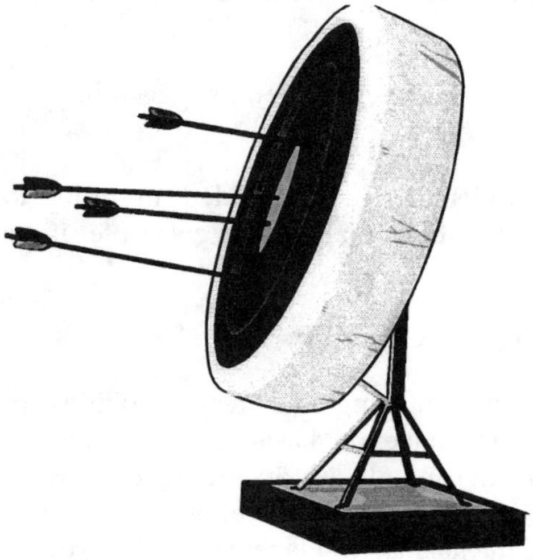

Where are we?? Before any improvements or problems can be solved, knowing where we are is essential. Statistical Process Control is the set of tools that provides a clear idea of where we are in relation to our target. Before an archer can hit the bull's-eye, he must know where the target is. He must also know where his arrows are falling so that any adjustments are made in the appropriate direction.

The details of archery are essential to hitting the bull's-eye. These same details are essential to a continuous operation. Now let's focus on the first detail of the correct and consistent running of the operation.

What does Control mean?? When we say that we are in control, we are only talking about operational issues. The term in control means that we are running the facility correctly and consistently. This gives us a way of knowing where we are.

We must have tools available to us to measure a facility's uniquely correct and consistent running parameters. Control charts were designed expressly to do the job of evaluating the correct and consistent running parameters of a machine. A control chart also functions as an alarm system to alert us to changes and deviations from these optimum parameters. Remember that changes can take the form of either improvements or deterioration of the process. However, control charts cannot identify whether the change is an improvement or deterioration. A control chart's mission is very specialized: to identify change only.

OPERATIONAL DECISIONS

When we understand the concept of control, we realize that the objective of operations is the correct and consistent running of the currently available and existing facility. Operations must keep a focus on the tactical needs by making tactical decisions and conducting tactical analysis.

Tactical decisions are defined as decisions employing the available means to accomplish an end. Operations makes tactical decisions.

Operations => Tactics: Operations uses tactical decisions to continually better understand the facility. With this knowledge, operations can use tactics to continue to correctly and consistently run the facility.

THE OPERATOR'S ROLE

The operator must focus his attention on the provided machine. The operator must run the machine as correctly and consistently as possible with the current state of knowledge. Running the machine to the maximum is the operator's responsibility for which he must be held accountable. Tools to assist the operator must be provided with the clear mission of supporting the correct and consistent running of the machine.

The objective of correctly and consistently running the machine means getting the most out of the machine no matter what the customer's specifications require. Our tools to support the operator will thus be independent of the customer and his requirements.

TOOLS TO SUPPORT THE OPERATION OF A CONTINUOUS PROCESS

There are many tactical analytical tools that are designed specifically to support operations. One tool, called a control chart, is used on continuous operations to detect change. Control charts provide the mechanism to determine whether or not a particular machine is running consistently, and are also a means of monitoring and detecting homogeneous groups. They could also be called "consistency charts," "change detectors," or "cause detectors."

Control Chart

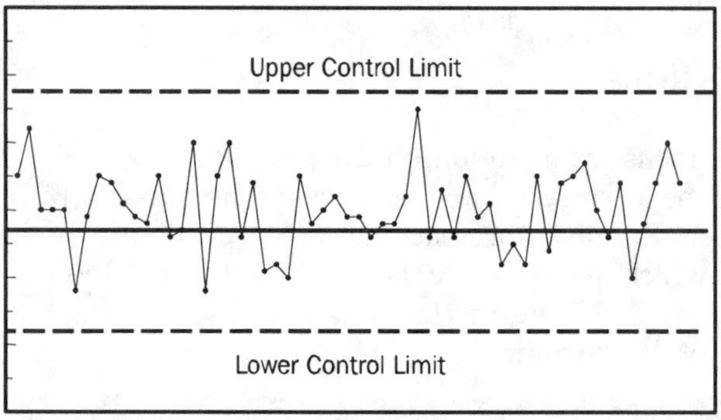

Many people attempt to make a control chart into both a management and an operations report by including specifications, goals, customer expectations, and tolerances on them. Control charts are operational tools, not management reports. Since specifications are strategic in nature, they NEVER appear on a control chart. The whole mathematical concept behind control charts assumes we are only discussing tactical issues. We will be concerned with specifications in the discussion of the strategic tool called "capability studies" discussed later in this section.

Control charts were never intended to be used as an indication of how well the product fits the customer's needs. Control charts are for the tactical decision of consistently running the facility and for detecting change.

WHAT EXACTLY IS A CONTROL CHART

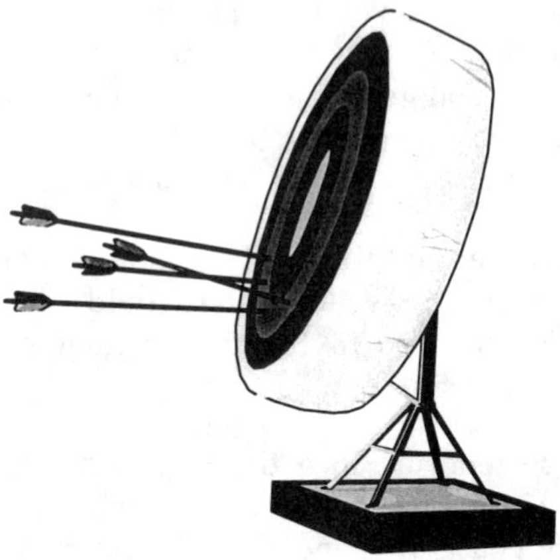

The objective of a control chart is to help an operator run a machine correctly and consistently (without change). This is referred to as being in control. Because change can be either an improvement or deterioration, any change must be identified immediately so that management can assess the impact to the customer.

Since the change must be detected quickly, a change detector is critical. That is exactly what a control chart is.

I hope you have a smoke detector in your house. The smoke detector sits quietly in the background until smoke or fire is detected. When the detector senses these situations, it sounds the call to arms loudly and aggressively. No action is taken based on the alarm alone, but immediate inquiry into the situation is required. We must know the cause of the fire before taking action because if we throw water on a grease fire, the fire will spread. Once the smoke detector alarm is activated, we immediately search the house to find the cause of the alarm. When the fire's cause is identified, we can make a decision about what to do. This is exactly how a control chart works - instantly alerting the operator to any change and triggering our research as to the cause.

Control Consistency Alarm Chart
System
Operator's Tool
1 Particular Entity

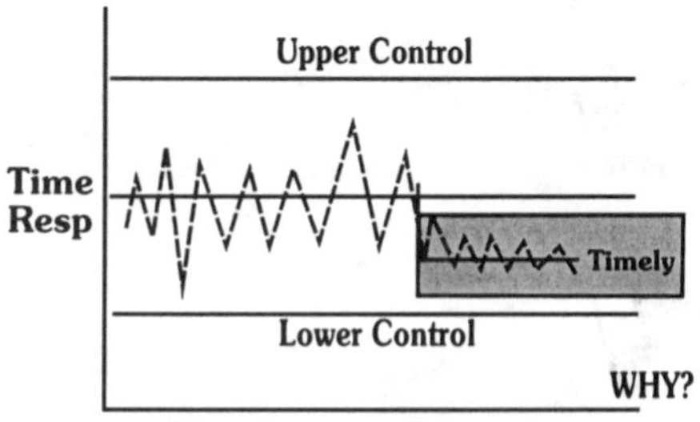

Time Sequence Orientation
Alarm System
AVE
$UCL = AVE + 3\ STD_{AVE}$
$LCL = AVE - 3\ STD_{AVE}$

When we are in control, we are running the machine in a steady fashion. In control is another way of saying that the machine is running with no change from the machine's typical running results.

Control charts, like the one to the left, show when a change has occurred for a particular machine.

WHY TIMELY REPORTING IS ESSENTIAL

In the early 70's, the comedian Flip Wilson had several characters that he portrayed in sketches. One of my favorite characters was Geraldine. She was well known for her lines, "What you see is what you get," in reference to herself and, "The Devil made me do it," when she was in trouble. She attended the Reverend Leroy's church that was named *The Church of What's Happening Now*.

Control charts are in many ways like Geraldine because the most important data point for a control chart is the most recent event or, as Geraldine would say, "What's Happening Now!" Conditions and changes in the past cannot be resolved and fixed but we can act upon the current situation.

Control chart alarms must be reported in a timely manner to allow us the opportunity to determine the reason why the change has occurred. Control charts demand that all results be posted immediately.

TACTICAL SUPPORT FOR THE OPERATOR

In a manufacturing setting, the operator is our tactician. The operator must use the available means to its optimum in order to run the facility as correctly and consistently as possible. A separate set of tools which alert the tactician to change are required to support the tactician's mission of consistently running the available facility. These statistical tools, based on averages and the use of standard error, are called confidence intervals and will be in the tactician's tool kit. The formula for confidence intervals is:

$$X_i = X_{Ave} \pm Z * Std_{Ave}$$

OR

$$X_i = X_{Ave} \pm Z * \frac{Std_{Ind}}{\sqrt{N}}$$

A second way to state confidence intervals is by using a term called confidence limits. Confidence limits are the spots on the extreme ends of the confidence interval. The interval is the range while limits are the end points of the interval. Intervals and limits are used for both confidence and prediction.

Confidence limits that detect change become our means of building control charts. The control chart uses a special kind of confidence limit called control limits. A control limit is an alarm that the product or process has changed from what has been the norm for this machine.

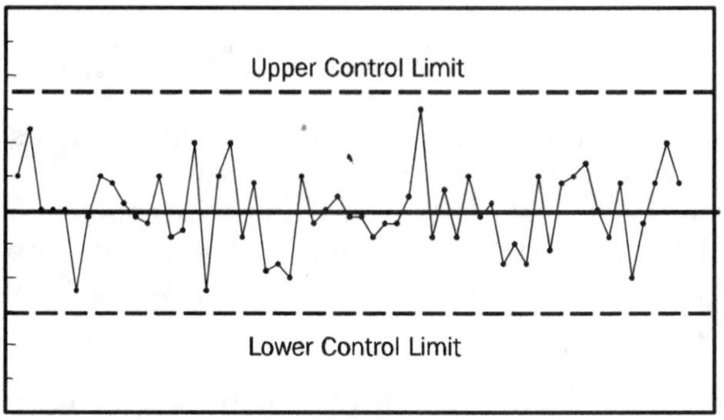

WHAT MAKES A CONTROL CHART

A control chart is the alarm system to note changes in a product or process function. The control chart monitors the various quantitative aspects of the function. This is a pictorial change alarm system.

The information to be plotted is comprised of two components: data and alarms.

Data or values to be monitored over time: Since we are looking only for an alarm of a shift or change, then the data will be massaged through averaging to assure a normal distribution.

Alarms to detect change: The following are the alarms that are used in control charts and are based on the fact that the data will be a normal distribution. This normality is because our data is averages of subgroups. These subgroup averages use the central limit theorem to guarantee a normal distribution.

The first alarm could be the average where 50% of the data points are above the average, while the remaining 50% fall below the average. A second alarm could be where 68% of the data points will fall inside the plus or minus one standard error interval. A third alarm could be when 95.4% of the data points will fall inside the plus or minus two standard error intervals. Continuing, another alarm could be when 99.8% of the data points will fall inside the plus or minus three standard error intervals. More zones could be created but the possibility of

having values in larger zones is so small that there is no need to include them. To reduce the confusion of so many lines and alarms, one control limit is required.

A control limit is a special kind of confidence limit used for the specific purpose of assisting the operator run a machine consistently. A control limit was defined in the 1920s with a Z value of three. This Z value was selected such that any data point outside the control limits would be a rarity. The control limits are as follows:

$$\text{Control Limits} = X_{Ave} \pm 3 * Std_{Ave}$$

The original developers of SPC defined the term control limits to mean a specific idea. Since control limits were defined so many years ago, any deviation from the definition is absolutely forbidden with no exceptions. This would be like trying to redefine the color red. We might be able to convince a few people to call red by the name of blue, but anyone to whom we had not talked would be extremely confused and rightly so.

In addition, ALL interpretation rules are based on control limits that are computed with a Z value of three. Any changes would require complete revisions of these interpretation rules. No matter what the reason, we have too much invested in our proper control limit definition to allow any changes or deviations. Thus, control limits must be set only at a Z value of THREE.

Normally, only the control limits appear on the control chart because more lines will create too much clutter for easy use of the control chart methodology.

In **Chapter Six** we will discuss the details of the calculations for the alarms associated with control charts. We will see some short cuts that were invented back in the 1920s to expedite the calculations of control limits and, most importantly, discover why these short cuts work.

MANAGEMENT'S ROLE

The concept of making what the customer wants is very important; we must be customer driven. At the same time, we can only evaluate capability when we are using the correct tool. Management must stay focused on strategic needs.

Management must understand its responsibility for providing a facility that will make what the customer wants. Management must understand that it will be held accountable for this mission regarding the capability of the machine. We provide very targeted tools to support operations' mission. Likewise, tools must be provided to assess management's mission of providing facilities that can meet the customer's needs.

When we say that we are capable, we are only talking about management and customer issues. The term capable means that the facility is making what the customer wants. There is a difference between the correct and consistent running of the facility and how well we are meeting our customer's expectations. When we understand the concept of capability, we realize that the objective of management is to assure that we are providing a facility that can make what the customer wants.

As management makes strategic decisions to plan for a goal, the limiting factor of availability that was placed on tactical decisions is removed. Management must find the means or facilities to supply operations. Strategic decisions involve determining the time, place, and resources required to accomplish our goal just as a general must obtain the resources, determine the place for the battle, and pick the time of the battle.

Strategic decisions are categorized as the defining and obtaining of the appropriate resources and then determining when and where to use them. Management uses strategies and strategic decisions to continually evaluate the adequacy of the facility in making what the customer wants. This strategic decision is based on the tool we mentioned above, the capability study. If the facility is not capable, a strategic decision must be made concerning a proper course of action.

TOOLS TO SUPPORT THE MANAGEMENT/SALES/CUSTOMER ISSUES OF A CONTINUOUS OPERATION

There are many strategic analysis tools to support management/sales/customer decisions. One of these, a capability study, assesses how well what we are producing matches what the customer wants. A capability study would evaluate how well the product meets our customer's expectations. These studies are for a continuous process and assume the process is in control.

This chart is an example of a capability chart. Management uses a graph like this for reports:

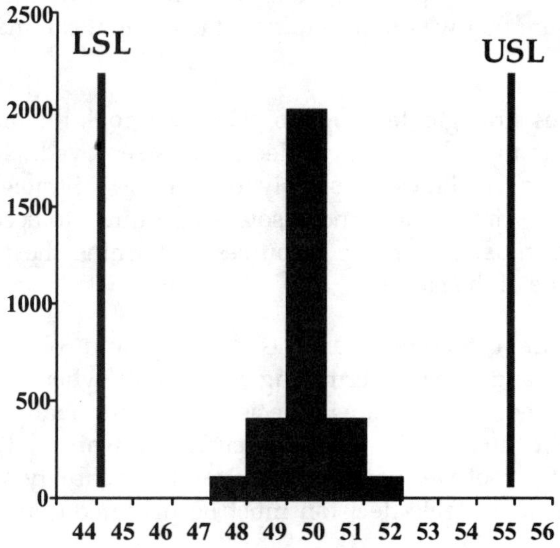

Because strategic decisions involve defining and obtaining appropriate resources and then assesssing when and where to use those resources, facility determination is clearly a management/sales/customer function. The capability study gives a strategist the information he needs to make appropriate decisions.

The archer assesses how the arrows are hitting the target and how many of them have hit the bull's-eye. As our picture shows, improvement is required to become a master. Control does not mean capable and capable does not mean control. Control and capable are two independent functions. When we manipulate them with one another, spectacular things will happen! Later we will see how they form a team.

STRATEGIC SUPPORT FOR MANAGEMENT

In **Chapter One** we discussed the use of average, standard deviation, and the Z value to build an interval. This idea of intervals was covered in **Chapter Two** for the two sets of analytical books to support Division of Labor. Now we are ready to use the strategic books called prediction intervals.

Management decisions are strategic and assess impact. Management, or strategy, selects, assesses, and provides the means. All strategic analysis must support this mission. Since our management must assess the impact to the customer, customer specifications and the individual values must be used.

In a manufacturing quality setting, strategic issues deal with assuring that we have the correct facility to make what the customer wants. Thus we must compare our data to the customer's specification. To accomplish the strategic mission, the individual values must be used. To make the objective a more general statement, the strategist is responsible for providing the correct facility and also assuring that any change to the facility is capable.

Prediction intervals are the statistical tools based on individuals and the use of standard deviation. All the statistical tools based on prediction intervals will be the strategist's tool kit. The formula for prediction intervals is:

$$X_i = X_{Ave} \pm Z * Std_{Ind}$$

In **Chapter Ten** we will discuss the details of capability study calculations.

THE STATISTICAL PROCESS CONTROL TEAM

SPC is comprised of the team that includes both control charts (for running the facility) and capability studies (assessing the impact). When working together and in harmony, the team is an unbeatable combination.

The SPC Team

All changes are quickly detected by operations and then immediately reported to management. While operations investigates to find the cause of the change, management assesses the impact of the change on the customer. When both the cause and the impact are determined, then and only then can an action plan be plotted.

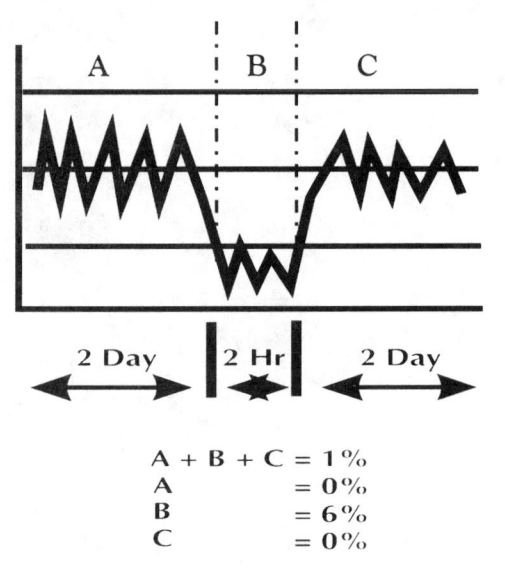

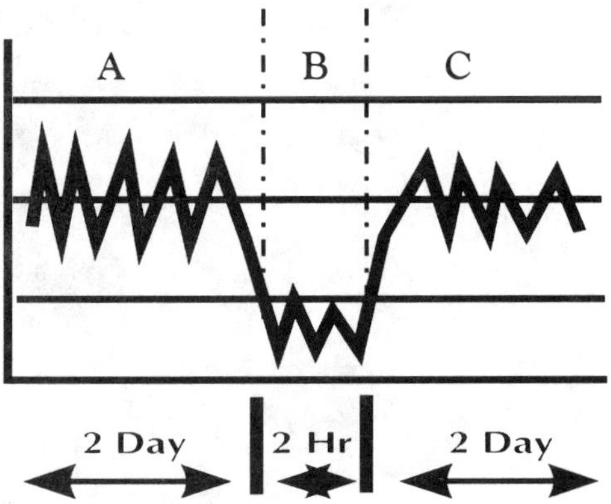

A + B + C = 1%
A = 0%
B = 6%
C = 0%

The chart to the left shows candy weights at the time of production. The weight of the candy has shifted from time period A to time period B. A second shift is shown from time period B to time period C.

The control chart keeps us from repeating the time-series grouping mistake that so often is made in capability studies. Only data that is produced during a time of statistical control can be grouped together in a capability study.

When we analyze the candy weights being produced for time period A, this capability study results:

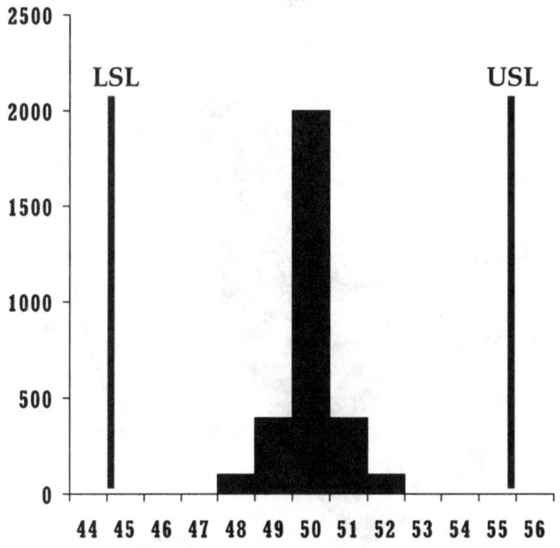

The histogram above is the results from time frame A with the specification limits overlaid. This gives us a look at how the candy production for time frame A would meet the customer's specifications.

Time frame A = 0% defective

The defective percentage for time period A is zero, for time period B is six, and for time period C is zero. Two distinctly different groups can be seen. If we attempted to group all the time periods together (A, B, and C), we would compute a defect rate of one percent which would be completely misleading and erroneous.

The tool to analyze this situation is called Statistical Process Control (SPC). SPC is the analysis tool of choice for a continuous operation.

The SPC team detects all changes and allows us to keep the improvements while getting rid of the deterioration. All changes, no matter how small, are addressed with equal fervor. Therefore, a series of very, very minute shifts are not allowed to slowly accumulate into one large problem.

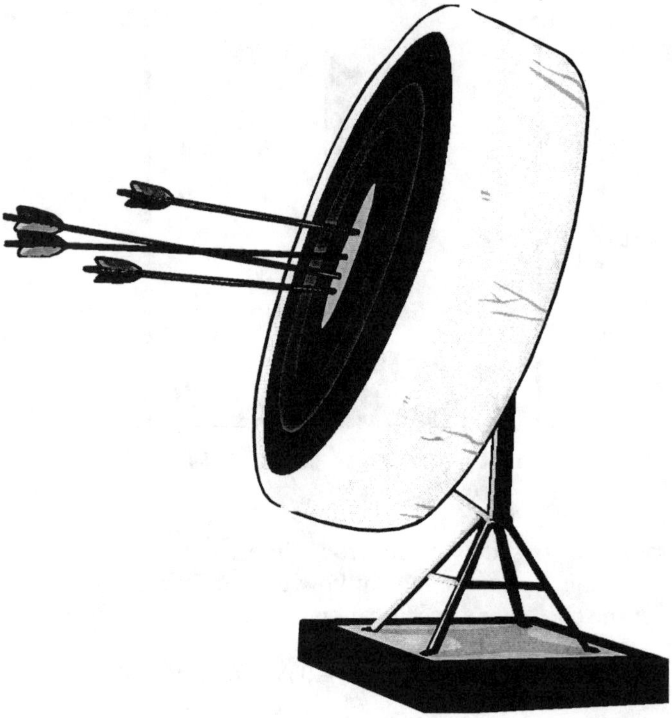

Using capability studies and control charts for consistency, we, like the archer, can consistently hit the bull's-eye.

CHAPTER SUMMARY

Statistical Process Control (SPC) is the set of tools to monitor and control a continuous process. Control charts are the tactical tools to assist operations in the correct and consistent running of the facility. Capability studies are the strategic companion of control charts. They assess the impact of all changes on the customer so that management is never caught off guard.

The combined tools of control charts and capability studies allow our efforts to be focused to improve the product and the process. The SPC team can now support both strategic and tactical decisions with very specialized decision-making tools.

The SPC Team

CONTROL CHARTS

The control chart is the operator's friend in accomplishing the tactical role of correctly and consistently running the machine. The following summarizes this chapter's explanation of a control chart and provides guidance as to which situations require this tool.

Consistency Alarm System Checklist: Functions of the Control Chart

- Operator's Tool
- One Particular Machine
- Continuous Process
- Time Production Oriented
- Zones - (based on bell shaped curve)
  - Average
  - Average ± 1 Std_{Ave}
  - Average ± 2 Std_{Ave}
  - Average ± 3 Std_{Ave} ! !
  - UCL - Upper Control Limit
  - LCL - Lower Control Limit
- Recalibration
- COWHN (*Church of What's Happening Now*)

Control Consistency Alarm Chart
System
Operator's Tool
1 Particular Entity

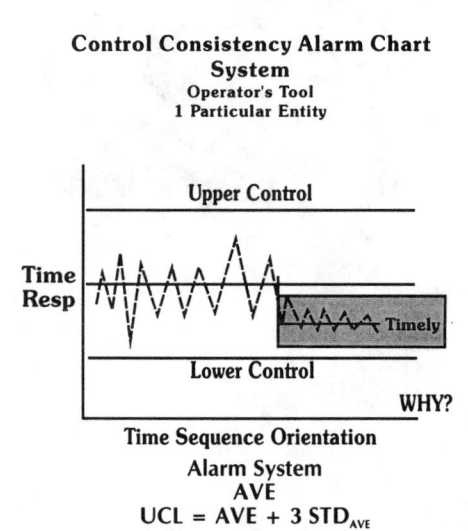

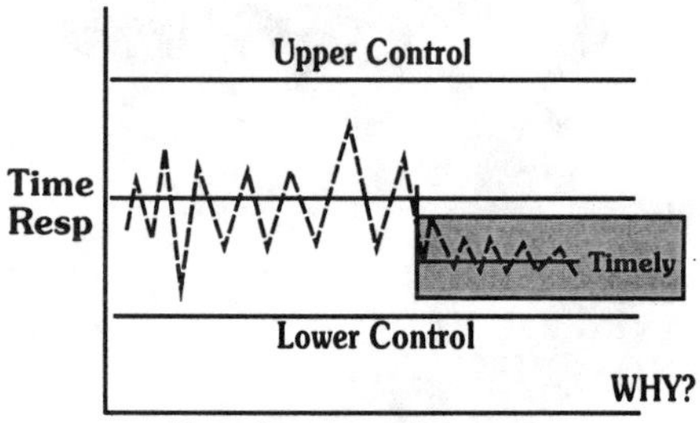

Time Sequence Orientation
Alarm System
AVE
UCL = AVE + 3 STD_{AVE}
LCL = AVE - 3 STD_{AVE}

Remember that control chart methodology is a charter member of the *Church of What's Happening Now*, commonly referred to as COWHN!

The chart to the left is an example of a control chart that has detected a shift. Operations will investigate the shift/change. Remember, a customer's requirements or specifications have no place on a control chart. This shift does not imply either an improvement or deterioration, but simply that a change has occurred.

CAPABILITY STUDIES

The capability study is management's tool to assess how well the facility meets the customer's requirements. The capability study must work with the control chart to assess all changes and to determine the impact of the change on the customer.

Control charts and capability studies form the dynamic team of SPC that is on a continuous search for improvements that are to be retained and deterioration that is to be eliminated.

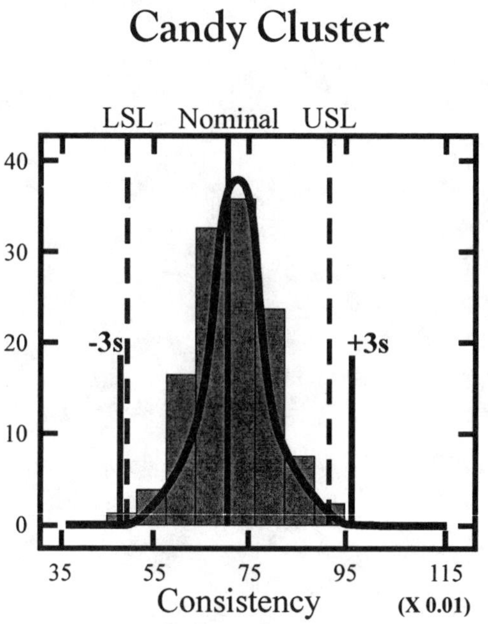

The chart to the left is an example of a capability study that is used to assess the impact on the customer. The control chart has detected a change and now our strategic decision-makers must assess the impact on the customer through the use of a capability study. Customer requirements and specifications belong on this tool.

This chapter provided a general look at control charts and capability studies. **Chapters Six, Eight,** and **Nine** will explain the math for computing control charts, while **Chapter Seven** will explain how to read the charts. **Chapter Ten** will explain the mathematical computations for capability studies.

Chapter Five:
Where Do We Start?

MISSION

To assure that control charts and capability studies are being used correctly, their purpose must be stated clearly. Furthermore, this statement of purpose should be placed directly on the control chart. All participants (management, line supervisors, and most importantly, operators) should understand the purpose of the charts and how these tools will provide information to improve the process.

If all parties understand why we have control charts and why we are using them on a particular process, all parties will be focused on the mission of continuous improvement. If all parties are not using the tools correctly and monitoring the proper metrics, we will make inappropriate decisions. Not only will we not make improvements but the reverse, deterioration, will occur. We must understand the First Principle of Process Management in order to focus on the right target.

Remember, a metric blueprint is a prerequisite for improvement to occur. A metric is a study area for which the blueprint gives focus and direction. The metric blueprint answers the question, "Are we monitoring the right thing?" This will assure that not only are we working hard, but also that we are working on the most important areas. The tool that contains the metric blueprint is called the *Walkabout™*. It will be explained later in this chapter.

In my book, *Optimize Your Operation,* I told the story of my mother learning the art of biscuit-making from my grandmother. Since Grandma was an accomplished biscuit chef but my mother was not, the knowledge transfer was very difficult. Without the proper analysis tools used in the correct areas, Mama burned many biscuits and the baking knowledge was never transferred. My story showed how improper focus keeps us from making improvements. Let's give a brief summary and recap of the first Principle of Process Management.

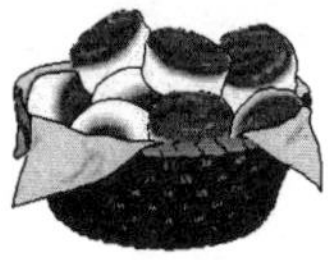

First Principle of Process Management

A fundamental understanding of BOTH the product and process is essential to improvement. Both the product and the process must be described and understood individually and separately. The underlying component for improving the product is the process.

Don't forget, the first Principle of Process Management is crucial to improvement. There are two broad areas: product and process. We must have data from each area, and in order to improve the product, we must understand the process better.

A product is...
- Noun
- Result

When we are discussing products, we are focusing on the result of our activities. The product is always a noun.

Product

A process is...
- Verb
- Activity
- Something that builds the product

Process discussions are focused on the activities that build the product. The process is always a verb.

Process

The *Walkabout ™* Dependency Diagram is the tool designed to help us understand the product, the process, and their relationship to each other. The *Walkabout ™*construction is covered in detail in *Optimize Your Operation*. Since the *Walkabout*™ provides a metric blueprint, a brief summary of its role is explained in this chapter.

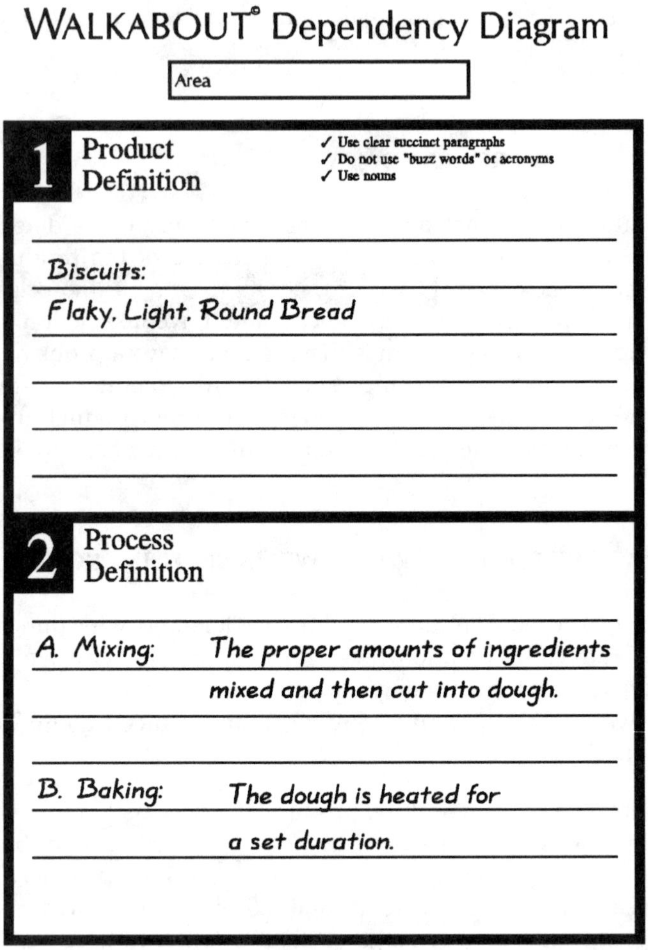
WALKABOUT© Dependency Diagram
Area
1 Product Definition
✓ Use clear succinct paragraphs
✓ Do not use "buzz words" or acronyms
✓ Use nouns
Biscuits:
Flaky, Light, Round Bread
2 Process Definition
A. Mixing: The proper amounts of ingredients mixed and then cut into dough.
B. Baking: The dough is heated for a set duration.

Since the product is the goal and objective, many people monitor only the product, but to achieve the goal, an equal knowledge of the process is required. A clear understanding of the first Principle adds focus to what we monitor. The importance of product and process knowledge must be clear because metrics and quantitative measures are vital to understanding the product and process. We will learn how to identify and measure metrics from the tool called the *Walkabout ™*Dependency Diagram.

The front side of the *Walkabout ™*, shown above, gives us the techniques and facilities for documenting the product and process. The diagram provides the

structure so that we will never skip a step or forget a component. The first step is to define and document the product. The second step is to define and document each step in the process. We write this information on the front of the *Walkabout* ™.

With this information, we have started on our journey to improvement. Many people have difficulty making a clear distinction between product and process. The important issue is to monitor both with equal fervor. Over-emphasis on either one will result in mistakes.

THE IMPORTANCE OF PROCESS DATA

When we monitor the product only, we are aware only of its deterioration or improvement. However, this awareness of the change of the product does not give us a reason for the change. Thus product monitoring is important, but it is reactionary. When a product problem is encountered, we take action to correct it. The drawback to acting on a problem is that we must have a problem in order to act on it! The product monitoring and actions tolerate waste with no understanding of the cause. When improvements in the product are found, no knowledge of the cause is determined thus the improvement cannot be repeated.

WITHOUT A KNOWLEDGE OF "WHY", WE CANNOT IMPROVE

For us to make Grandma's biscuits, we must understand why things occur the way they do. Product information gives no insight into why we made good biscuits or why we burnt the biscuits. Since we don't know why we are making good biscuits, we cannot repeat the activities that produced them. **This loss of knowledge is tragic.**

When we monitor the process and the product, the process parameters allow us to know the conditions that caused the change. The monitoring of both product and process is essential for proactive decision-making. With product and process knowledge, measurable improvements and elimination of waste will occur. Understanding the cause of change will increase knowledge, leading to improvement.

Note that SPC stands for Statistical **Process** Control. This should keep our focus on the process to improve the product. Too often we only use SPC to monitor the product as if the title is Statistical Product Control. Remember to use SPC (process) to monitor both the product **and** the process metrics.

THE KNOWLEDGE OF "WHY" ALLOWS US TO IMPROVE CONTINUOUSLY

By adding knowledge about the activities required to make a biscuit (process or oven), we begin to learn what is required to make good biscuits. The additional information about the different processes that were used for good biscuits and defective biscuits allows us to continue to repeat the improvements and to discontinue the defects.

In the perfect world of my grandmother and her biscuits, I never saw her check the biscuits when she removed them from the oven. She kept her focus on the process. Since she knew all the subtleties of baking, she took corrective action as the biscuits were baking in the oven, so that, in a proactive manner, she avoided ever producing any burnt biscuits. She was a perfect chef; unfortunately, most of us are not perfect chefs of our processes.

Often we spend a great deal of effort monitoring defects. However, when we are talking about defects, we are actually discussing the product. The problem with focusing on these undesirable product characteristics is that once the information arrives, it is history because the product has already been produced. If a defect is present, we now have waste, unhappy customers, scrap, and re-work.

Since we live in a not-so-perfect world, and our knowledge of our process is not nearly so complete as my grandmother's was about her oven, we must continue to monitor both our biscuits and our oven with equal intensity. More precisely, we must monitor both process and product.

As we gather data and knowledge, we must accumulate equal amounts of knowledge about both the product and the process. This will allow us to build the knowledge base for both the product and the process.

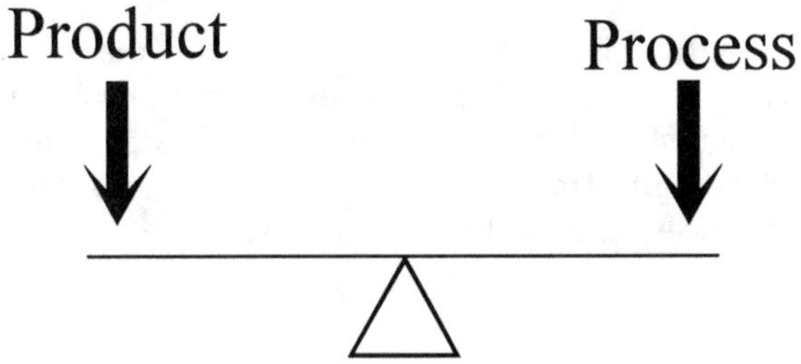

The first Principle explains the interconnection between product and process. We cannot improve the end product without improving the process, and in order to improve the process, our knowledge base must be dramatically increased. In this chapter, we will draw a clear picture of the product/process relationship as a system of interacting and intertwined components. To simplify our efforts, we will use simple techniques to draw a schematic of the system. The system picture is called a dependency diagram and is part of the *Walkabout* ™ we discussed earlier.

HOW DOES THE *WALKABOUT ™* DEPENDENCY DIAGRAM LOOK?

The chart below is the *Walkabout ™* Dependency Diagram for baking Grandma's biscuits. The dependency diagram shows the sequence of activities. Let's use this example to explain how to read the *Walkabout ™*. We discussed the first two sections, found on the front of the *Walkabout ™*, earlier.

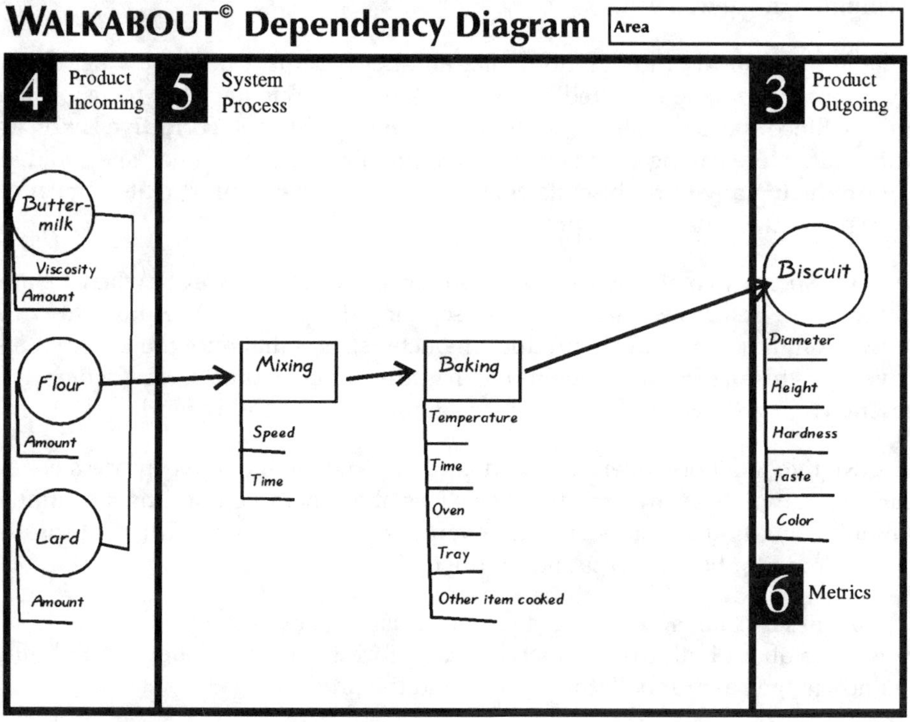

The dependency diagram is shown with circles for the products (think of southern biscuits) and rectangles for the processes (imagine an oven for baking). The schematic diagram shows the sequence in which each activity occurs. This simple diagram clearly illustrates that we mix before we bake. This picture makes the learning process easy and easy-to-follow.

WHAT ARE METRICS?

Metrics are study areas about the product and the process. Metrics are our means of capturing this product and process knowledge. We will have many metrics for which we must set targets, measure, monitor, and analyze. To deal with all of these study areas (metrics) we will need a metric blueprint to guide us and keep our research focused.

Hanging from the products and processes are legs that have the metrics (study areas) that we will want to study. The dependency diagram and the legs of the metrics form the blueprint.

The *Walkabout ™* provides a communication medium for each and every associate to learn, share findings from bottom to top, and retain this knowledge for current and future associates. This communication tool will allow us to:

- **Learn** our product and process.
- **Share** our knowledge and what we have learned with our associates.
- **Teach** and train others in what we have learned.
- **Build a metric** and all its components through the use of the *Walkabout ™* as a metric blueprint.
- **Have a checklist** to assure we don't forget any of the details of our knowledge.

The *Walkabout ™* gives us one common language and framework to share and increase the knowledge that we will learn. Failing to have a common language leaves us in a chaotic state, but a common language gives us a method to get the best knowledge from all associates. Progress and knowledge will not occur if we don't have a common language.

The *Walkabout ™* describes our dependencies and defines metrics. With the *Walkabout ™* in place, we have a tool that will give us both a short and long-range plan for metrics, which will guide us in all our studies. Quantitative analysis is required for a vivid picture of the product and process. Techniques required for defining metrics, measurements, and targets are explained in this section.

USING THE *WALKABOUT ™* AS A METRIC BLUEPRINT

The *Walkabout ™* Dependency Diagram is the comprehensive tool to evaluate how well the effort has been described and also becomes the tool to monitor compliance.

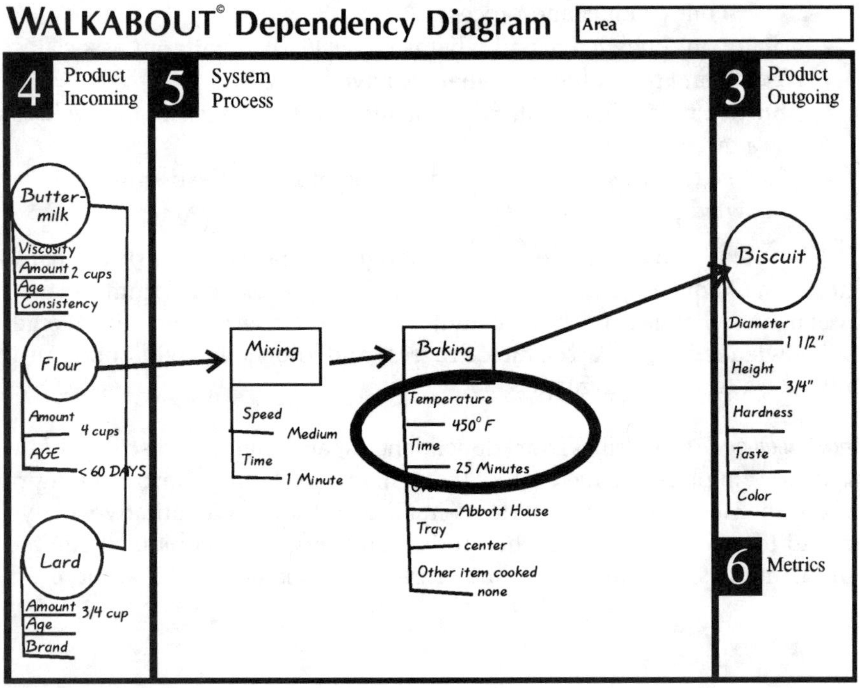

The *Walkabout ™* is a tool that allows us to make use of the first Principle of Process Management in order to document and improve our particular product and process. Again, the dependency diagram documents the product and process and is driven by the first Principle of Process Management.

The *Walkabout ™* Dependency Diagram is the tool to examine the system of incoming products, manufacturing processes, and outgoing products. It shows the sequence of processes and their dependencies. Metrics (study areas) are shown in relation to the products and processes.

Being able to see all the metrics in picture form provides a mechanism for identifying which metric to monitor. The *Walkabout ™*, as a metric blueprint, provides the picture for selecting which metrics to start monitoring, which future metrics to monitor, and which measurements to determine. This allows us to understand and monitor our progress of current and future information needs.

My Grandmother used the *Walkabout ™* to clearly document the products, the process, and the product/process relationship for baking biscuits. The

Walkabout™ also contained all present and future product and process metrics, measurements, and target values and was first and foremost a tool to document how Grandma made the biscuits. Grandma used the completed diagram to teach my mother how to make southern biscuits.

When a metric is selected, we have a place to start our efforts and are ready to begin Statistical Process Control.

As Mama and Grandma worked to improve the biscuits, the *Walkabout*™ grew and grew. Both the process and product understanding are shown on the form. This tool provides the medium to share the knowledge with future generations so that the legacy of southern biscuits will live on.

We must strive to accomplish the levels of expertise in our process that my grandmother and mother achieved in their biscuit-making production. Grandma and Mama did not achieve their expertise by easy and lazy efforts. Improving our knowledge base is a worthwhile objective, but it requires hard work on the appropriate things. It is not enough to know what to do, but we must actually do it. We must build and understand the tools of process management, use our knowledge, and execute our plans.

WHICH METRIC DO WE MONITOR FIRST?

Three issues are the driving forces for picking metrics for analysis. These issues are:

- The cost of monitoring the metric.
- What and how much information is to be gleaned.
- The feasibility of measuring the metric.

These three issues will guide us to determine which metrics to monitor first. All of our metrics will ultimately be monitored, but only so many can be monitored at once. Thus we must make strategic decisions as to which metrics to monitor first, second, third, and so on until all metrics have been monitored to give us complete knowledge of the product and process.

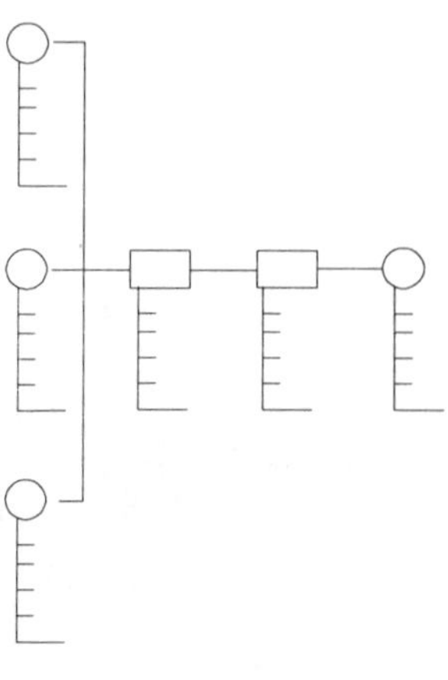

As we pick our metrics, a balance of incoming product, manufacturing process, and outgoing product metrics must be maintained. These three must be kept balanced. A correct balance of information would result in a *Walkabout*™ as shown to the left, where there are close to the same number of metrics for all areas. This will provide a tremendous amount of information. We can learn in a balanced way about both the product and the process.

Remember, keep a balance of product and process metrics. This will give us accurate information that will facilitate our process and product improvement.

WHAT DID MAMA CHOOSE AS METRICS FOR SPC?

She knew that SPC was a tool to assist in the monitoring of a continuous operation. Let's see how Mama approached the selection of metrics and then used SPC for monitoring them. From our *Walkabout*™ metric blueprint we can now begin to narrow our list of metrics to those SPC metrics that would be appropriate.

Continuous operations are found in many situations. According to the completed *Walkabout ™*, some of Grandma's metrics are continuous in nature. We will need to monitor these metrics with SPC, our tool of choice for continuous operations. Our completed *Walkabout ™* guides us by keeping all of our metrics organized, so that we can pick our first monitor areas.

A continuous operation is one in which the same activities happen over and over again. Many operations fit this criteria. Statistical Process Control (SPC) is a set of tools that was designed specifically for this kind of situation. Now we must determine which metrics are continuous and thus a candidate for SPC. Our statistical tool selection process must move from situation to tool.

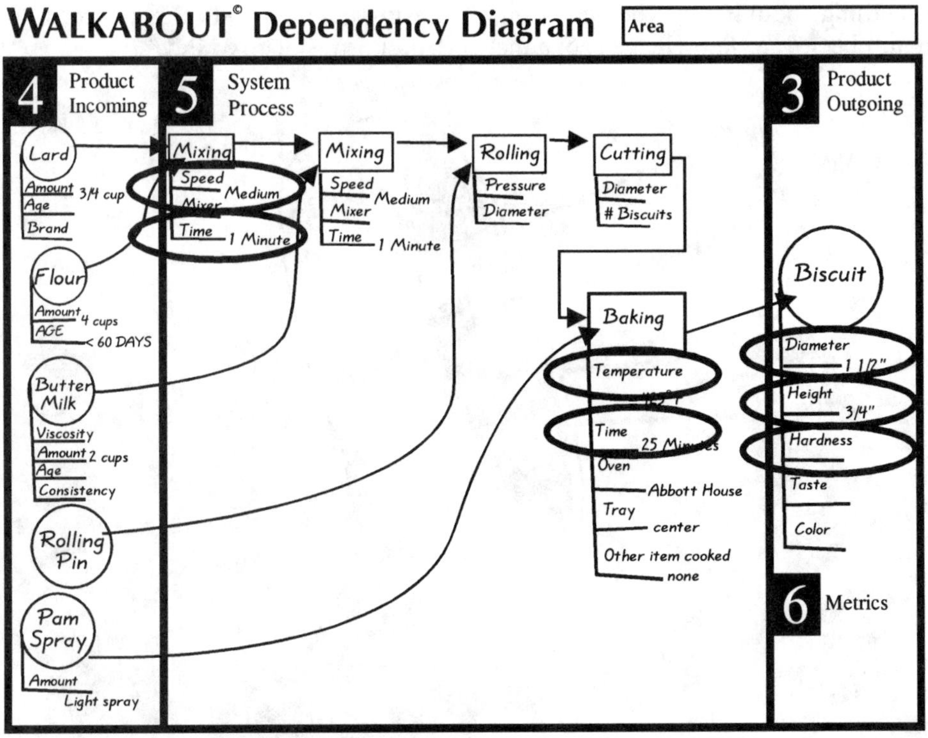

Oven Temperature - Grandma and Mama believed that oven metrics are important to good southern biscuits. Since the temperature may continuously change, a continuous surveillance method must be used to monitor it. SPC is the tool for the task of continuously monitoring the oven temperature.

Other biscuit and oven metrics may be candidates for SPC monitoring -- these metrics include the mixer speed and length of mixing time; the oven duration; and the biscuit diameter, height, and hardness. We would have control charts to assess the consistency of each metric. Each metric could then be compared against the specifications and targets to assess the capability of the process. Once a metric is selected, we must learn to measure the metric.

HOW WILL WE MEASURE THE METRIC?

Measuring the metric is essential to the learning process. If we never shoot the bow, we will never know for certain how good our archery skills are. Similarly, taking readings is essential to our learning efforts. No measurements mean no knowledge.

Measuring our metric is key to learning. In 1883 Lord Kelvin said, "When you can measure what you are speaking about, and express it in numbers, you know

something about it. But when you cannot measure it, when you cannot express it in numbers, your knowledge is of a meager and unsatisfactory kind."

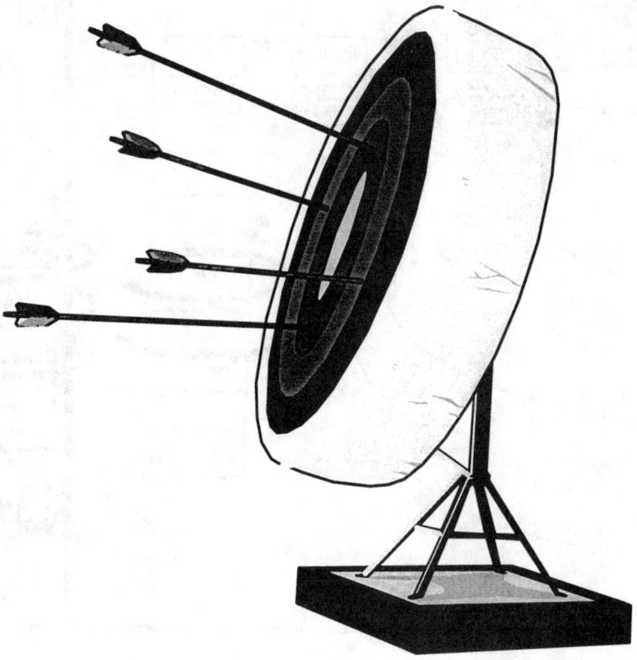

When an archer shoots an arrow into a target, the different locations of the arrows in the target paint a picture about how he should improve. When the target includes numbered circles, the knowledge of the archer's accuracy is increased. Adding numbers to the target advances our ability to learn. We can measure how many arrows fell in each area to obtain a better picture of our archery skills. Measuring against a target allows us to understand both how consistent we are and the capability that we possess.

This consistency and capability knowledge becomes essential for any business or operation. To achieve the consistency and capability knowledge, measurements are required.

WALKABOUT ™ AS A MEASUREMENT BLUEPRINT

The completed *Walkabout ™* will provide the blueprint for all measurement definitions.

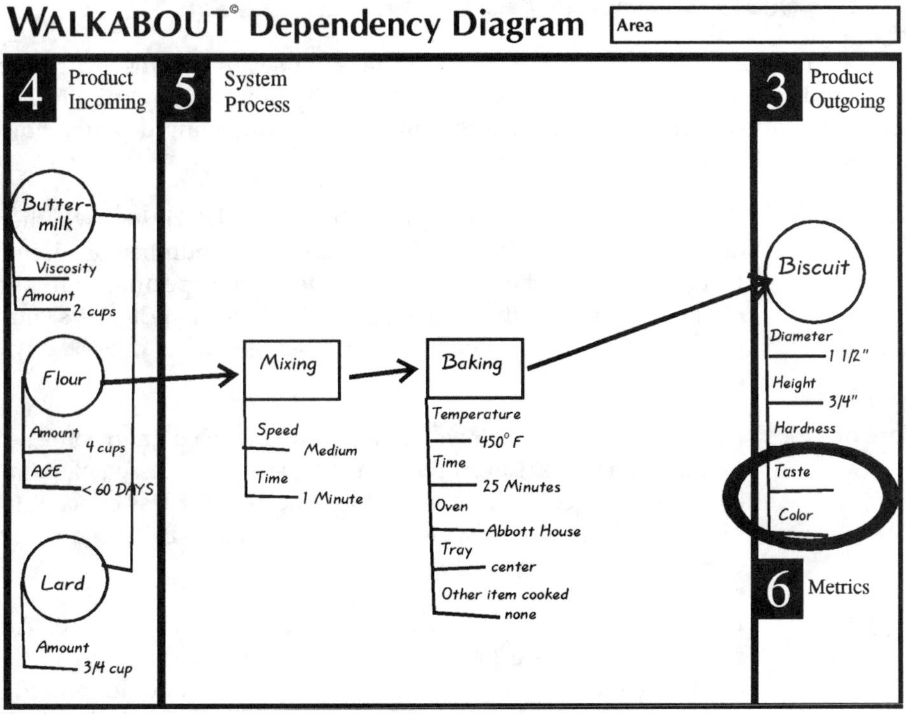

Some metrics will be either difficult or impossible to measure while other measurements may also be very expensive. In these situations, we do not want to lose our metric, but we may simply defer our measurement until taking it is feasible. With a blueprint of our metrics and measurements, we will never lose sight of our need to gather more information, and we will also know what information is missing. In the example above, technology is not available to measure taste or color. These are still metrics, but they will be added when the technology is available in the future.

WHAT MEASUREMENT TYPES ARE AVAILABLE?

There are two metric measurement types. The first type, called attribute, has pass/fail, true/false, or counts as its properties. Attribute data is also referred to as categorical data. The second type has measurable properties and is called a variable. Variable data is also referred to as continuous data.

ATTRIBUTE DATA

Attribute or categorical data is pass/fail and counts. This type of data is generally thought of in the passing of a part in manufacturing or in service industry (administrative) tasks. Even though this type of data is pass/fail, we can count the frequency of occurrence. Attribute data is "yes" or "no", "good" or "bad", "go" or "no go". Another example of attribute data is the count of the number of red M&Ms in an M&M bag.

How we measure the metric "flour age" can take on several forms. Attribute data could be one possible choice for determining the flour age by monitoring the number of bags produced before a certain date. The following describe how that could be accomplished:

All or Nothing: This most elementary type of attribute data determines whether an item is good or bad. We might count the number of biscuit batches in which the flour age exceeded a pre-specified number of days. If we set the target age to be less than 30 days, our measurement would then be the number of batches over 30 days old.

More or Less: In this next level of refinement, we compare our data to some set of benchmarks. An example is a comparison to a set of paint chips or a range. Grandma could use the more or less concept to identify when the biscuit dough is mixed to the proper consistency.

Sequence: In this example, we compare to a scale, such as 1 to 10. An example of this is a hardness scale in which a diamond is 10. Counting the number of batches within ranges could provide more insight into the age of flour. We could tabulate the flour bags' batches into ranges of age days.

VARIABLE DATA

Variable data is a continuous measurement. This type of data is thought of in terms that can be measured like temperature, length, width, diameter, shading, and days. Continuous data can be recorded on a scale: meters, grams, inches, or viscosity. The following describe how variable data can be expressed:

Units: Examples of this are length, width, time, and weight. We might want to know the flour age in number of days since it was milled.

Multi-dimension: We are now measuring against multiple units. An example of this is density, which is weight per volume. We want to know the flour age but rather than simply monitoring number of days, we want to divide the number of days by the number of biscuits in the batch.

Several methods and types of measurement may be available to us. During our flour age discussion of data types, many methods were discussed but more are available. A key to deciding how to measure and what data type to use is the context and objective of the metrics.

STEPS TO METRIC MEASUREMENTS

There will always be several options available to us in our metric measurements. Consideration must be given to the amount of information to be gleaned, the cost of the measurement, the accuracy of the measurement, and the difficulty of the test procedure to accomplish the measurement. Over time, I would expect the technique for gathering the measurement to change and improve. These improvements should not be confused with more costs or just more precision; instead the improvements must increase product and process knowledge.

Determining the kind of measurement (attribute or variable) and the technique for gathering the measurements are key to increasing our knowledge base.

In addition to the obvious things like temperature and duration, metric measurements must be established for our housekeeping cleanliness. For example, a frequency check for the cleanliness of the oven must be established because this is a vital metric measurement. Similarly, checking for incorrect operations must be a regular part of the housekeeping effort. It is reasonable then that these checks for incorrect operation must be included in the *Walkabout* ™.

We first determine the measurement technique and procedure for each metric. The intended use of our information will drive our test method. The need for

different measurement methods to support operations versus protection of the customer should come as no surprise.

A list of the metric measurements that will (or can) be used for each incoming product, outgoing product, and process is developed. Consider the following in determining those measurements:

- amount of information to be gleaned
- resource availability as a function of how much time the people have to do the measurement
- skill of the people that will be asked to make the reading
- cost of the measurement

Once we have determined the measurement and the procedure for taking the measurement, we are ready to move to the next step and define the mission of the control chart.

A clear measurement mission is key to the successful gathering of product and process knowledge. The objective and purpose of the information is key to how to measure the metric. A measurement technique that requires eight hours to perform a test may be very acceptable for a quality assurance function but unacceptable for an operational function. Running a machine requires a much more timely response than a quality assurance function. Having multiple measurement techniques available, and having to decide which one(s) to use, poses a common dilemma; the context of the metric resolves this question.

Having a clear mission gives the metric purpose. With this purpose in hand, the measurement of the metric has a start and an end because when we have learned all that we need to know about the mission, the measurement chart may be no longer necessary.

Remember, the measurement process benefits from SPC techniques. Measurement capability is called repeatability, reproducibility and accuracy. Measurement control is called stability.

HOW WILL WE GATHER OUR MEASUREMENTS?

Many people want to analyze all our data, but when all the products are measured, the cost of our testing will increase. A plan must be developed to monitor enough data but not too much. The testing plan must be both cost effective and accurate.

Population Statistics refers to the monitoring of all the data available for a set of information. For some situations, gathering all the data can be impossible or expensive. For example, taste testing each and every one of our biscuits would leave us without any product to sell.

Population statistics mistakes are often made when all defects are analyzed and labeled a population simply because we are looking at all the defects. The information from this type of study is very biased and paints a very distorted picture. The defects are really a biased sample of the total population. Then what is a sample?

Sample Statistics refers to the monitoring of a subset of information about a population while attempting to estimate the population statistics. In order to achieve our objective of estimating the population through a subset, bias must be avoided at all costs. Avoiding bias is done through a technique called random samples. Since random samples can be accomplished in many ways, the technique we choose depends on the situation.

For a continuous process, our objective is to detect any change as the process runs. Therefore, chronological sequence is important to avoiding a biased picture. We must track all data in its time of occurrence.

Population = Sample + Error

The only way to avoid a risk of no sample error is to test all of our products. But again, to test all the product is prohibitive from a cost, time, and product impact perspective. With this in mind, a certain amount of risk of getting bad information is possible. Later we will discuss the accuracy of our results.

WHEN ARE READINGS TAKEN?

Since control charts are tactical tools and invoke central limit theorem to normalize our data, then clusters of readings will be captured. SPC is a tool for a continuous process and, with this in mind, our readings must be captured in chronological sequence. The readings will be pulled to form a grouping called a subgroup. The subgroups must maintain their time sequence and have equal amounts of time passed between each of the subgroups.

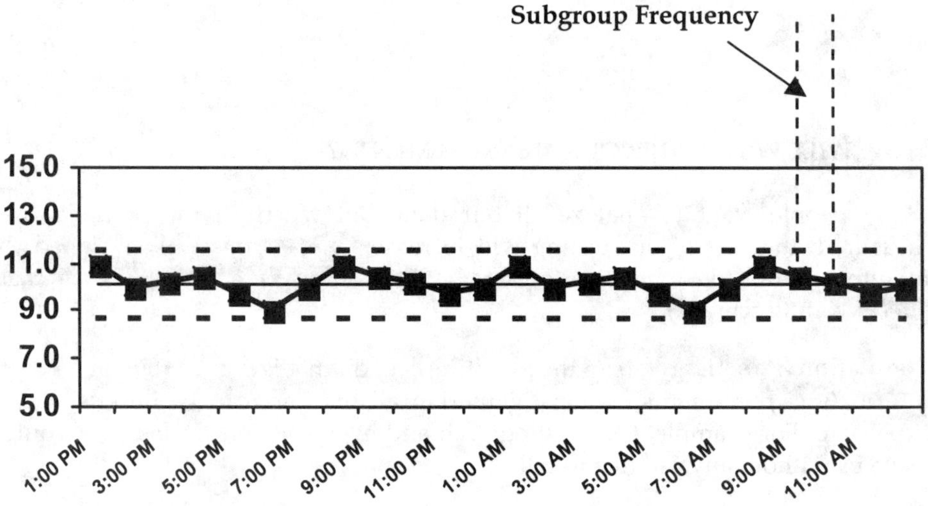

The spacing between each subgroup should be the same, if at all possible. The time spacing is called the subgroup frequency.

HOW ARE THE INDIVIDUAL READINGS OF THE SUBGROUP PULLED?

Samples of product must not be drawn haphazardly and must not introduce bias toward either good or bad. As nearly as possible, a single subgroup must include product or process readings produced at the same time under the same conditions. In other words, the individuals will be consecutive readings if possible. In **Chapter Six** the reason for the consecutive sequence for the data points in the subgroup will be explained.

Remember, our measurement readings are intended to paint a total picture of the process and product; they are not just to detect the bad product. This total picture must include central tendency, subgroup to subgroup variability, and reading to reading variability. In addition, it must detect change, monitor consistency, and assess impact to the customer.

HOW OFTEN DO I TAKE A SUBGROUP READING?

Subgroup readings will be obtained as frequently as the process demands. As often as the operation changes, readings must be taken. This decision is dictated by the volatility of the operation and not by statistics. For instance, if we wish to detect variations in product due to worker "warm-up" over the first couple of

hours of a shift, we must measure product several times during those hours. Measuring once per shift will fail to detect the cause.

If the process distribution is stable (i.e. if the process is in control), we need only sample infrequently to detect changes in the distribution. If the distribution is not in control, we will need to sample more often to detect special causes.

Some processes are volatile or change can occur quickly. For these volatile situations the process must be monitored on a very frequent basis. Even if a volatile process is in control, we would still need to monitor it frequently to assure that all changes are detected.

HOW MANY WILL BE TESTED?

Central limit theorem (the math trick we learned in **Chapter Two**) is the reason for our multiple readings in a subgroup. Central limit theorem is the tactical medium for making a non-normal distribution into a normal distribution. As we learned in **Chapter Two**, five samples in our subgroups will almost always guarantee a normal distribution. This assures simple alarm methods for the operator to use.

More samples in a subgroup will simply make the forced normal distribution a better normal. Generally, if more samples are to be pulled, we prefer a more frequent number of subgroups rather than more samples within a subgroup. As an example, instead of pulling 20 samples in a subgroup every hour, we would rather pull five samples in four subgroups every 15 minutes.

Remember, the subgroup size in Statistical Process Control is driven by central limit theorem, not by sampling theory or any attempt to reduce the risk in sampling error. **As a rule of thumb, five samples are pulled in a subgroup if at all possible.**

CONTROL CHART MISCONCEPTION

Many people think that control charts are a tool to assist the quality assurance (QA) department in weeding out all of the defective product. However, the real use of a control chart is not just for the quality assurance department, but as part of a total system of both control charts and capability studies to improve a continuous operation. Too often the control chart is used by the QA department, and because they have taken the initiative to use the tool, management fails to get involved.

SPC cannot weed out defects but can only paint a picture of what is happening on a machine. This picture can be of tremendous value in the hands of operations to assess and build a plan of improvement. As such, the most asked question, "How many samples do I need to pull?" is not pertinent because once the process is in control, then all the values during this state can be collected in a time-series group for assessment.

ACCURACY OF THE CAPABILITY STUDY

The control chart below has detected a change. A capability study must be done from the point where the first change is detected.

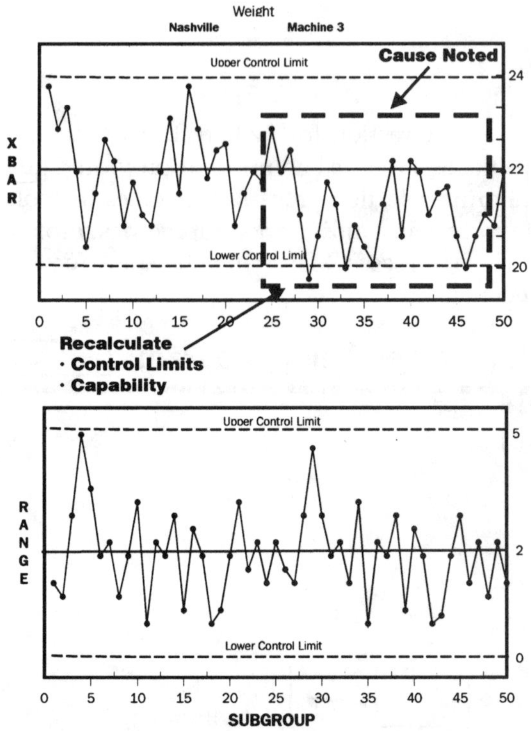

The capability study assumes that the process is in control (consistent). Since the capability study is based on a large number of subgroups that are all consistent, we would expect the accuracy of our data to give a very good picture of our product. In other words, we are looking at a very large sample of data to approximate the population. This large sample of data is comprised of all data during the time frame when the process is in control. The picture shows that we are analyzing our data over time.

The longer we are consistent, the more comfortable we are that our product decisions are based on good estimates. A process that has been in control for a long period of time, validated with control charts, yields very accurate capability study results. **Statistical Process Control cannot weed out all defective products but SPC was designed to predict how much defective product we should expect.**

Control charts and capability studies must work as the SPC team to obtain the improvement results desired. Control charts detect change. Change can be either an improvement or deterioration. A control chart alarm must be assessed with the strategic tool of capability to determine the impact. The SPC team is powerful in its ability to learn the process and product of a continuous process.

CHAPTER SUMMARY

This chapter gives us a direction for "where to start the SPC effort". First, a *Walkabout* ™ is essential as a metric blueprint for providing guidance and balance to our metric monitoring selection process. This gives us tools to assure that we are monitoring the correct and most important metrics. From our understanding of the first Principle of Process Management, equal focus is placed on both process and product metrics.

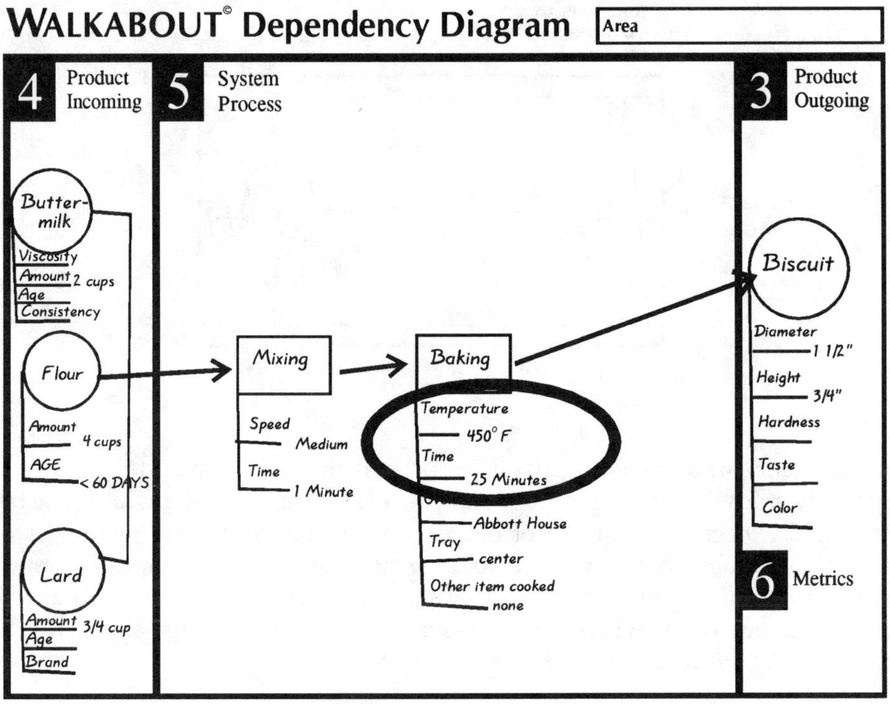

We determine which metric to monitor first based on the cost of monitoring, the information desired, and the feasibility of measuring.

Metric measurements may be expressed as attribute data (categorical) or variable data (continuous).

The steps for measuring each metric are established. Finally the how, when, where, and how many is established for the SPC process.

With these issues under our belt we are ready to begin our SPC efforts. The next chapter takes us into the details of SPC.

Chapter Six:

$\overline{X}$ and R Chart Construction

Statistical Process Control is comprised of 1) control charts and 2) capability studies.

A control chart is the operator's tool to monitor a particular machine or system over its time of function. It includes an alarm system with a mechanism for detecting any type of shift or change. This alarm must be dynamically recalibrated to reflect the current status. The control chart supports both variable and attribute types of data. The variable control charts are $\overline{X}$ and R, $\overline{X}$ and S, and Individuals. The attribute control charts are NP, P, C, and U.

A capability study is the management tool to assess how well the product we produce matches the product the customer desires.

To make our learning efforts easier, we will narrow our scope of interest to include only the operator and the tools that are designed to assist him. With this approach in mind, we will focus all our attention and work on covering control chart methods in detail. We will first cover the most used control chart: $\overline{X}$ and R charts. This chapter will cover the construction details of the $\overline{X}$ and R.

To support this chapter, **Chapter Seven** will cover the interpretation, reading, and use of the $\overline{X}$ and R. Since all control charts are based on a normal distribution, coverage of the $\overline{X}$ and R interpretation should make all other charts' use and reading very simple. All control charts use the same set of alarms to detect change.

Chapter Eight will cover the other two variable charts' construction. **Chapter Nine** covers the construction and use of attribute charts.

The overall objective of control chart methods is to detect product or process change. The demonstrated effectiveness of a control chart is attributable to its objective and systematic analytical methods. Shortcuts and "make-do" procedures lead to invalid conclusions and costly mistakes.

The methods for effective control include the following steps:

- Calculate the initial control limits.
- Establish that the process is in control.
- Continually survey the control charts for alarms (out of control conditions).
- Assess the capability of the in control process.

CALCULATE THE INITIAL CONTROL LIMITS

To set the initial control limits, data must be gathered. As a guideline, thirty sets of values are captured to calculate and post on the charts. Remember, since a control chart is for one particular machine, the data points must come from that one machine and their chronological order kept intact. Our readings are taken from 1:00 PM until 9:00 AM, giving us twenty subgroup points to plot for an example.

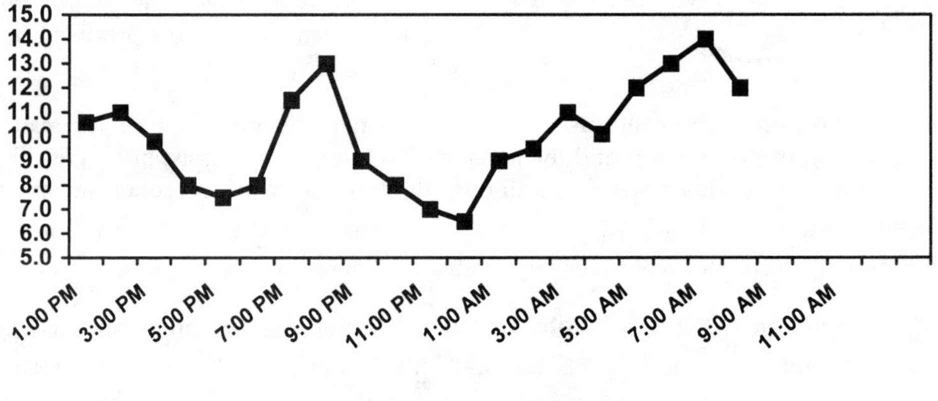

Different control alarms for each machine would not be surprising. These same thirty subgroups are then used to compute initial control limits. The subgroup reading and the alarms are then posted on the chart for statistical control interpretation. This chapter will explain the mechanics and calculations for control limits.

When our initial control limits are calculated, an out of control situation is never a surprise.

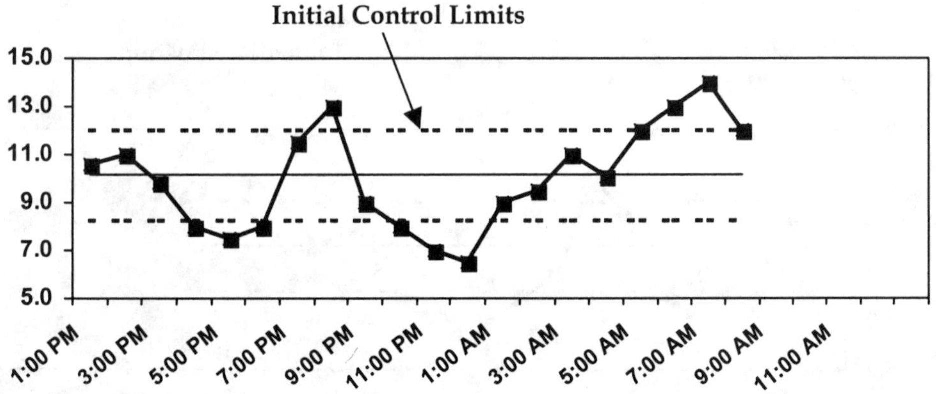

These out of control conditions are researched to find out why the change has occurred. This research must be conducted in the plant, in the vicinity of the machine. Now we are adding process and product knowledge. Using very old, historical data is typically a futile effort because determining the causes of old data is virtually impossible.

With our initial control limits we post each reading as quickly as possible to assess for out of control conditions. The next hour's reading (10:00 AM) is immediately posted.

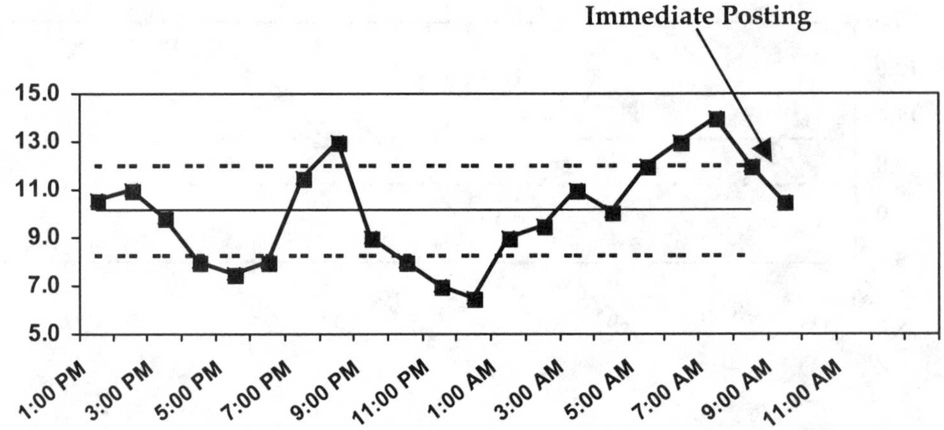

Our knowledge of the process and product will quickly grow through our disciplined research. We will quickly learn the correct and consistent means of running the machine. Now our operator is focusing on his role and doing his tactical function.

As our process is run more correctly and consistently, the machine will typically smooth out.

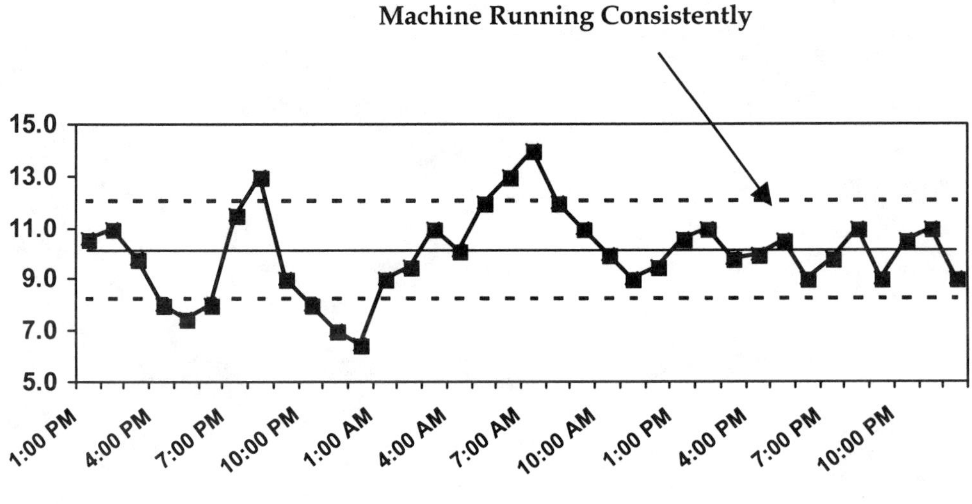

Now revised control limits will be calculated based on our increased product and process knowledge. These limits will use only our new more consistent data prepared with our new knowledge of how to run this machine. Notice how the revised control limits have tightened.

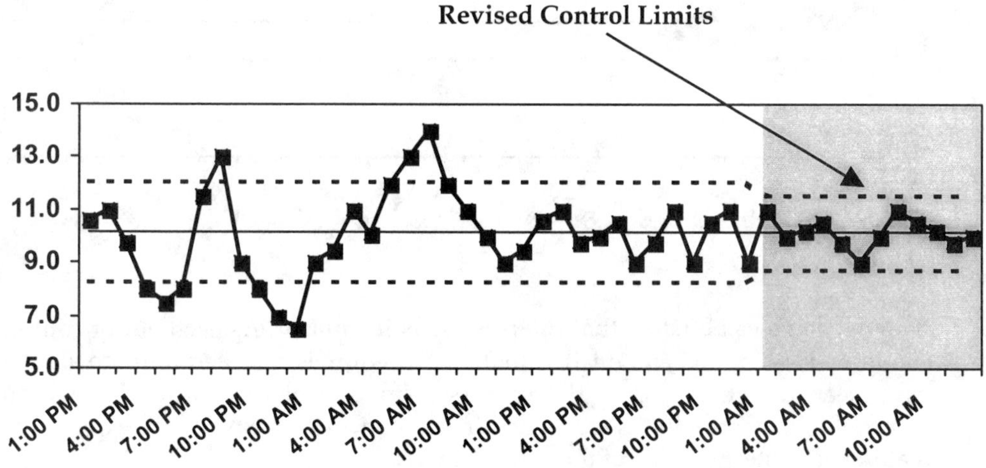

We will continue with this cycle until the process is stable as noted by the control chart. The cycle is: gather data and post, learn about the product and process, and reset the control limits. This effort will continue until all points are in control. The control chart will then reflect all points in control. This process of revising the control limits and learning may require several iterations to build our knowledge of the product and process.

Finally, the control limits can be locked to reflect our current understanding of the product and process when the process is in a state of statistical control.

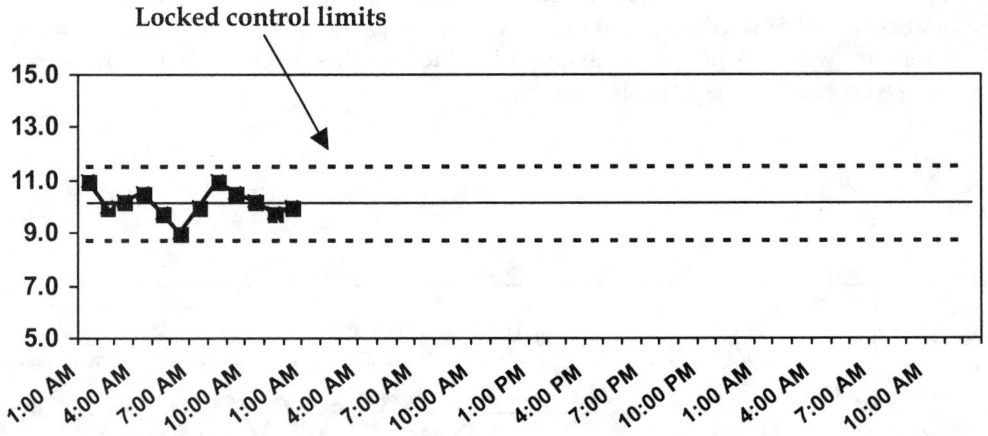

Now we have established that the process is in control. As each out of control condition is identified and dealt with, this procedure is repeated until no alarms have been detected. When the process is in control (no alarms have been detected), the control limits are locked in place. **Chapter Seven** will explain the reading and interpretation of the control charts.

CONTINUALLY SURVEY CONTROL CHARTS FOR ALARMS (OUT OF CONTROL CONDITIONS)

Data is gathered to monitor against the alarm mechanism (control limits) for changes in the conditions of the machine. When an out of control situation or change is detected, the chart has done its job. The following tasks then must be undertaken:

1. Investigate the cause.
2. Alert management to the change so that a strategic assessment of the impact can be made.
3. Decide what to do.

Chapter Seven will explain the task details associated with handling out of control conditions. **Chapter Ten** will deal with our actions and what to do.

ASSESSING THE CAPABILITY OF THE IN CONTROL PROCESS

The process that is in control is then assessed for its suitability to produce product that meets the customer's needs. **Chapter Ten** will explain the calculations, assumptions, and use of capability studies.

Now let's focus our attention on the details dealing with variable data and the control charts that will monitor this type of data.

VARIABLE DATA CONTROL CHARTS

Variable data is continuous measurement of things like temperature, length, width, diameter, and time. A set of monitors exists for monitoring this kind of situation. As we know from our coverage of basic statistical analysis, all three statistical components must be monitored: central tendency, variability, and distribution. Our control charts are the ongoing surveillance tools for a continuous process to alert us to any change in the statistical components.

Most control charts use the central limit theorem, which eliminates the need to monitor the distribution. The exception is the individual chart that will be covered in **Chapter Eight**. A control chart displays changes over time. The charts then are analyzed in pairs to monitor central tendency and variability.

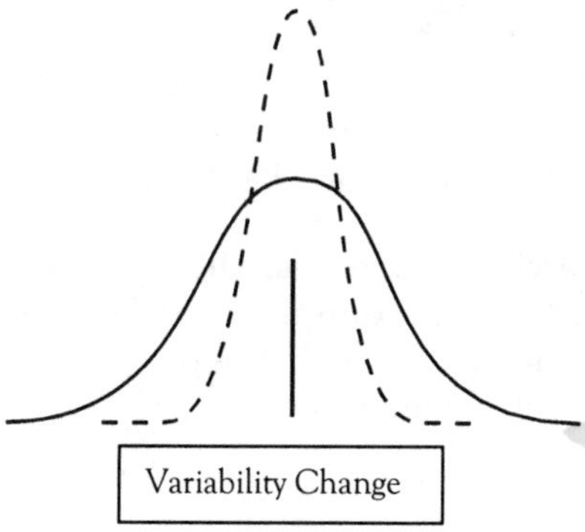

Variability: One chart displays changes in the variability of the measurements. The variability can either tighten or spread. The example here shows the variability collapsing. The solid line in this chart shows the original distribution. The dotted curve of our changed process is tightened because of the variability change. This picture depicts the effect of the reduced variability.

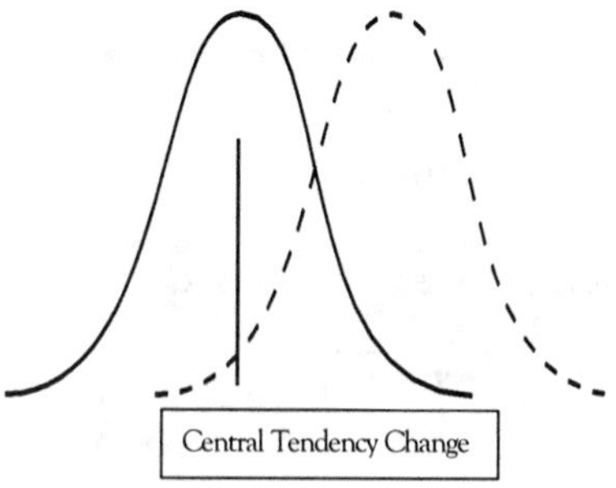

Average: A second chart displays the average values of the samples to detect shifts in the central tendency. The solid curve represents the original distribution. The central tendency can shift left or right from its current position. In this example, the center has moved to the right from the current center position. The dotted curve shows the center point of the distribution changing to a higher level.

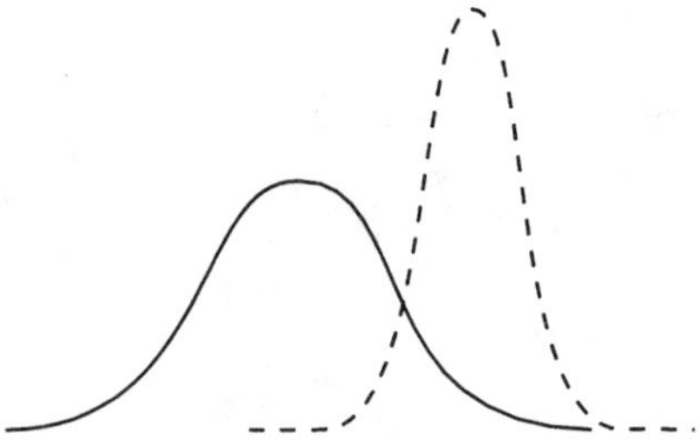

Both Central Tendency and Variability Changing

Shifts in both the central tendency and variability can occur, and each can occur by itself. Control charts must be able to detect both the central tendency shift and the variability shift.

Now, we see in the graph that shifts in both central tendency and variability can occur simultaneously as well. If only one control chart attempted to detect two simultaneous shifts, the alarm might not draw attention to both areas.

Let's return to our home smoke detector example from **Chapter Four**. The reason for having two smoke detectors, one in the kitchen and one in the bedroom, is to help reduce the search area for the fire causing the alarm. If the smoke detector in the kitchen is buzzing, then our first investigation is going to be in the kitchen. No one would start looking for the fire at the end of the house opposite from the smoke detector that is sounding. This reduces the area that we must search and investigate. We can quickly go to the area of the house where the alarm has sounded. Now our fire search is focused in one specific area to determine the cause and what appropriate action will be needed. It is much easier to determine the proper action to take when our efforts have been focused.

In like manner, we always need two control charts, one to monitor variability and one to monitor central tendency. This, like the multiple smoke detectors, will help us reduce our search and investigation area. Now let's look at the pairs of charts that are classically used to monitor variable data.

THE CLASSIC VARIABLE CONTROL CHARTS

In the 1920s, Dr. W. A. Skewhart developed a series of control charts to monitor variable data. Each set was designed to monitor for a particular situation. The three classic charts are $\overline{X}$ and R, $\overline{X}$ and S, and Individual charts.

$\overline{X}$ and R are the prime charts for monitoring a high volume continuous manufacturing facility. The $\overline{X}$ and S charts are appropriate for the situation in which a large number of samples are in a subgroup. The last classic control chart is the individual chart for times when subgrouping is impossible or undesirable.

All of the classic control charts are actually comprised of two control charts. One chart monitors central tendency for any changes. The other control chart monitors for changes in the variability of the process. The following table shows what each chart is designed to monitor:

Chart	Central Tendency	Variability	Distribution
$\overline{X}$ and R	$\overline{X}$	R	Central Limit Theorem
$\overline{X}$ and S	$\overline{X}$	S	Central Limit Theorem
Individual	X	Moving Range	Histogram

As the chart shows, the $\overline{X}$ and R and the $\overline{X}$ and S use central limit theorem which guarantees a normal distribution.

Remember, do not confuse control charts and control limits with a management chart to assess customer specifications. Control limits help us determine if a process is producing consistent output: that is, whether its distribution is stable and the process is in control and not changing. Later, we will apply specification limits to the distribution of a controlled process to determine its capability. Then, we will see that a process can be in control, but consistently producing defects.

Now let's focus on the $\overline{X}$ and R. This will allow us to complete all the calculations of one set of charts then move into **Chapter Seven** to discuss use of the control chart. This approach will allow us to cover one chart completely. The remaining charts are continuations of this same approach. **Chapter Eight** will then cover the remaining variable charts, and **Chapter Nine** will explain the attribute charts.

In **Chapter Five: Where Do We Start?,** we covered the details of how many samples to take, when to pull the samples, how to pull the samples, and how to measure the metric. Now we move on to the construction of $\overline{X}$ and R charts.

WHEN TO USE THE $\overline{X}$ AND R CHART

This chart, the most commonly used, is geared to high volume manufacturing. Users typically monitor product metrics such as the weight of a biscuit, the diameter of a drinking glass, or the weight of a candy bar. This chart typically uses samples of five in a subgroup. Be sure that you plan for adequate resources to handle this large quantity of data. The $\overline{X}$ and R are normally used to monitor a high volume discrete product.

$\overline{X}$ chart is designed to monitor the movement or changes in the central tendency of the process. Throughout this book the term $\overline{X}$ will be used for the average of the subgroup and $\overline{\overline{X}}$ for the average of the averages. The $\overline{X}$ chart has the plot lines for data points and alarms.

$\overline{X}$ Chart

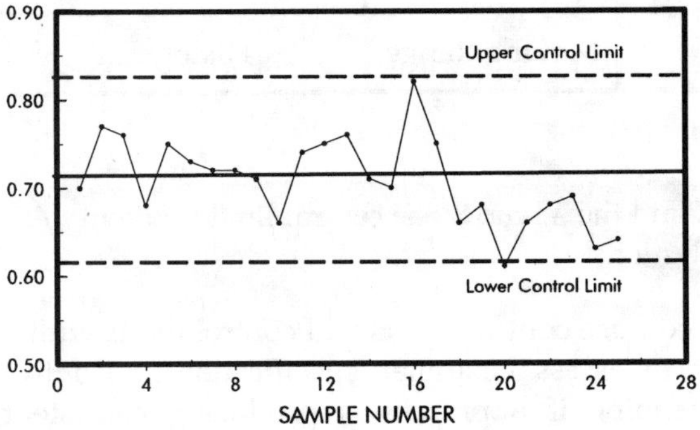

This chart is an example of an $\overline{X}$ chart; the remainder of this chapter will explain how to compute the data and control limits for this chart.

$\overline{X}$ chart alarms: $\overline{\overline{X}}$ is the benchmark of the central tendency of the process. UCL_{Ave} is the upper control limit and is three (3) standard errors above the mean. LCL_{Ave} is the lower control limit and is three (3) standard errors below the mean. $\overline{X}$ is the average of each subgroup and becomes the data point to be monitored.

R chart is designed to monitor the movement or changes in the variability of the process. The R chart has the plot lines for data points and alarms.

R Chart

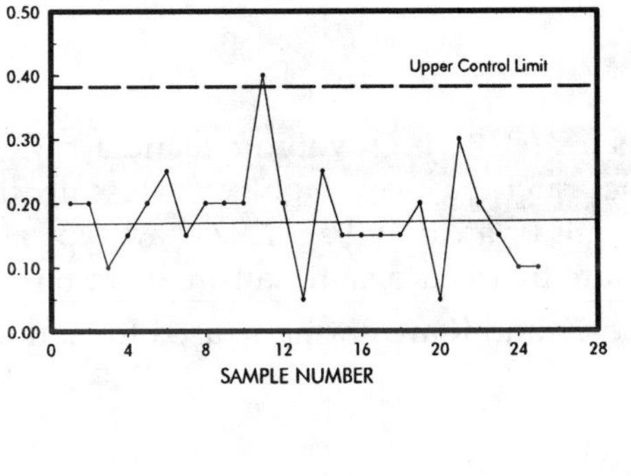

This chart is an example of an R chart and the remainder of this chapter will explain how to compute the data and control limits for this chart.

R chart alarms: $\overline{R}$ is the benchmark, or center, of the variability of the process. UCL is the upper control limit and is three (3) standard errors above the mean. LCL is the lower control limit and is three (3) standard errors below the mean. R is the range of each subgroup and becomes the data point to be monitored.

The $\overline{X}$ chart and R chart form a powerful team with the $\overline{X}$ chart monitoring central tendency and the R chart monitoring variability. The prime objective is detection of minor shifts or changes while the changes are still small and manageable. Now let's learn how to construct both charts.

For a simple text example, I have prepared the following product metric measurement data to analyze. Our manufacturing facility for this exercise is a high volume candy plant. Candy is coming from one machine down a conveyor belt in the sequence that it is produced. Each set of readings is taken consecutively and the subgroups are taken every hour. We have test data for the 1:00, 2:00, 3:00, and 4:00 time periods. This data will be used to generate our initial control limits.

This volume of data is only for this text and would not be sufficient volume to build a good set of limits. In the real world and in actual practice, larger volumes are required to provide a vivid picture of the process. As a rule of thumb, thirty subgroups would be required to determine the initial control limits.

Subgroup	**1:00**	**2:00**	**3:00**	**4:00**	**5:00**	**6:00**
Sample						
1	10	14	10	10		
2	11	8	10	11		
3	13	10	9	9		
4	9	10	10	10		
5	10	9	10	10		

$\overline{X}$ AND R CONTROL CHART DATA

The following are the algebraic formulas to compute the 1:00 subgroup control chart data points. They are used to derive the data to plot for the $\overline{X}$ and R charts. Average data is used to provide a means to alert operators when a shift in the process has occurred. This should eliminate the potential for over adjusting control or eliminating a test due to an overzealous alarm.

X_N is the central tendency data reading for the particular subgroup where N equals the size of the subgroup. $\overline{X}$ is the average of the subgroup while R is the range for the subgroup.

$$\overline{X} = \frac{X_1 + X_2 + X_3 + \ldots + X_N}{N}$$

where N equals the number of samples in the subgroup.

$$R = \left| X_{highest} - X_{lowest} \right|$$

Look in-depth at the 1:00 readings of 10, 11, 13, 9, and 10. These are taken at precisely 1:00 and each reading is from the next five consecutive candy clusters. The actual readings are fed into the control chart mechanism. The data for control charts is the normalized values or averages. The $\overline{X}$ value is the average of the five readings. The R value is the difference between the high of the five readings (13) in the 1:00 subgroup and the low of the five readings (9) in the 1:00 subgroup.

The 1:00 control chart readings of $\overline{X}$ is computed as follows:

$$\overline{X}_{1:00} = \frac{10+11+13+9+10}{5}$$

$$= \frac{53}{5}$$

$$= 10.6$$

The 1:00 control chart reading for R is completed as follows:

$$R_{1:00} = 13\text{-}9$$

$$R_{1:00} = 4$$

Now each one of the hourly subgroups must be calculated in the same manner. The results of these calculations are shown below:

Subgroup	1:00	2:00	3:00	4:00	5:00	6:00
Sample						
1	10	14	10	10		
2	11	8	10	11		
3	13	10	9	9		
4	9	10	10	10		
5	10	9	10	10		
Total	53	51	49	50		
Samples	5	5	5	5		
$\overline{X}$ = Total / Samples	10.6	10.2	9.8	10		
R	4	6	1	2		

On a control chart, the actual individual candy readings will not be used. From this point on in this chapter, no use of the individual readings will be made. Therefore in the tables that follow, all of the individual readings have been eliminated. When we return in **Chapter Ten** to discuss capability studies, the individual readings will become significant again.

Subgroup	1:00	2:00	3:00	4:00	5:00	6:00
$\overline{X}$	10.6	10.2	9.8	10.0		
R	4	6	1	2		

Now we can take these values and use them in the calculation of our control limits.

HOW $\overline{X}$ CHART AND CONTROL LIMITS ARE CALCULATED

Revisiting our definition of control limits, we remember that control limits are operational tools to detect a change and are the average plus or minus three standard errors. The upper control limit is plus while the lower limit is minus.

In a manufacturing setting, the operator is our tactician. The operator must use the available means to its maximum and optimum. The operator must run the facility as correctly and consistently as possible. Control limits are the tool required to support the tactician's mission of consistently running the available facility. This tool will alert the operator (tactician) to change that is unusual for his machine. Control limits are based on confidence intervals for a particular machine. Remember, control limits were defined in the 1920s with a Z value of three. This Z value was selected such that any data point outside the control limits would be a rarity. The control limits formula uses confidence intervals and is as follows:

$$\text{Control Limits} = X_{Ave} \pm 3 * Std_{Ave}$$

Bringing the relationship of standard deviation and standard error forward, we know that:

$$\frac{Std_{Ind}}{\sqrt{N}} = Std_{\text{~~Ind~~ AVE}}$$

Now, if we combine the formula above with the relationship of standard deviation and standard error, the following formula results:

$$\text{Control Limits} = X_{Ave} \pm 3 * \frac{Std_{Ind}}{\sqrt{N}}$$

Since control limits were developed in the 1920s for operators, the inventors knew that asking an operator to do the math in the above equation was an impractical task. Obviously, some simplifications were required. This necessity drove the development of a series of very good approximations that made the math requirements less complex. Standard deviation is a rather laborious calculation with all the ranges, squaring, and summing. An approximation for standard deviation was found using the range value. Range is not only an easier number to compute but also an easier number to conceptually understand. The formula shows that range and standard deviation are related by a factor. As standard deviation goes up so too does the range. This range and factor allow us to use range in our control limit calculations for ease and simplicity.

$$\text{Factor} * \text{Standard Deviation} = \text{Range}$$

Remember, all these are approximations, not exact values. As a matter of fact, all statistics are made of numbers that are an approximation of the exact number.

Standard deviation is an approximation of the variability of the process, not the exact value. Therefore using approximations does not detrimentally affect our monitoring of the process.

The prior equation can be rearranged to give the equation below:

$$\text{Standard Deviation} = \frac{\text{Range}}{\text{Factor}}$$

Using our naming convention for standard deviation of STD_{Ind}, the equation reads as follows:

$$Std_{Ind} = \frac{\text{Range}}{\text{Factor}}$$

Returning to the original equation for control limits as shown below:

$$\text{Control Limits} = X_{Ave} \pm 3 * \frac{Std_{Ind}}{\sqrt{N}}$$

This equation can now have the standard deviation (Std_{Ind}) replaced with the range divided by a factor equivalent value. This replacement is shown below:

$$\text{Control Limits} = X_{Ave} \pm 3 * \frac{\frac{\text{Range}}{\text{Factor}}}{\sqrt{N}}$$

The interval piece of the equation is composed of the number three, the square root of the number of samples in the subgroup, and the range standard deviation conversion factor. To reduce the operator's workload then, the mathematics can be done one time and inserted into a table that only changes as the size of the subgroup changes. The table is shown on the next page.

Subgroup Size	Factor A_2
2	1.880
3	1.023
4	0.729
5	0.577
6	0.483
7	0.419
8	0.373

Notice the factor for converting the range to three standard errors is called A_2. The A_2 gets smaller as the subgroup size gets larger. This happens because the factor A_2 is derived from a group of constants with only the square root of N changing. Since the square root is our dividing number, the A_2 will get smaller as this number gets bigger.

Now our final version of the control limit formula is shown:

$$\textbf{Control limits} = \bar{\bar{X}} \pm A_2 \bar{R}$$

As the control limits are plotted on the control chart, only three standard errors are used because more lines will create too much clutter. Having a cluttered chart conflicts with the control chart methodology of keeping things simple and easy.

SUMMARY OF $\bar{X}$ CHART EQUATIONS AND TABLES

Data: The following formula computes the data points to plot and monitor on the $\bar{X}$ Chart. X_N is the data reading for the particular sample in the subgroup where n equals the sample number.

$$\overline{X} = \frac{X_1 + X_2 + X_3 + \ldots + X_N}{N}$$

where N equals the number of samples in the subgroup.

The following summarizes the alarms and the calculations to arrive at them:

Center Point: The first alarm is the average of the averages as calculated in the following formula:

$$\overline{\overline{X}} = \frac{\overline{X}_1 + \overline{X}_2 + \overline{X}_3 + \ldots + \overline{X}_K}{K}$$

where K equals the number of subgroups.

The R values for each subgroup were calculated earlier and these values are now used to compute the control limits. The next formula is used to compute the average R called $\overline{R}$.

$$\overline{R} = \frac{R_1 + R_2 + R_3 + \ldots + R_K}{K}$$

where K equals the number of subgroups.

This $\overline{R}$ is used to approximate and compute the interval around the center. The factor that was derived in the previous section will be used to compute the interval of three standard errors above and below the center.

Control Limits: The general equation for the control limits for the $\overline{X}$ chart has already been explained in detail. Now let's summarize all of the elements.

$$\text{Control Limits} = X_{Ave} \pm 3 * Std_{Ave}$$

or, using the constant derived earlier, the equation is now expressed as follows:

$$\text{Control Limits} = \overline{\overline{X}} \pm A_2 * \overline{R}$$

The upper control limit is computed by adding three standard errors to the average. This interval is approximated by multiplying the $\overline{R}$ by the factor called A_2. The table below is used to find the appropriate A_2 value. First the number of samples in the subgroup must be known. This number is found in the first column labeled "Subgroup Size" and the A_2 value is then obtained from the first column to the right. This same methodology can be used to compute the lower control limits.

Subgroup Size	A_2	d_2	D_3	D_4
2	1.880	1.128		3.267
3	1.023	1.693		2.574
4	0.729	2.059		2.282
5	0.577	2.326		2.114
6	0.483	2.534		2.004
7	0.419	2.704	0.076	1.924
8	0.373	2.847	0.136	1.864
9	0.337	2.970	0.184	1.816
10	0.308	3.078	0.223	1.777
11	0.285	3.173	0.256	1.744
12	0.266	3.258	0.283	1.717
13	0.249	3.336	0.307	1.693
14	0.235	3.407	0.328	1.672
15	0.223	3.472	0.347	1.653

$\overline{X}$ & R Chart Conversion

This table consists of all the constants used in conjunction with the $\overline{X}$ and R charts. A_2 is the conversion factor to arrive at three standard errors for use in determining UCL and LCL of the $\overline{X}$ chart. The other factors on this table will be covered later in this chapter and in **Chapter Ten**.

From above, note the selection of A_2 from the factor table. For a subgroup sample size example of five, the A_2 value is .577. This A_2 of .577 is the most commonly used because of the high use of samples of five in the subgroup to normalize the data.

This A_2 value of .577 is then inserted in the equations below where $A_2 * \overline{R}$ is an approximation of three standard errors.

$$UCL_{Ave} = \overline{\overline{X}} + .577 * \overline{R}$$

$$LCL_{Ave} = \overline{\overline{X}} - .577 * \overline{R}.$$

Now let's move back to our simple example and compute all the alarms and plot the chart.

EXAMPLE ALARM CALCULATION

Our example's data is shown in the table below.

Subgroup	1:00	2:00	3:00	4:00	5:00	6:00
$\overline{X}$	10.6	10.2	9.8	10.0		
R	4	6	1	2		

Note we only include the $\overline{X}$ and R for each subgroup. The following computes the alarms or control limits for the $\overline{X}$ chart for our simple example. First, the alarm of the average of the averages is calculated:

$$\overline{\overline{X}} = \frac{\overline{X}_1 + \overline{X}_2 + \overline{X}_3 + \ldots + \overline{X}_K}{K}$$

$$= \frac{\overline{X}_{1:00} + \overline{X}_{2:00} + \overline{X}_{3:00} + \overline{X}_{4:00}}{4}$$

$$= \frac{10.6 + 10.2 + 9.8 + 10.0}{4}$$

$$= \frac{40.6}{4}$$

$$= 10.15$$

The R values for each subgroup are calculated and these values are used to compute the control limits. The next formula is used to compute the average R called $\overline{R}$:

$$\overline{R} = \frac{R_1 + R_2 + R_3 + \ldots + R_K}{K}$$

$$= \frac{R_{1:00} + R_{2:00} + R_{3:00} + R_{4:00}}{4}$$

$$= \frac{4 + 6 + 1 + 2}{4}$$

$$= \frac{13}{4}$$

$$= 3.25$$

With our $\bar{\bar{X}}$ and $\bar{R}$ calculated we can now use our factors to compute the control limits for the $\bar{X}$ chart. Remember that in the factor table the size we are concerned with is the subgroup size. The subgroup size is the number of readings in each group of data that is pulled.

Subgroup Size	A_2	d_2	D_3	D_4
2	1.880	1.128		3.267
3	1.023	1.693		2.574
4	0.729	2.059		2.282
5	0.577	2.326		2.114
6	0.483	2.534		2.004
7	0.419	2.704	0.076	1.924
8	0.373	2.847	0.136	1.864
9	0.337	2.970	0.184	1.816
10	0.308	3.078	0.223	1.777
11	0.285	3.173	0.256	1.744
12	0.266	3.258	0.283	1.717
13	0.249	3.336	0.307	1.693
14	0.235	3.407	0.328	1.672
15	0.223	3.472	0.347	1.653

$\bar{X}$ and R CHART Conversion

This $\bar{R}$ is used to approximate and compute the interval around the center of the $\bar{X}$ chart. The factor that was derived in the previous section will be used to compute the interval of three standard errors above and below the center. The subgroup size for the example is five, the A_2 value is .577. This value is then inserted in the equations below.

$$UCL_{Ave} = \bar{\bar{X}} + A_2 * \bar{R}$$
$$= 10.15 + .577 * 3.25$$
$$= 10.15 + 1.88$$
$$= 12.03$$

$$LCL_{Ave} = \bar{\bar{X}} - A_2 * \bar{R}$$
$$= 10.15 - .577 * 3.25$$
$$= 10.15 - 1.88$$
$$= 8.27$$

The table below shows all the details of the example.

$\overline{X}$ CHART EXAMPLE

Subgroup	1:00	2:00	3:00	4:00	5:00	6:00
Samples	5	5	5	5		
$\overline{X}$	10.6	10.2	9.8	10		
R	4	6	1	2		

$$\overline{\overline{X}} = \frac{10.6+10.2+9.8+10}{4} = \frac{40.6}{4} = 10.15$$

$$\overline{R} = \frac{4+6+1+2}{4} = \frac{13}{4} = 3.25$$

$$UCL_{\overline{\overline{X}}} = \overline{\overline{X}} + A_2 * \overline{R} = 10.15 + .577 * 3.25 = 12.03$$

$$LCL_{\overline{\overline{X}}} = \overline{\overline{X}} - A_2 * \overline{R} = 10.15 - .577 * 3.25 = 8.27$$

R CHART FORMULA

Data: The following formula computes the data points to plot and monitor on the R chart. Range, or R, is the data reading for the particular sample in the subgroup where K equals the subgroup number. To find the range, subtract the minimum value of the subgroup data (X_{Min}) from the maximum value of the subgroup data (X_{Max}).

Range or R = X_{max}-X_{min}

Subgroup	1:00	2:00	3:00	4:00	5:00	6:00
$\overline{X}$	10.6	10.2	9.8	10.0		
R	4	6	1	2		

The previous table shows our example's R data. Remember, our individual data is not important for control charts.

Alarms: The following summarize the alarms and the calculations to arrive at them. These alarms consist of a center point and control limits.

Center Point: The next formulas compute the alarms or control limits for the R chart. The first alarm is the average of the averages as calculated in the next formula. The R values for each subgroup were calculated earlier and these values are now used to compute the control limits. The next formula is used to compute the average R called $\overline{R}$.

$$\overline{R} = \frac{R_1 + R_2 + R_3 + \ldots + R_K}{K}$$

where K equals the number of subgroups.

Control Limits: The general equation for the control limits for $\overline{X}$ has already been explained in detail. Now let's take our knowledge from the $\overline{X}$ chart and use it to compute control limits for the R chart. First the general equation for control limits is still the following:

$$\text{Control Limits} = X_{Ave} \pm 3 * Std_{Ave}$$

The $\overline{R}$ value is used to approximate and compute the interval around the center. The factor that was derived in the previous section will be used to compute the interval of three standard errors above and below the center of the $\overline{R}$.

COMPUTING $\overline{R}$ UPPER CONTROL LIMITS

Our first derivation will be of the upper control limit for the R chart.

$$UCL = Ave + 3 * Std_{Ave}$$

The $\overline{R}$ value is inserted for the average and the factor multiplied by $\overline{R}$ is inserted for three standard errors.

$$UCL = \overline{R} + Factor * \overline{R}$$

$$UCL = \overline{R} * (1 + Factor)$$

Now using algebra, the $\overline{R}$ can be pulled outside the parenthesis. The summing of the number one and a single remaining factor (1+ factor) are done to arrive at a single factor. The new factor is labeled, temporarily, $Factor_2$.

$$UCL = \overline{R} * (Factor_2)$$

The $Factor_2$ from above is called D_4. The D_4 name was established by Dr. Skewhart. The upper control limit for the R chart equals $D_4 * \overline{R}$ where $D_4 * \overline{R}$ is an approximation of three standard errors. This leaves us with a much simpler equation for computing the upper control limit. Now the lower control limit must be computed separately because D_4 only works for the upper control limit. Finally, the UCL equation reads as follows:

$$UCL_R = \overline{R} * D_4$$

The D_4 table is shown below:

Subgroup Size	Factor D_4
2	3.267
3	2.574
4	2.282
5	2.114
6	2.004
7	1.924
8	1.864

Notice the factor for the upper control limit is called D_4. The D_4 gets smaller as the subgroup size gets larger. This happens because the factor D_4, like A_2, is derived from a group of constants with the square root of N changing. Since the square root of N is our dividing number, the D_4 will get smaller as this number gets bigger.

COMPUTING $\overline{R}$ LOWER CONTROL LIMITS

Our first derivation computed upper control limits. Now the lower control limits for the R chart must be calculated.

The $\overline{R}$ is again used to approximate and compute the interval below the center. Another factor will be derived to compute the interval of three standard errors

below the center. This second factor is caused because we are subtracting three standard errors.

$$LCL = Ave - 3 * Std_{Ave}$$

The $\overline{R}$ is inserted for Ave and Factor $* \overline{R}$ is inserted for three standard errors, which is shown in the equation below.

$$LCL = \overline{R} - Factor * \overline{R}$$

Now we algebraically rearrange our equation, as shown below.

$$LCL = \overline{R} * (1 - Factor)$$

Finally, we total (1-Factor) to arrive at the $Factor_3$.

$$LCL = \overline{R} * (Factor_3)$$

The $Factor_3$ is called D_3 which was also defined and developed by Dr. Skewhart. The lower control limit for the R chart equals $D_3 * \overline{R}$ where $D_3 * \overline{R}$ is an approximation of three standard errors. Finally the equation reads as follows:

$$LCL_R = \overline{R} * D_3$$

The D_3 table, for computing the R chart lower control limit is shown below:

Subgroup Size	**Factor D_3**
2	
3	
4	
5	
6	
7	0.076
8	0.136

Notice the factor is called D_3. Just as all the other factors got smaller as the subgroup size got bigger, the D_3 also gets smaller as the subgroup size gets larger. Notice that for subgroup sizes of six or less there is no D_3 constant because negative variability is impossible.

Now to summarize our R chart control limits:

The upper control limit is computed by adding three standard errors to the average. This interval is approximated by multiplying the $\overline{R}$ by the factor called D_4. The table on the following page is used to find the appropriate D_4 value. First, the number of samples in the subgroup must be known. This number is found in the first column labeled "Subgroup Size" and the D_4 value is then obtained from the D_4 column to the right. This same methodology can be used to find the D_3 value and to compute the lower control limits.

The following summarizes the calculations used to derive the data plots for the R chart:

$$R = \left| X_{Highest} - X_{Lowest} \right|$$

$$\overline{R} = \frac{R_1 + R_2 + R_3 + \ldots + R_K}{K}$$

where K equals the number of subgroups.

$$UCL_R = D_4 * \overline{R}$$

where $D_4 * \overline{R}$ is an approximation of three standard errors above the center for the R chart.

$$LCL_R = D_3 * \overline{R}$$

where $D_3 * \overline{R}$ is an approximation of three standard errors below the center of the R chart.

Subgroup Size	A_2	d_2	D_3	D_4
2	1.880	1.128		3.267
3	1.023	1.693		2.574
4	0.729	2.059		2.282
5	0.577	2.326		2.114
6	0.483	2.534		2.004
7	0.419	2.704	0.076	1.924
8	0.373	2.847	0.136	1.864
9	0.337	2.970	0.184	1.816
10	0.308	3.078	0.223	1.777
11	0.285	3.173	0.256	1.744
12	0.266	3.258	0.283	1.717
13	0.249	3.336	0.307	1.693
14	0.235	3.407	0.328	1.672
15	0.223	3.472	0.347	1.653

$\overline{X}$ and R CHART Conversion

D_3 is the conversion factor to arrive at three (3) standard errors for use in determining the LCL of R chart.

D_4 is the conversion factor to arrive at three (3) standard errors for use in determining the UCL of R chart.

For a subgroup sample size example of five, the D_4 value is 2.114 and the D_3 value is blank. These values are then inserted in the equations. Now let's move back to our simple example, compute the alarms, and plot the chart.

EXPLANATION OF R CHART EXAMPLE

The table below shows our example's data:

Subgroup	1:00	2:00	3:00	4:00	5:00	6:00
$\overline{X}$	10.6	10.2	9.8	10.0		
R	4	6	1	2		

The R values for each subgroup are calculated and these values are used to compute the control limits.

The next formula is used to compute the average R called $\overline{R}$ which becomes our first alarm on the R chart.

$$\overline{R} = \frac{R_1 + R_2 + R_3 + \ldots + R_K}{K}$$

$$= \frac{4+6+1+2}{4}$$

$$= \frac{13}{4}$$

$$= 3.25$$

Subgroup Size	A_2	d_2	D_3	D_4
2	1.880	1.128		3.267
3	1.023	1.693		2.574
4	0.729	2.059		2.282
5	0.577	2.326		2.114
6	0.483	2.534		2.004
7	0.419	2.704	0.076	1.924
8	0.373	2.847	0.136	1.864
9	0.337	2.970	0.184	1.816
10	0.308	3.078	0.223	1.777
11	0.285	3.173	0.256	1.744
12	0.266	3.258	0.283	1.717
13	0.249	3.336	0.307	1.693
14	0.235	3.407	0.328	1.672
15	0.223	3.472	0.347	1.653

$\overline{X}$ and R CHART Conversion

This $\overline{R}$ value of 3.25 is used to approximate and compute the interval around the center. The factor that was derived in the previous section will be used to compute the interval of three standard errors above and below the center. The subgroup size for the example is five, the D_4 value is 2.114, and the D_3 value is blank.

These values are then inserted in the equations below:

$$UCL_R = D_4 * \overline{R}$$
$$= 2.114 * 3.25$$
$$= 6.87$$

Our R chart upper control limit has been calculated and found to equal 6.87.

The D_3 value (lower control limit) from the above table is left blank. This D_3 value of zero is inserted in the following equation:

$$LCL_R = D_3 * \overline{R}$$
$$= 0 * 3.25$$
$$= 0$$

Our R chart lower control limit is zero.

The table below shows the results of our R chart calculations.

R CHART EXAMPLE

Subgroup	1:00	2:00	3:00	4:00	5:00	6:00
Samples	5	5	5	5		
$\overline{X}$	10.6	10.2	9.8	10		
R	4	6	1	2		

$$\overline{R} = \frac{4+6+1+2}{4} = \frac{13}{4} = 3.25$$

$$UCL_R = D_4 * \overline{R} = (2.114) * (3.25) = 6.87$$

$$LCL_R = D_3 * \overline{R} = (0) * (3.25) = 0$$

$\overline{X}$ AND R CHART EXAMPLES PLOTTED

The $\overline{X}$ chart is designed to monitor the movement or changes in the central tendency of the process. The $\overline{X}$ chart from our simple example is shown below:

$\overline{X}$ Chart Example

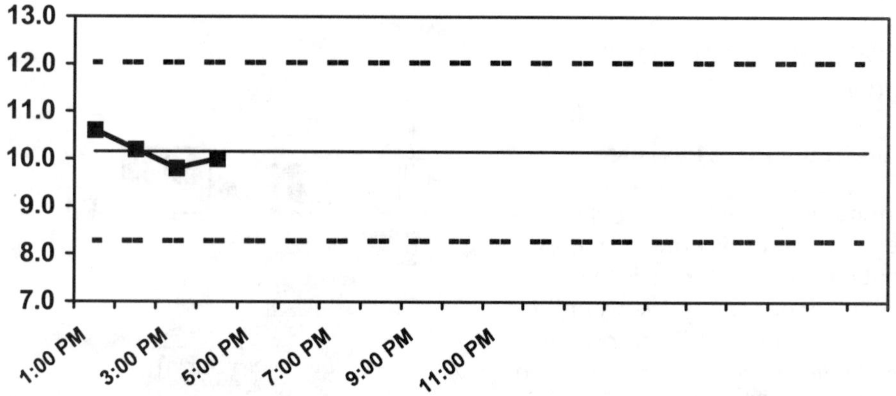

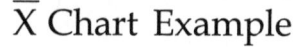

The R chart is designed to monitor the movement or changes in the variability of the process. The R chart from our simple example is shown below:

R Chart Example

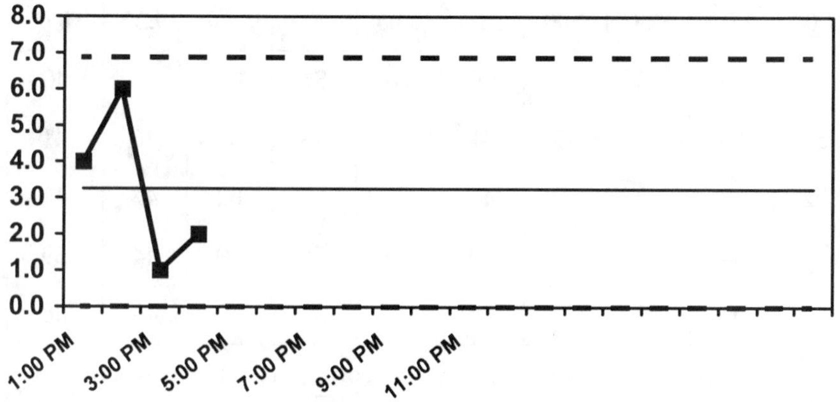

CAUTION! Once the process is in control, stop recalculating the control limits. The recalculation of control limits is a joint decision of both strategic and tactical decision-makers. Never let computers automatically recompute your control limits without direct human decisions.

$\overline{X}$ AND R CHART SAMPLE PROBLEM

The Candy Plant Revisited

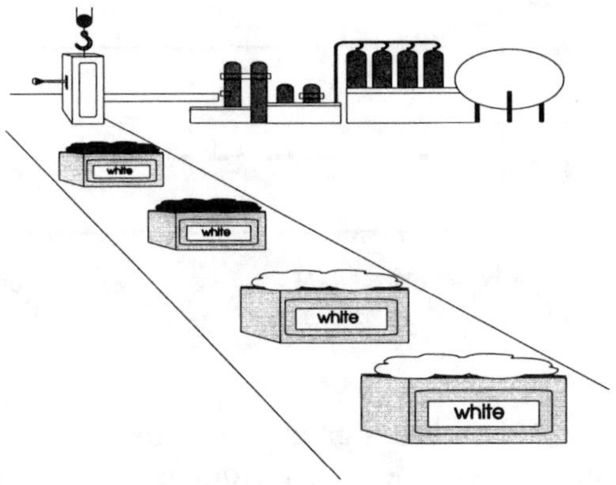

For our exercise, the candy plant is revisited and this time the metric that we are monitoring is the weight of our candy. We want this target weight to be 50 grams. In the table below, readings are taken every hour. The hourly readings are pulled from the conveyor belt in a subgroup of five chocolate candy clusters. These individual chocolate clusters are pulled from the conveyor in consecutive order with the objective of better understanding the weight of the candy as it is produced. The 1:00 to 10:00 readings are shown next:

1:00	2:00	3:00	4:00	5:00	6:00	7:00	8:00	9:00	10:00
50	55	60	45	40	50	55	60	45	40
51	56	61	46	41	51	56	61	46	41
52	57	62	47	42	52	57	62	47	42
49	54	59	44	39	49	54	59	44	39
48	53	58	43	38	48	53	58	43	38

On the following pages, we reinforce the control chart construction. In this example, we will assure that you can construct $\overline{X}$ and R control charts. We are back at the candy plant making chocolate clusters that should weigh 50 grams.

EXERCISE FOR $\overline{X}$ CONTROL CHART

The $\overline{X}$ control chart detects shifts in central tendency. Does our data have any shifts? To answer this question, we must build a control chart. Therefore, the following exercise is designed to complete the control chart that will answer the question. This table with those values is shown below. First, calculate the $\overline{X}$ and R values for our candy machine.

	1:00	2:00	3:00	4:00	5:00	6:00	7:00	8:00	9:00	10:00
	50	55	60	45	40	50	55	60	45	40
	51	56	61	46	41	51	56	61	46	41
	52	57	62	47	42	52	57	62	47	42
	49	54	59	44	39	49	54	59	44	39
	48	53	58	43	38	48	53	58	43	38
$\overline{X}$										
R										

Next, calculate the $\overline{\overline{X}}$ and $\overline{R}$ values for our 1:00 to 10:00 candy machine readings.

$\overline{\overline{X}}$ =

$\overline{R}$ =

Based on the information we have already learned and the previous data, calculate the control limits of the $\overline{X}$ control chart and note them below, then construct the chart on a piece of blank paper.

UCL =

LCL =

EXERCISE FOR R CONTROL CHART

The R control chart detects shifts in variability. Does our data have any of those shifts? Again, we must build a control chart. The following exercise is designed to complete the control chart that will answer that question. Use the previous information to calculate the control limits for R chart in the space below, and then construct the R chart on a blank piece of paper.

UCL =

LCL =

BETWEEN AND WITHIN GROUP SHIFTS

Many people are surprised that the posted results of the computed values do not provide charts that are in control. Our exercise shows this situation. The charts below could be a broader example of the situation encountered in our exercise.

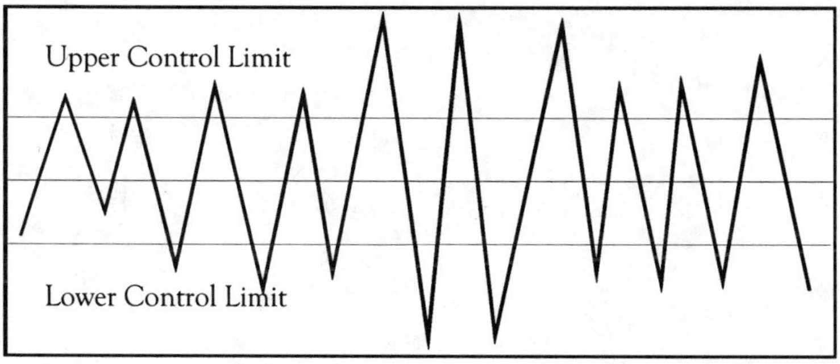

$\overline{X}$ monitors central tendency

The above $\overline{X}$ chart shows a very erratic process while the following R chart shows a very stable process.

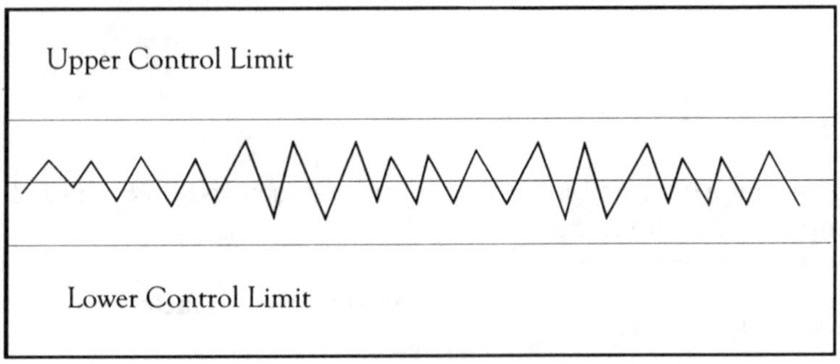

Not only does the $\overline{X}$ chart monitor shifts, patterns, and trends associated with central tendency, but the $\overline{X}$ also monitors between group shifts. The R chart monitors shifts, patterns, and trends associated with variability and part to part variation; the R chart monitors within group shifts.

How can the $\overline{X}$ chart be so erratic when the control limits are from the data? This is a very typical question. The alarms of a control chart are computed from R values. The R is the least variability that we would expect from a machine because the R values are calculated from consecutive readings in the subgroup. Since we normally pull five units, the variability that we use to compute the alarms should be very low. By using $\overline{R}$ to derive our control limits, we are using a very aggressive alarm system that is based on this minimum variation from part to part. This aggressive alarm system shows how well the machine could possibly run.

Often charts that look like the above are examples of violations of the second Principle of Process Management. Rather than run the process correctly and consistently by using control charts, operators make opinion-driven adjustments that are not needed. This is symptomatic of something happening in between the subgroup readings. I would immediately begin to take more frequent readings to understand what is causing these changes. Extra subgroup readings allow us to begin to identify what is happening between subgroups.

Between Group Shifts: The $\overline{X}$ control chart not only monitors the central tendency but also can detect shifts from group to group. The mechanics of using the part to part variability to compute the control limits provides this additional information. **Within Group Shifts**: The R chart in addition to its main purpose of monitoring variability is also checking for any shifts in part to part change.

This is the tip of the iceberg for control charts. Now we must summarize what we have learned about the construction of a control chart and move on to understanding how to interpret and use this tool.

CHAPTER SUMMARY

The table below is used to compute our control limits and is based on the use of the number of samples in the subgroup.

Subgroup Size	A_2	d_2	D_3	D_4
2	1.880	1.128		3.267
3	1.023	1.693		2.574
4	0.729	2.059		2.282
5	0.577	2.326		2.114
6	0.483	2.534		2.004
7	0.419	2.704	0.076	1.924
8	0.373	2.847	0.136	1.864
9	0.337	2.970	0.184	1.816
10	0.308	3.078	0.223	1.777
11	0.285	3.173	0.256	1.744
12	0.266	3.258	0.283	1.717
13	0.249	3.336	0.307	1.693
14	0.235	3.407	0.328	1.672
15	0.223	3.472	0.347	1.653

$\overline{X}$ and R CHART Conversion

A_2 is the conversion factor to arrive at three (3) standard errors for use in determining the upper control limit (UCL) and lower control limit (LCL) of $\overline{X}$ chart.

D_3 is the conversion factor to arrive at three (3) standard errors for use in determining the lower control limit (LCL) of R chart.

D_4 is the conversion factor to arrive at three (3) standard errors for use in determining upper control limit (UCL) of R chart.

$\overline{X}$ Chart Control Limit Calculations

$$UCL_{Ave} = \overline{\overline{X}} + A_2 * \overline{R}$$

$$LCL_{Ave} = \overline{\overline{X}} - A_2 * \overline{R}$$

R Chart Control Limit Calculations

$$UCL_R = D_4 * \overline{R}$$

$$LCL_R = D_3 * \overline{R}$$

Remember, all control charts are tactical tools to detect change in the product and process. A control chart can never tell you how well the product meets the customer's expectation. This will come in **Chapter 10: Capability** when we cover the strategic tools for management and customers.

Chapter Seven:
Using a Control Chart

Chapter Seven will cover the interpretation, reading, and use of control charts. Since control charts are based on a normal distribution, coverage of the $\overline{X}$ and R interpretation should make all the other charts' use and reading very simple. All control charts use the same set of alarms to detect change.

The overall objective of control chart methods is to detect product or process changes. The term "out of control" simply means a change has been detected. The demonstrated effectiveness of a control chart is attributable to its objective and systematic analytical methods. Shortcuts and "make-do" procedures lead to invalid conclusions and costly mistakes.

Chapter Six explained the methods to effectively construct an $\overline{X}$ and R control chart to control a process and product. **Chapter Six** also covered the initial control limit calculations for $\overline{X}$ and R charts, as well as the details necessary for calculating and constructing these charts. Different control alarms for each machine are not surprising -- as a matter of fact they are expected. We also explained the mechanics and calculations for control limits and discussed how to draw the control chart. Now that we have the control chart, we must learn to use it effectively. This chapter deals with the steps for getting the process in control and then assuring a continuous surveillance program to detect any changes.

In **Chapter Seven** we will learn how to:

Read control charts. The alarms associated with control charts and why they work will be explained. These alarms will act as change detectors for our tactical decision-makers and as alerts to our strategic decision-makers.

Establish that the process is in control. As each out of control condition is identified and dealt with, this procedure is repeated until no alarms have been detected. When the process is in control (no alarms have been detected), the control limits are locked in place. At this point we will read and interpret the control charts.

Continually survey the control charts for alarms (out of control conditions). Data is gathered to monitor against the alarm mechanism (control limits) for changes in the conditions of the machine. When an out of control situation, or change, is detected the chart has done its job.

Investigate the cause. When a change is detected our tactical decision-makers must research and find the cause of the change. This chapter will explain the types of causes and how to research them. In **Chapter Ten** we will explain management change alerts and the decisions regarding what to do about them.

This chapter will explain the details of the tasks associated with dealing with an alarm - both what must be done and who should do it.

THE USE OF CONTROL CHARTS

The flow diagram that is presented later in this chapter shows the general steps of a control methodology. The control chart component is one player on the SPC team. A control chart helps the operator understand his machine and establish how to correctly and consistently run it. The chart also establishes the typical patterns for the machine and alerts the operator to any deviations from the norm. These deviations are change or out of control. Many people are confused by the term out of control but it simply is another word for change.

Remember, control charts are only one player on the team. We must have all the players in place for SPC to be effective. The flow shows that an ongoing, never-ending data gathering effort must be maintained. If no change is detected, we must wait for the next readings. If a change is detected, our investigation begins to determine the cause and assess the impact. We decide what action to take once all the prior steps are complete.

CHANGE DETECTION

Control charts are a tactical tool to detect change in a continuous operation. A series of easy to use and read alarms must be developed for the tactician (operator). These alarms must be simple but effective.

Chapter Two covered the math tricks that force a normal distribution. Normal distribution makes the alarms simple because no decision is required by the operator as to the type of distributions. All our alarms are based on the normal distribution.

This chapter will discuss the interpretation rules for control charts and how they were derived.

Once a change is detected, we are just at the start of our journey; we must move on to our investigation efforts.

INITIATE INVESTIGATION

Our investigation is comprised of two parts: one tactical and one strategic. A clear understanding of the roles of both the strategic and tactical players is key. Once the individual roles are clear, the players must function together as a team for effective action.

The tactical decision-makers (operators) begin investigating to determine the cause of the alarm. These causes will increase our understanding of the process and product. This knowledge is crucial for improvement. Once the knowledge has been learned, it must be shared and retained for all associates. The tacticians must also alert the strategic decision-makers that a change has occurred so that an assessment of the impact of the change can be made.

The strategic decision-makers must simultaneously (while the cause is being investigated) assess the impact of product or process change on the customer.

Once the cause has been identified and the capability determined, a course of action must be chosen. This is a team decision by both the strategic and tactical decision-makers.

WHEN A CHANGE IS REAL

Often the natural ebb and flow of a process is mistaken for real change. With these false changes, operators begin to adjust the machine incorrectly. These incorrect adjustments lead to more false change alarms and, thus, more incorrect adjustments.

To prevent that misinterpretation, a set of benchmarks is required to establish what is typical for a particular machine. The control chart's limits provide the means to differentiate between what is typical and what is unusual behavior for a process and product. Remember, what is usual for one machine may be bizarre for another. SPC provides the tools to separate the typical from the unusual.

The SPC tool of control charts is comprised of a few simple alarms that note a change is taking place and that an immediate initiation of the causal search should be advanced at full speed. The next pages describe the common patterns found in control charts, and where to begin looking for causes.

We are narrowing our scope to focus our attention on the tactical issue of consistency. The following flow is how we should use our control charts. Our data is gathered and each set is then immediately tested for a shift. If no shift is detected, no action or adjustments are necessary. Only when a real change is detected is research required. Since our tactician's (operator's) time is so precious, the tactician must only research a real change. He must not waste his time researching what is the natural ebb and flow of a process or product. We are following a method of "management by change."

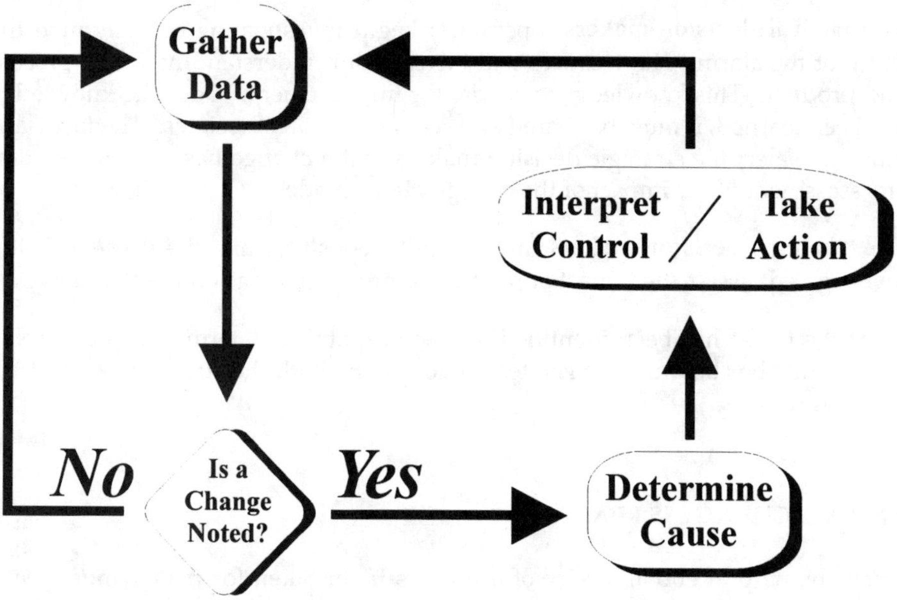

The above chart depicts the steps to action based on a control chart alarm. We regularly gather our data and test for change. If no change is detected, then the tactician continues his work until the next reading is taken. If a change is detected, the tactician begins the research for determining the cause of the change. After the change is determined, we are ready to begin the decision of how to act.

Remember, never take action just because an alarm is noted. The cause must always be found before taking action. Earlier we discussed the smoke detector. We would never bring the garden hose into the house to put out a fire without an investigation. If the fire turns out to be a grease fire, our water and good intentions will simply make the situation worse by spreading the fire. The cause must be identified before any action is taken.

STEPS FOR INTERPRETING AN ALARM

From our earlier discussion of basic statistics, we know that we must be aware of both variability and central tendency. A chart is provided to monitor both of these areas. Variability is so often skipped, misunderstood, and ignored. Thus, I always monitor the R chart to check variability first, and then go to the $\overline{X}$ chart to check central tendency second. Once each component has been monitored for change, then I look at both charts together.

To summarize, these three steps are as follows:

1. Check Variability
2. Check Central Tendency
3. Check Both - variability and central tendency together

We must assure that we always check both variability and central tendency for change. The most common mistake in controlling a process is to test only for shifts in the central tendency or center.

HOW DID CONTROL CHART ALARMS ORIGINATE?

The alarms of a control chart are based on the area under the curve that represents the probability of occurrence. Remember in **Chapter Two: Math Tricks to Make SPC Work** we formed our data into a normal distribution. This is accomplished by using the central limit theorem or simply using averages of our data. This trick guarantees a normal distribution and its associated probabilities.

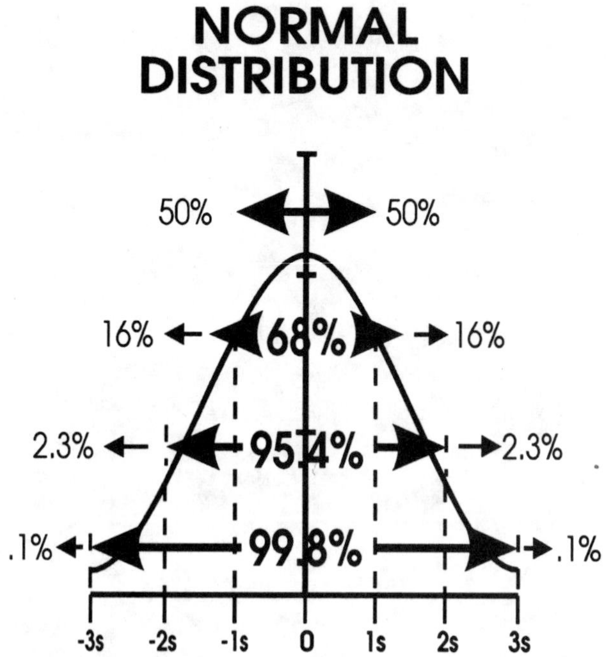

An occurrence outside plus or minus one standard deviation (one is the Z value) equates to a probability of 16% above or 16% below or 68% inside. An occurrence outside plus or minus two standard deviations (two is the Z value) equates to a probability of 2.3% above or 2.3% below or 95.4% inside. An

occurrence outside plus or minus three standard deviations (three is the Z value) equates to a probability of 0.1% above or 0.1% below or 99.8% inside.

Remember, our control limits were defined as being three standard errors away from the mean. The control limits are set such that the odds of having a value outside either of the limits is 0.1% or, stated very simply, the odds are very remote that a point will be outside the limits without truly being a change. Since we are very sure that a change is taking place, then an immediate investigation as to the cause is initiated.

Since the odds of being outside the control limits are remote, a change alarm and the search for the cause is seldom a wild goose chase. This rarity of the alarm is the reason that the other alarms are all based on about the same probability. The next section of this chapter covers the basic set of control chart alarms and how they were each developed.

SINGLE POINT OUTSIDE CONTROL LIMITS

Any data point outside control limits requires investigation, because the odds that a controlled process could produce such a measurement purely by accident are very remote. This rule applies to both the $\overline{X}$ and the R control charts.

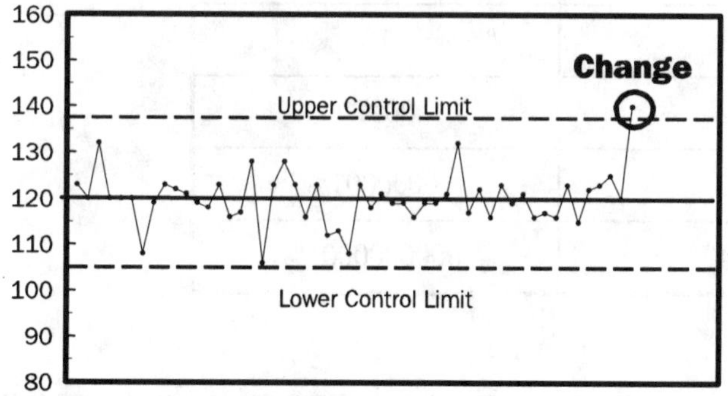

The chart should trigger an alert to investigate and determine the cause and the impact of the change.

Any subgroup average falling outside the $\overline{X}$ chart control limits is an indication that the central tendency is changing. Any subgroup range value falling outside the R chart control limits is an indication that variability is changing. An immediate investigation is required.

Acting on the alarm would be like immediately throwing water on a kitchen fire after a smoke detector sounds, only to find out later that the fire is a grease fire and water causes a grease fire to spread.

Remember, as we stated before, never act on the alarm. Before any action can be taken, the cause of the alarm must be identified. Later in this chapter we will discuss causes. The control chart does not tell us the cause but only alerts us to start the investigation. The quicker our investigation starts the better our chances that we will determine the cause.

A SERIES OF POINTS OUTSIDE OF THE CONTROL LIMITS

Since the odds of a single data point outside the control limits is 0.1%, or .001, then a **series** of data points outside the limits must really be rare.

The second occurrence of having a point outside the control limits is also 0.1% or 0.001. The odds of having **two consecutive** points outside the control limits are the first probability multiplied by the second probability. Thus the probability of having two consecutive outside the control limits is 0.001 multiplied by 0.001 which equals 0.000001 or 0.0001%.

Number of points outside the control limits	Probability of Occurrence
1	.1%
2	.0001%
3	.0000001%
4	.0000000001%

As is evident in the table above, the probability of having multiple consecutive data points outside the control limits is very rare. Four straight data points outside the control limits which do not reflect a change would be almost impossible. This leads us to the conclusion that this must truly be a shift in the metric that is being monitored. The control chart below shows this particular situation.

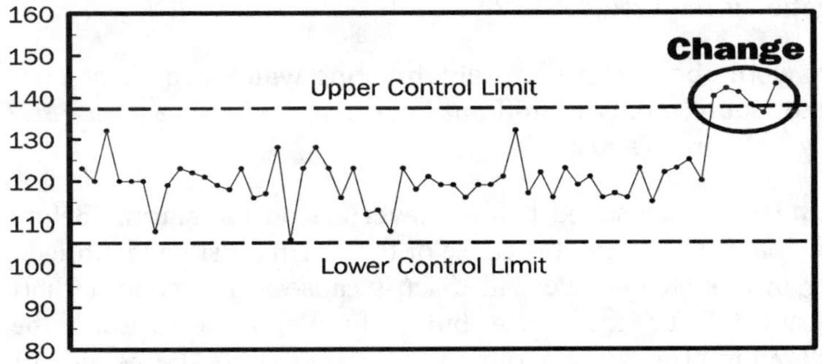

A series of values outside the control limits is an alarm.

All our alarms apply to control charts for both central tendency and variability because the alarms are based on the probabilities of a normal distribution.

SUDDEN JUMP IN LEVEL - SEVEN CONSECUTIVE DATA POINTS ON ONE SIDE OF CENTER

Many people mistakenly look only for the alarms that we just covered. Control charts were designed to detect much more subtle changes than those. Because

control chart methods are designed to detect minor changes, many of our alarms are based around values that are inside the control limits. These alarms are geared to detect the most minor of shifts that are outside the typical for any one particular machine. The first change that is detected with data inside the control limits is a jump in data.

This particular alarm was geared for minor shifts above the mean of the central tendency or variability, or minor shifts below the center.

The alarm is seven consecutive data points above the center point of the control chart, with none of the data points falling outside the control limits. The chart below reflects this particular alarm.

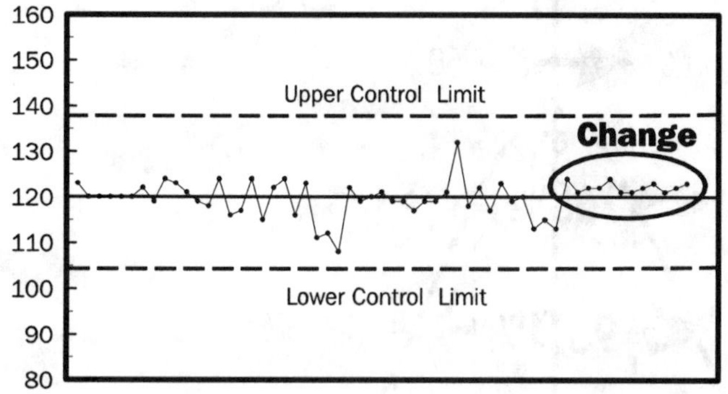

This chart shows a series of data points all above the centerline.

The first indication of an alarm is when seven consecutive points are on the same side of the centerline. The more consecutive the values on one side of the center, the bigger the alarm.

An alarm similar to the above is seven consecutive data points all below the center point of the control chart, but none of the data points are outside the control limits. Restated, the alarm is seven consecutive values on one side of the center of the control chart with none of the values falling outside the control limits.

All the alarms are alerts that a change has occurred in the process or product. Never stop the machine because of an alarm on the control chart. This alarm may be a signal of an improvement!

WHY USE SEVEN CONSECUTIVE POINTS AS THE ALARM?

This is one of the most frequently asked questions associated with the control chart alarms. Let's explain the logic of seven points in a row.

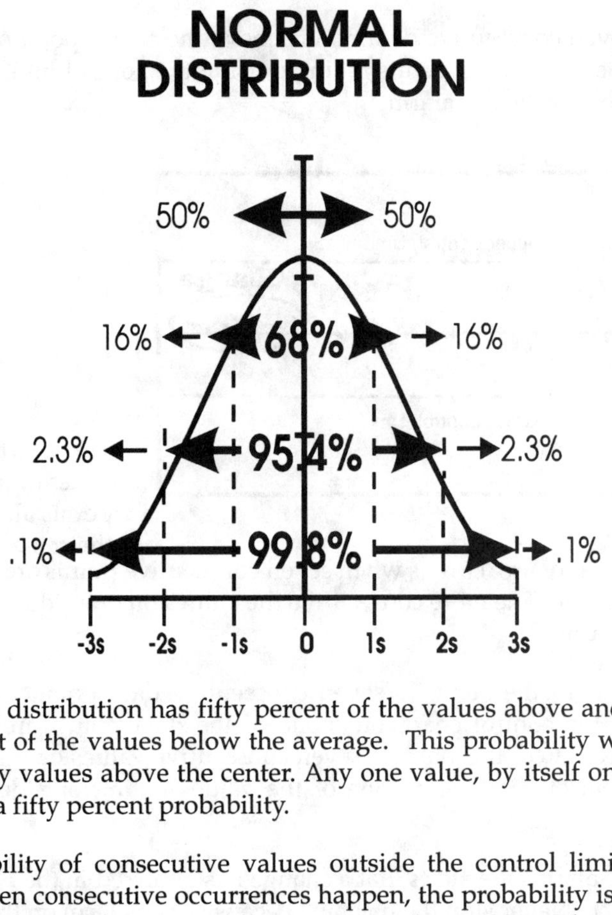

The normal distribution has fifty percent of the values above and the remaining fifty percent of the values below the average. This probability would lead us to expect many values above the center. Any one value, by itself on one side of the average, is a fifty percent probability.

The probability of consecutive values outside the control limits was covered earlier. When consecutive occurrences happen, the probability is multiplicative. The probability of having two consecutive data points above the center is calculated by multiplying together the probability of occurrence of the individual data points.

One data point above the center is itself a 0.5 probability. Therefore, the probability of two straight data points occurring consecutively above the center line is 0.5 multiplied by 0.5 or a 0.25 probability.

The table below shows the probability of having seven straight values on one and only one side of the center and no values outside the control limits. As the number of consecutive points increases, the probability decreases that this shift is just chance. This leads to the conclusion that the probability of this being a real change is very large.

Consecutive Points on one side of the Center	Probability Calculations	Probability
1	.5	.5
2	.5*.5	.25
3	.5*.5*.5	.125
4	$.5^4$	.06
5	$.5^5$	.03
6	$.5^6$	.016
7	$.5^7$	.008

The seven consecutive points on one side of the center (either seven above the center or seven below the center) applies for both the $\overline{X}$ and R charts monitoring the central tendency and variability.

The seven consecutive points rule is used because its probability of occurrence is very close to the probability of occurrence for one point falling outside the control limits. This keeps us using the same basic logic for all our alarm conditions.

TREND - SEVEN CONSECUTIVE DECREASING (OR INCREASING) DATA POINTS

Another minor shift that is important is a trend. Trends can take the form of going up or coming down. Once again, minor shifts are the objective of the control chart's detection mechanism. A trend can also be found where the data is inside the control limits.

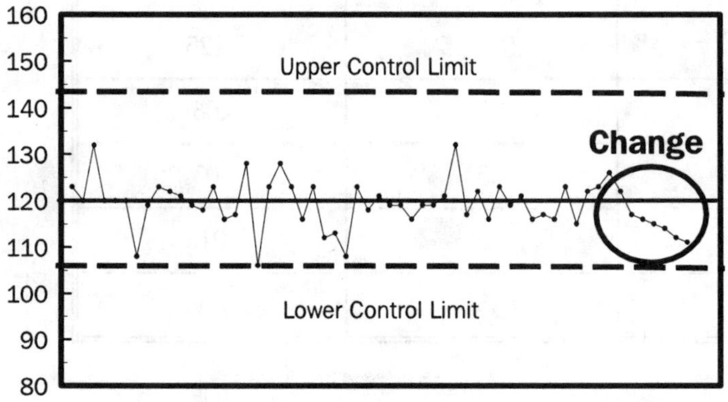

This particular alarm, illustrated to the left, is geared to detect a slow shift in a downward direction ("trending down"). It is described as seven consecutive points with each point lower than the last point and no points outside the control limits.

The same idea applies to the reverse, where the trend is increasing. This particular alarm is geared to detect a slow shift in an upward direction ("trending up"). This alarm is seven consecutive points with each point higher than the last point and none of the points outside the control limits.

Remember, the normal distribution is symmetrical. The symmetry of the normal distribution explains how this alarm was developed and why we use seven points. The probability calculation for this alarm is similar to the alarm of seven points on one side of the center.

Keep in mind, control charts must be viewed in a total context of all the information that is available. Just because no control chart alarms have gone off does not mean that other information might not cause an alert. As an example, if a drill bit is dull (needs replacing) the information about the bit should tell us to change the bit even though no control chart alarms have sounded.

TOO CLOSE - MORE THAN 68% OF THE DATA WITHIN ZONE ONE

Many people take the normal distribution and break it into three areas for use on the bell shaped curve. The first area, or zone one, is that area formed by plus and minus one standard error. The second zone is the area outside plus and minus one standard error, up to plus and minus two standard errors. The third zone is outside two standard error, to plus or minus three standard errors.

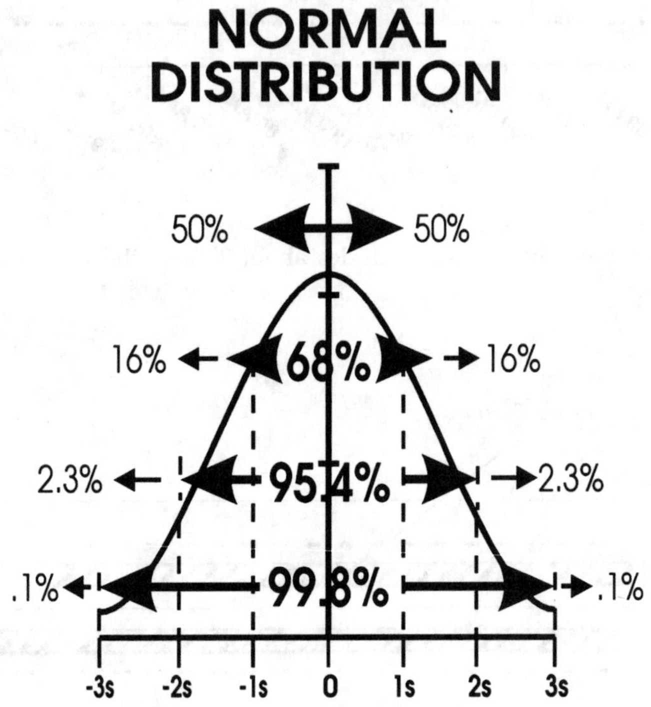

These three zones can then be used to subdivide the control chart into zones. These zones can be used because the control chart is based on a normal distribution.

The zone one area on a control chart includes 68% of the values and is shown below:

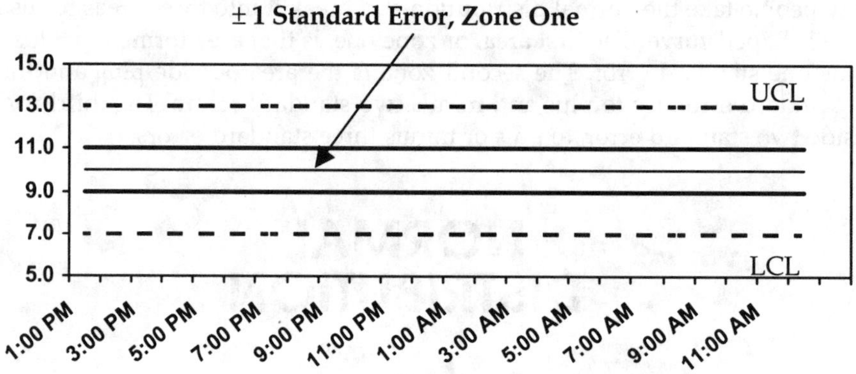

Zone two on the control chart includes about 27% of the values and is shown below:

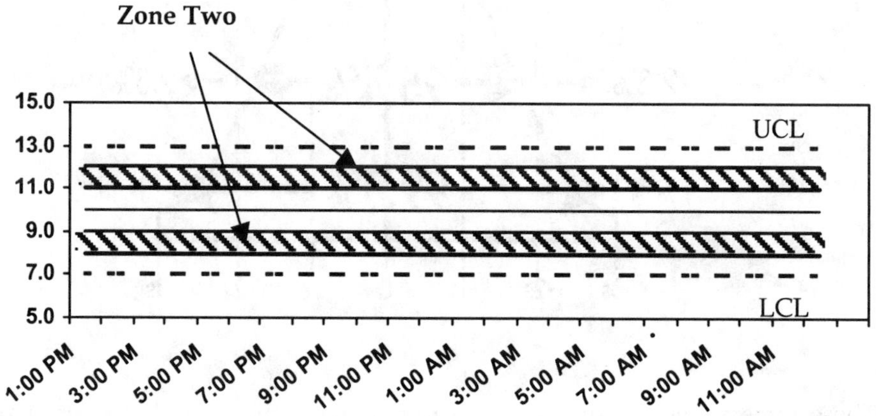

Zone three on the control chart is about five percent of the values and is shown below:

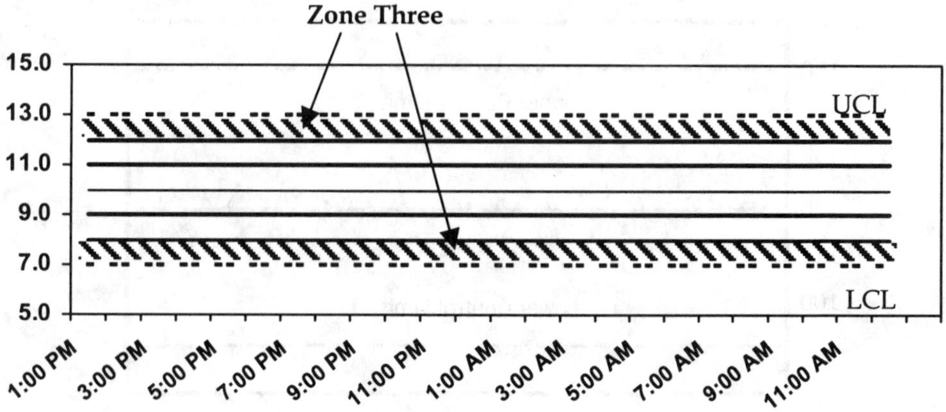

Revisiting the probabilities of a normal distribution, we find that 68% of the values should fall inside plus or minus one standard deviation. For our application, 68% should also fall inside one standard error. Based on our understanding of a normal distribution then, approximately 68% of the data points should be within one standard deviation of the average. Many people refer to the area inside plus and minus one standard deviation as the zone one area.

If too many of the values are clustered around the mean, an alarm is indicated. Remember, this is not an indication of bad product or good product, but an indication of change that needs to be investigated. The control chart on the next page shows a zone one alarm where more than 68% of the data points are in the zone one area.

On the control chart below, all the data points are inside the zone one area (plus and minus one standard deviation). This chart is an example of the "too close" alarm going off. This alarm like all the other alarms must be investigated immediately.

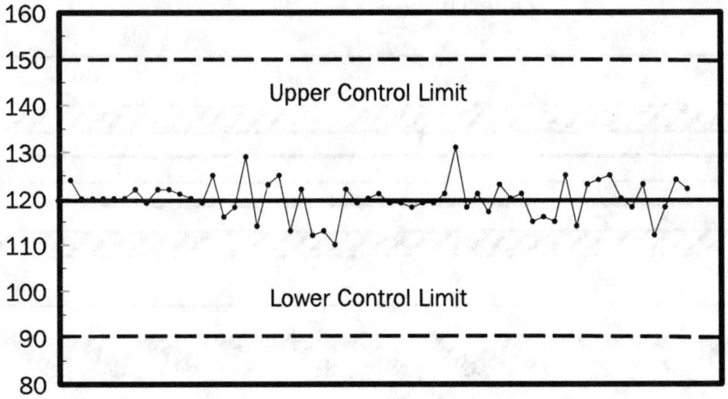

Minor change going unnoticed over time may seem trivial, but these minor changes have a compounding affect and over time allow us to miss major improvement opportunities or slide into major defect problems.

TOO FAR APART

Still viewing a normal distribution, the number of data points above one standard error but with no points outside the control limits should be 16% of the data points. The number of data points below one standard error with none outside the lower control limits is also 16%. The total data points within the control limits and outside zone one is 32%.

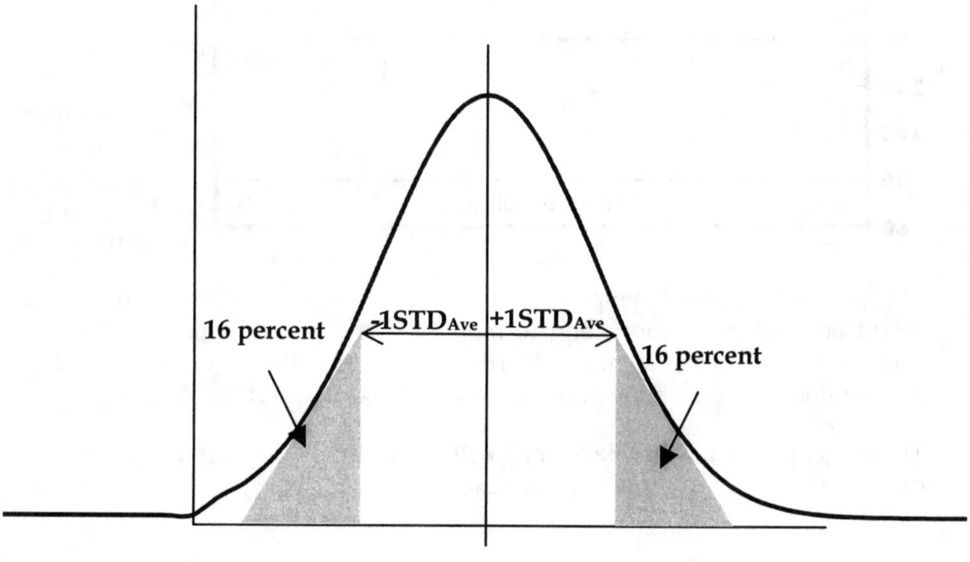

The area is comprised of the area from one standard error to two standard errors is referred to as zone two. The area from two standard errors to the control limits is called zone three. The total number of data points in zones two and three is 32%.

The alarm here is if more than 32% of the data points are in zones two and three. This becomes just as big an alarm as all the prior alarms.

MORE THAN A TOTAL OF 32% OF THE DATA IN ZONES TWO AND THREE

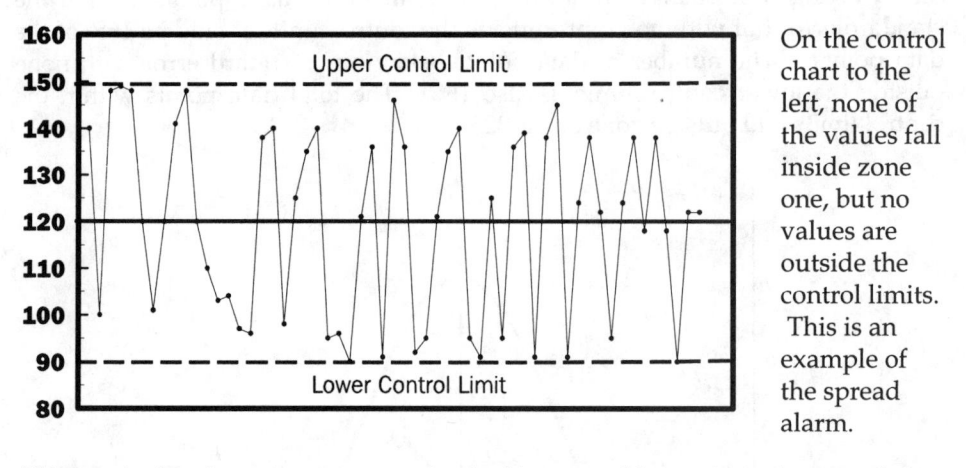

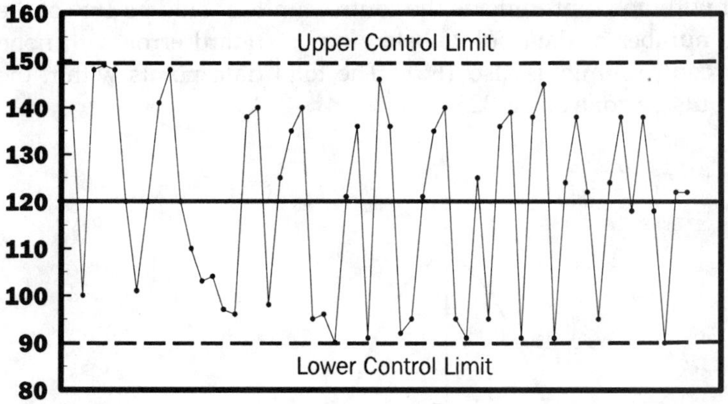

On the control chart to the left, none of the values fall inside zone one, but no values are outside the control limits. This is an example of the spread alarm.

This particular alarm is symptomatic of a bigger problem. A single control chart might be used (inappropriately) to monitor more than one machine. Because each machine has its own distribution, when these unique machines' distributions are laid on top of one another, a false distribution results.

The bigger problem might be formed with the individual distribution of machine one and machine two shown on the next pages.

Candy Machine One

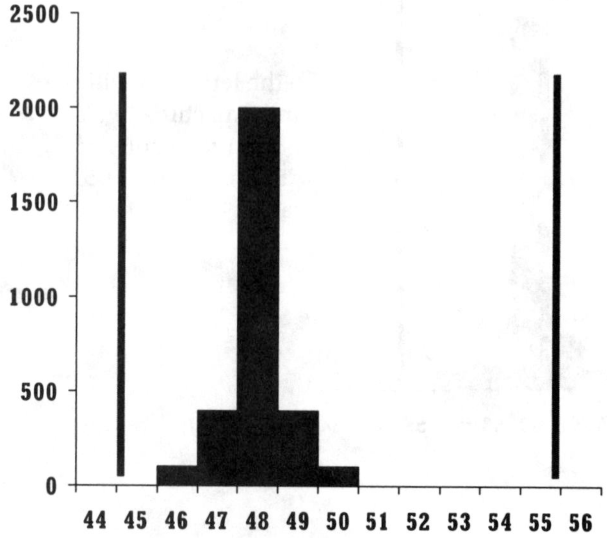

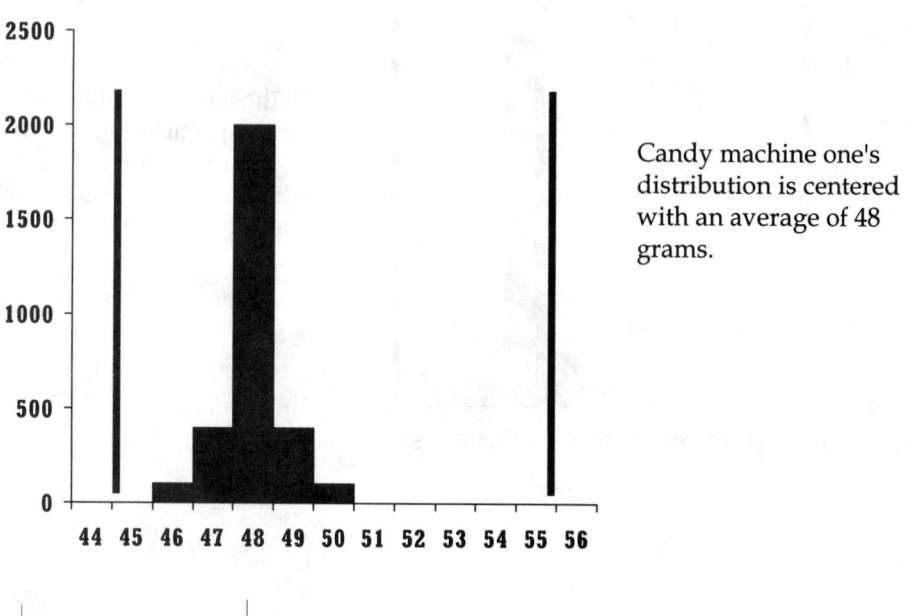

Candy machine one's distribution is centered with an average of 48 grams.

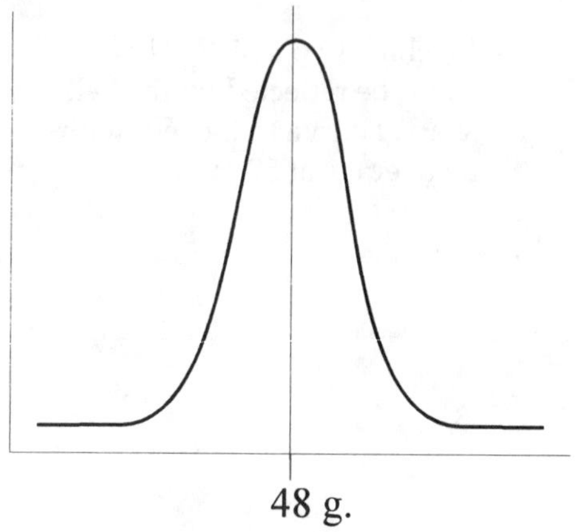

The machine one histogram could be reflected by the bell shaped curve to the left, with the average at 48 grams.

Candy Machine Two

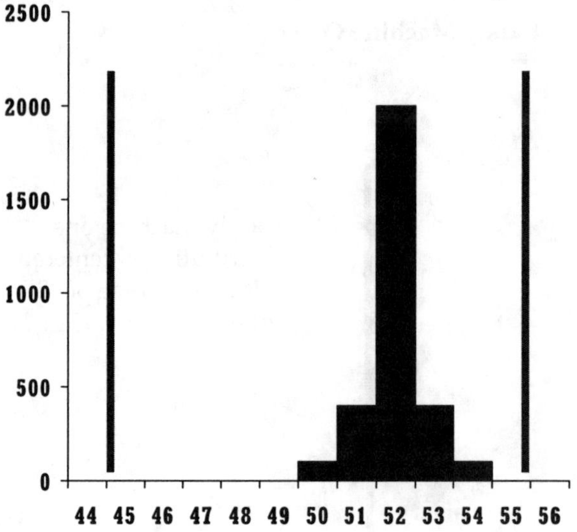

To the left, you will see candy machine two's distribution centered with an average of 52 grams.

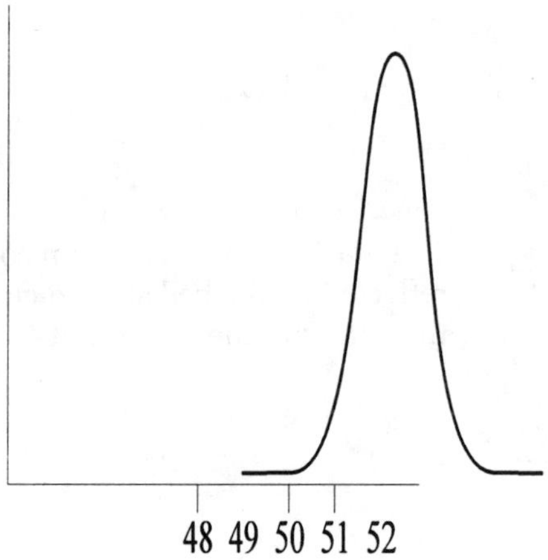

Machine two's histogram could be reflected by the bell shaped curve to the left, with an average at 52 grams.

Care must be taken to assure proper grouping and to avoid the mixing of the two machines' production.

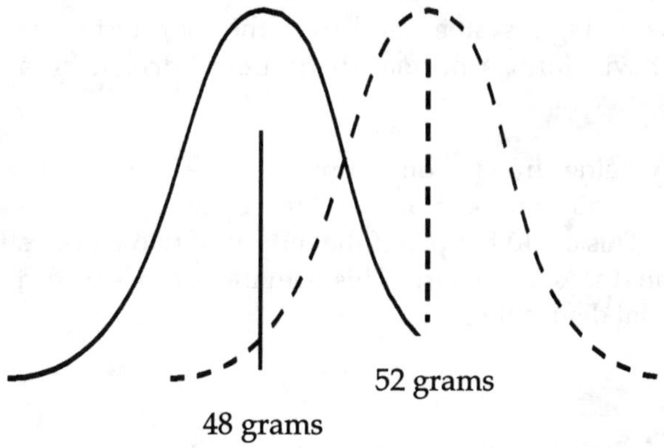

When the machine one and two graphs are superimposed on each other the graph to the left is created.

Candy Machines
One and Two

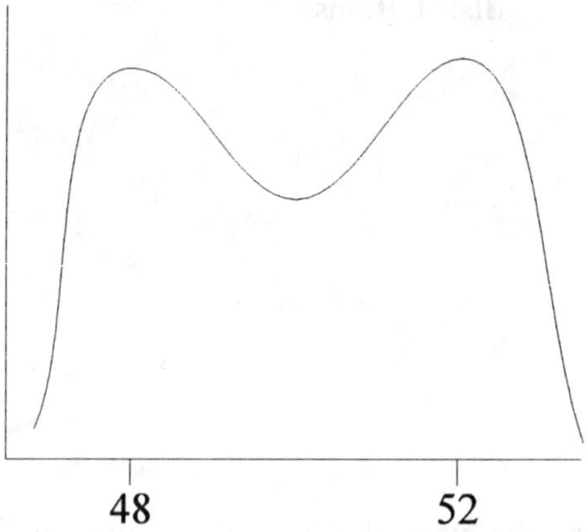

When the two machines' metric measurements are lumped together, an improper distribution is formed. The two candy machines' distributions looks like the graph to the left. By viewing them as one distribution, a confusing picture is drawn. Is this only one process' distribution?

ARE WE LOOKING AT ONE PROCESS OR MANY?

A controlled process behaves as a single system, and over the long term, the sample averages drawn from it will form a normal distribution, driven by a single system of common causes.

If the measurements are actually being drawn from more than one process, the distribution of sample averages will not be normal, but lopsided or even bimodal (with two peak values). This could happen if the output of two workers or machines were combined on the same chart. This situation can cause a distribution that is called a bimodal distribution.

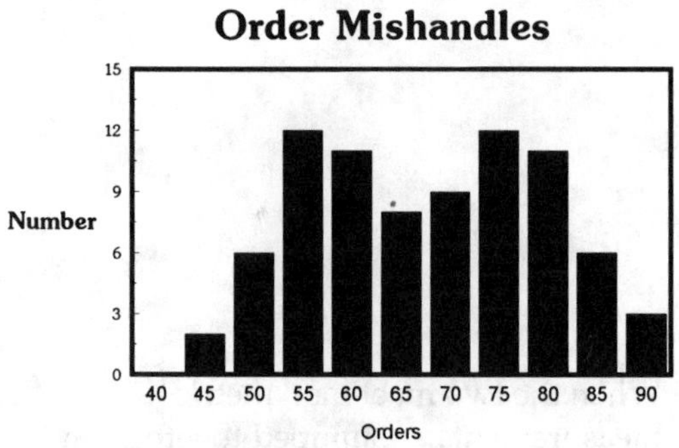

The histogram to the left is representative of how a bimodal distribution (two machines' distributions) might look. Notice the two spikes that are caused from the two different distributions.

RECURRING CYCLES

Any recurring pattern that deviates from the normal distribution must be viewed as an alarm. This alarm is not as specific as the others. Since control charts are based on the probabilities of a normal distribution, the 68% within one standard error of the mean, 95% within two standard error, and 99.8% within three standard error of the mean must be used to search for these patterns. For example, when a pattern of values outside the two standard error area is detected, an alarm to start the investigation must be initiated.

NORMAL DISTRIBUTION

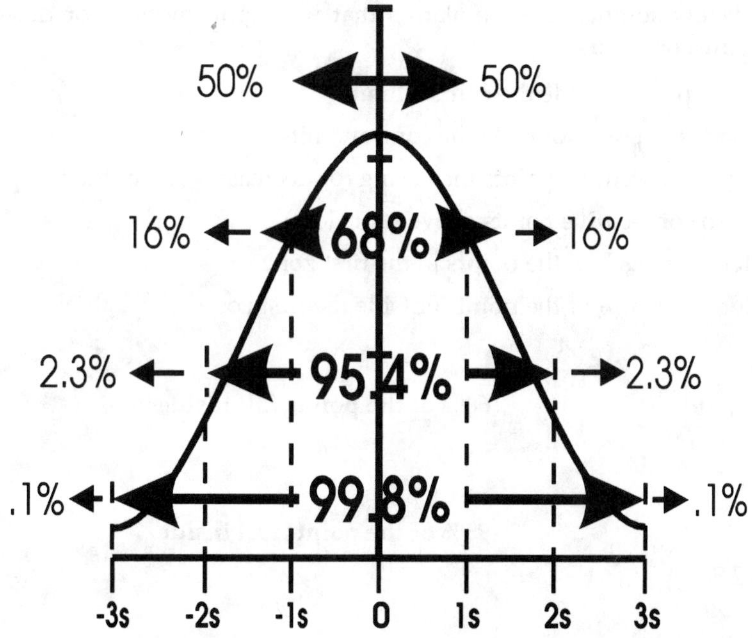

When any pattern or cycle violates the normal distribution, an alarm is triggered. These alarms are just as critical and important as all of the standard alarms.

SUMMARY OF INTERPRETATION GUIDELINES

The table below summarizes the alarms that we use to monitor or detect any shifts, patterns, or trends.

- Single point outside the control limits
- A series of points outside the control limits
- Seven consecutive points increasing (or decreasing) from the last point
- Seven consecutive points above (or below) the average
- More than 68% of the points in the first zone
- More than 32% of the points outside the first zone

Alarm Zones

Average + 1 Std_{Ave} Average - 1 Std_{Ave}	**68% of the points fall inside**
Average + 2 Std_{Ave} Average - 2 Std_{Ave}	**95% of the points fall inside**
Average + 3 Std_{Ave} Average - 3 Std_{Ave}	**99.8% of the points fall inside**

The zone one area on a control chart includes 68% of the values. The zone three area on a control chart is about five percent of the values.

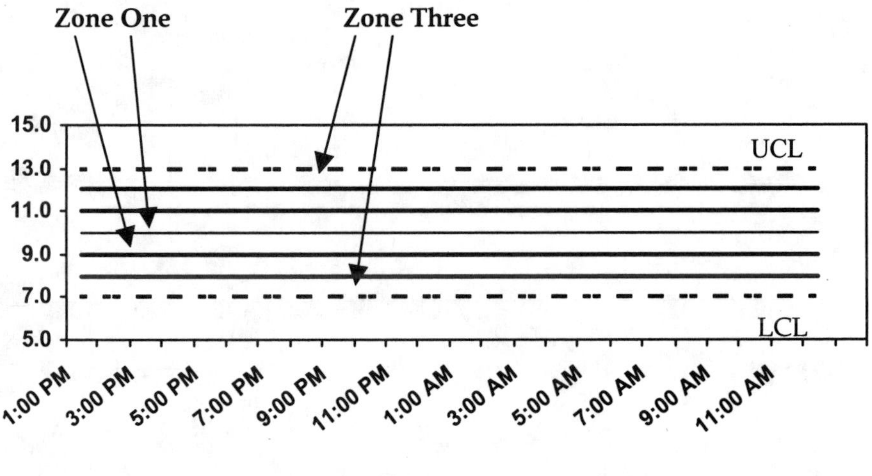

WHAT IS A CONTROL CHART ALARM

The control chart alarm is a change detection mechanism. These process or product changes are outside the typical behavior of the machine. Remember that change is not always bad; it can be either an improvement or deterioration. For progress (improvement) to be made, change has to occur.

The control chart is the tactical tool to identify when the change warrants our investigation. Our investigation is an attempt to determine the reason the change took place that is referred to as finding the cause. As we find the cause or causes our knowledge will grow, and with knowledge comes improvement.

In many ways the control chart (when used in conjunction with strategic tools) is our improvement detector. Actually the control chart can only find change, but without the control chart, change will go unnoticed. This is particularly true of minor change. Over time, many small, minor changes will accumulate to major change.

Once a change has been documented as more than just a fluke, the tactical role becomes even more focused on the correct and consistent running of the machine. The tactical operator must now focus on what caused the change while the strategic focus is to assess the impact. What is a cause and how do they work?

WHAT ARE CAUSES

Our knowledge base linking is the attempt to determine what caused something to happen. Effects are the things that happened. The deduction of what caused the effect is the most difficult task we will encounter. Since all facts are never known, making the determination of the cause of an effect is often difficult. The true cause or causes may be quite unknown. True cause identification is an ongoing effort that requires a vast amount of analytical experience. It will require much time, analysis, thought, and effort. We will be continually adding to our true causes, and in doing so, we will increase our knowledge base.

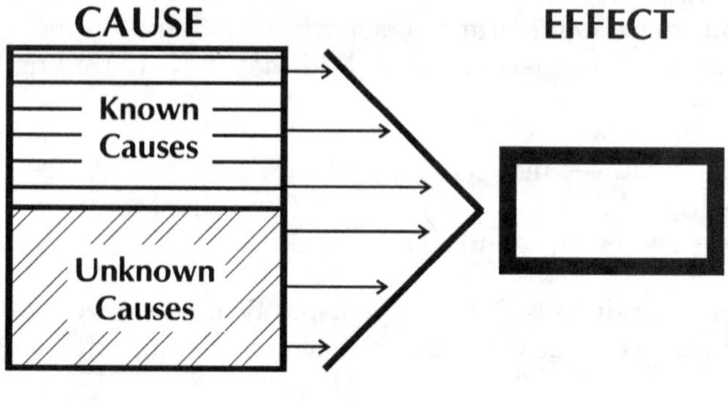

Since we never know all the facts or have a complete picture, we must continually review our determinations and findings. We must never view our determinations as laws or standards that cannot be improved. The disparity of known causes directly impacts our determinations and is due to a lack of all the facts or a failure to understand the meaning of the facts we have. The magnitude of this disparity must continually be investigated.

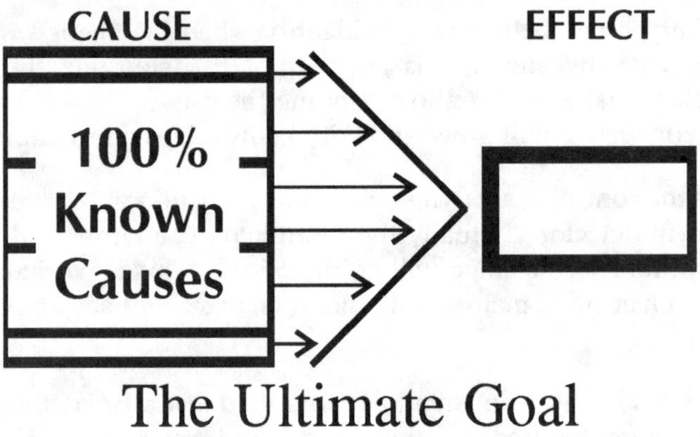

WHO IS BEST EQUIPPED TO FIND THE CAUSE

We first think of the machine designer, product designer, or process engineer as the most likely candidate to determine the cause of the change. These individuals are well equipped with technical skills. However, the investigation process must begin quickly so that the causal identification trail does not get cold. The problem with all the people listed is that their timely availability is questionable. Engineers, management, and designers are strategic and must be involved in the final action plan.

Change happens at all times of the day, weekends, holidays, and even at 3:00 AM on Saturday. Since our efforts must follow the *Church of What's Happening Now* philosophy, the person closest to the machine must be the causal searcher. This narrows our scope to the prime person most familiar with the machine - the operator. The operator, our tactician, will lead the efforts to finding the cause of the change.

All the technical resources that can support the operator must be brought into play to find the cause. As the operator finds these causes, the knowledge base about the process and product will be increased.

Our objective is to continually reduce this disparity and achieve total knowledge of the true causes. Over time we must strive to increase our knowledge base.

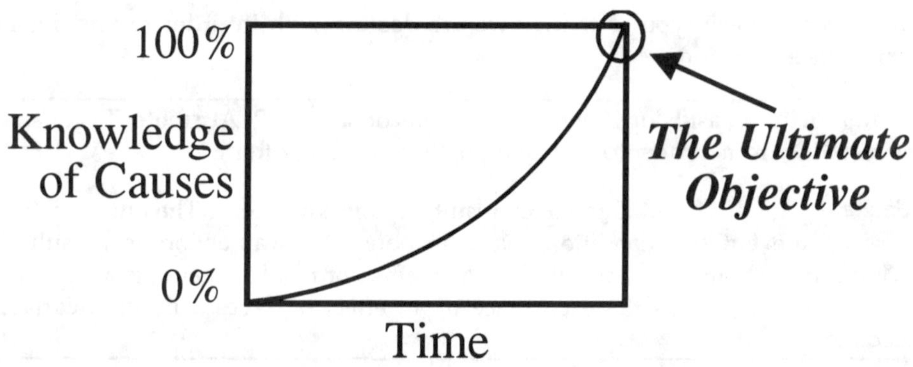

Effects are rarely the result of a single simple cause. Since most causes are seldom known, we should expect gaps in our knowledge base. These gaps of knowledge should keep us alert to the fact that effects are not always the result of known causes. Serious trouble will be encountered if the facts are forcibly stretched to explain the effect. A wise person is one who appreciates his lack of total knowledge.

To build our total knowledge base, our analysis must be based only on a historical record. The historical records allow us to begin to build a causal linking. This will not preclude our adding knowledge of changes in the future to better understand the cause. This is like driving a car. We look through the rear view mirror to understand where we have been. This view also allows us to see cars coming from the rear. We look through the front windshield to understand things coming up such as a curve in the road or a car on our side of the street.

The data for our analysis must begin at the basic element. Our analysis must begin both from the bottom and from the top, allowing the art of causal analysis to take place.

Our causal linking is easy when we view the most immediate occurrence that is known. The further removed the causes are from the effect, the more difficult the linking task. This linking must track the links of the chain from process to product. All products and processes are interrelated. This interrelationship impacts the outcome (effect).

To better understand the investigation and analysis that will be required, let's define the type of causes that can come into play.

ASSIGNABLE CAUSES

As we begin to study our information, a clear understanding of what a cause means and the types of causes which are possible is crucial to understanding what actions are required. We must first understand that we are looking for change. Change includes both improvements and deterioration. We must

understand which type of change we are dealing with in order to understand our courses of action.

Assign: 1. To set aside or give out in portions or shares. 2. Attribute; To consider as resulting from, proper to, or belonging to a person or thing.

Cause: 1. The producer of an effect, result, or consequence. 2. The one, such as a person, an event, or a condition, that is responsible for an action or a result. 3. What brings about or is associated with an effect or result. A cause is an agent or condition that permits the occurrence of an effect or necessarily or invariably leads to a result.

When we put the dictionary's definitions into action, we conclude that assignable causes are those which definitely result in a particular effect. As we read the definitions, we see that all causes do not have equal impact.

As we increase our knowledge base, we must strive to include all causes no matter how small their impact. A series of minor causes can lead to a cumulative impact that is very large. Too often we are only looking for the Big Bang. We are searching for both major and minor causes, so that we can build our knowledge base to be all-inclusive.

Causes are neither good nor bad but simply a statement of fact. A cause is why something happened or changed. For us to make improvements, we must first detect change and then determine its cause. We will diligently search for all causes, both those bringing about improvement and those resulting in deterioration. This information will allow us to increase our knowledge base of the process.

The reason causes are so important is that they give us the information to know what will happen in a particular situation. Many times an associate who has been on the job for twenty or thirty years will still run to the back end of the machine to find out what has happened every time that he changes a knob. There is major difference between thirty years on the job and thirty years of experience. With thirty years of experience, we have built a huge knowledge base that will tell us what is going to happen to the process. Our experienced operator's knowledge base allows him to know what will happen to the product when he turns that knob.

TYPES OF ASSIGNABLE CAUSES

For us to effectively make a decision, to understand its impact, and to know the correct type of decision, we must know what type of cause is involved. There are three kinds of causes: 1) Special, 2) Common, and 3) Tampering.

Special Causes are causes within one's control. The person running the machine is directly involved in the creation of a special cause. Special causes are isolated to one particular machine and impact only that one machine. As I drive down the street, the car's course adjustments are caused by my movement of the steering wheel. The car's speed is determined by my pressure on the accelerator.

In the same way, only an operator on a shop floor can make adjustments to his machine. These could include the speed the machine runs, the temperature of the machine, and the feed of the machine. No matter how the operator might desire these settings to impact other machines, it's pretty obvious that these changes, like the car's course adjustments, will have no effect on other machines.

Since special causes are local in nature (assigned to the driver or the operator), local action is required to resolve them. The operator must resolve the effects by dealing with the cause locally.

Special causes are the operator's responsibility for resolution. Local actions are usually required to eliminate these special causes and can usually be taken by people close to the process. Tactical decisions and tactical actions are generally used to deal with special causes. The driver of the car above must make course corrections to assure the safe driving of the vehicle. Such corrections are tactical decisions.

Common Causes are causes outside one's control. These influences generally occur across the board for all processes, thus the name common. The operator is usually not the generator of common causes. If the purchasing department buys bad peanuts for our chocolate-peanut clusters, the operator is not involved in this cause of change. Common causes are things that cross the boundaries of one machine into a group. Common causes impact multiple machines, and the impact is similar on all involved. Using the driving examples, I might choose to slow the speed of my car on a rainy day. This adjustment to my speed is caused by the rain, which is outside my control. Most other drivers would slow down also due to the bad weather conditions. All the cars are being impacted by the weather, and weather is common to all; no action by the drivers, either singularly or together, could change the weather.

All operators and their machines might be impacted by a shift to a new raw material such as new peanuts for our chocolate-peanut clusters. The raw material from the new source may be inferior and cause a rash of defective chocolate-peanut candy. No matter how sincere, conscientious, and diligent the operator, he cannot directly resolve the defects or change the raw material.

Since common causes are outside local control, sources outside the local area must resolve these causes. Generally this is thought of as a managerial issue because management has overall control of the facility and the actions on the system almost always require management action for correction. Strategic decisions and strategic actions are generally used to resolve common causes. Purchasing must resolve our bad peanut problem in order for good tasting

candy to be manufactured. Purchasing must make strategic decisions to resolve the problem or strategically decide to accept the defective candy clusters. No amount of local action can resolve this problem.

Tampering Causes are changes that are caused by too much control. Tampering occurs when we are trying to take action on something that should not be changed. This is typically caused by our failure to understand and comprehend the second Principle of Process Management.

SECOND PRINCIPLE OF PROCESS MANAGEMENT

Division of Labor is the framework for all aspects of decision-making. It must be clearly understood to separate the strategic and tactical decisions. Operations makes the tactical decisions of running the facility. Management makes the strategic decisions of assessing the facility's suitability for the job.

As we drive our cars, our driving habits and the outside conditions dictate how we act. If we get special causes and common causes confused, we could wind up trying to control the weather conditions. Since weather is outside our control and abilities, we would be trying to change the weather (an impossible task) and not trying to reduce our speed. The more we spend our energies trying to adjust the weather, the less time we have to actually drive. This would make our dangerous conditions even worse.

Please refer to my book, *Optimize Your Operation,* for a complete discussion of Division of Labor. There we rigorously discuss the potential violations to the second Principle. Since tampering is generally caused by a lack of understanding of the second Principle of Process Management (Division of Labor), we must assure that all appreciate this potential cause. Management must assure and take the responsibility that all associates understand Division of Labor.

We must research the many questions surrounding the chain of events that caused an effect. The real art of causal analysis and linking is determining which of these questions warrant an investment of the time and money required for further research. In many ways the research is like wildcatting for oil. Many causes will be confirmed. Many causes will be rejected. Often the research leads to more questions. The objective is to continue to build our knowledge base. This information can actually become a bigger asset than the manufacturing facility!

What is the cause of an event? Some people rush to explain the cause of an event as one single thing. These people talk as if the explanation for the event

can be determined by simply tracing a single line from an individual action. However, we are flirting with disaster by using overly simplistic reasoning. Instead, we must vigilantly watch for multiple causes and interactions in order to improve our knowledge base.

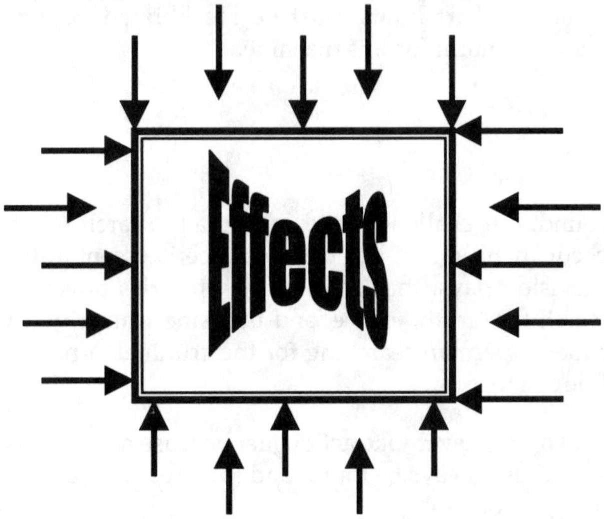

ASSESSING THE IMPACT OF THE CHANGE

Management, as the strategic decision-maker, must assess the impact of the change. While the tactical work force is working to determine the cause of the change, the strategist must assess the change through a capability study. The strategist's capability study will be covered in **Chapter Ten**.

DECISIONS FOR ACTION

The control chart is not a tool for action. The action must be driven from the determination of the cause and the results of the capability study.

IMPROVEMENT

If the capability has improved and the cause is found, then the cause is made a standard practice and the control chart limits are recalibrated. If the capability has improved and the cause cannot be found, then the best course of action is to bring more resources into play to continue and increase our search for the cause. Otherwise, we have missed an opportunity for improvement.

DETERIORATION

If the capability has deteriorated and the cause is found, then the cause must be fixed and the process brought back to its original method. If the cause cannot be fixed, then the control chart limits must be recalibrated because this level of performance is now the norm for this machine.

NO CAUSE FOUND

If no cause is found, our challenge is to continually search for the cause. This situation will occur many times, but perseverance is essential to this effort. In my boyhood television days, the "Superman" episodes always talked about a never-ending search for "truth, justice, and the American way." Our search for causes must be like Superman searching for the criminal: a never-ending search for the cause of our change.

Remember, never take action just because an alarm is noted. The cause must always be found and the capability assessed before taking action.

CHAPTER SUMMARY

Summary of Control Chart Interpretation Guidelines

- Single point outside the control limits
- A series of points outside the control limits
- Seven consecutive points increasing (or decreasing) from the last point
- Seven consecutive points above (or below) the average
- More than 68% of the points in the first zone
- More than 32% of the points outside the first zone

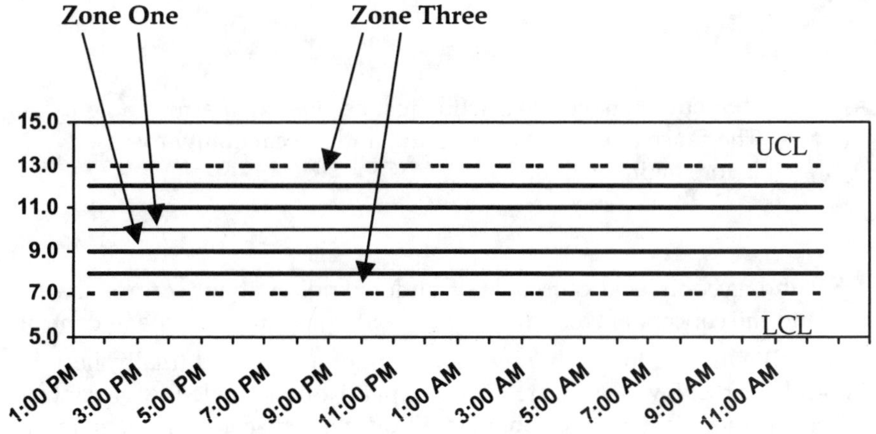

CAUSES

Special causes are within tactical control.

- Tactical action is required to deal with special causes
- Can be resolved by people (tactician) closest to the process

Common causes are within strategic control.

- Strategic Action is required to deal with common causes
- Common to all operators and machines
- Require strategic action for resolution

Tampering causes are caused by violations of Division of Labor.

- All associates must appreciate and understand their role and then execute the role

Remember, never take action just because an alarm is noted. The cause must always be found and the capability assessed before taking action.

Chapter Seven has completed our circle of understanding about control charts. We understand the concept of a control chart, how to prepare one type of control chart ($\overline{X}$ and R), what a control chart can and cannot tell us, and finally, how to read a control chart. Now we are ready to expand our knowledge of control charts to cover more situations. **Chapter Eight** will discuss the remaining variable control charts. **Chapter Nine** will explain attribute control charts.

Chapter Eight:

Other Variable Control Charts

We must now expand into other types of variable data. **Chapter Seven** covered the interpretation, reading, and use of control charts by covering the $\overline{X}$ and R charts in detail. Since all control charts are based on the normal distribution, the remaining charts are used and read in the same way. Remember that the overall objective of control chart methods is to detect product or process change. The term out of control simply means a change has been detected.

The initial control limit calculations were covered in **Chapter Six.** In that chapter all the methods to effectively control a process and product were discussed. As a review, the following steps were covered:

- Calculate the initial control limits.
- Establish that the process is in control.
- Continually survey the control charts for alarms (out of control conditions)

In **Chapter Seven** the use and reading of control charts was covered. The following summarizes the key points of **Chapter Seven**:

- **How to read control charts.** The alarms associated with control charts and why they work: the alarms act as change detectors for our tactical decision-makers and as alerts to our strategic decision-makers.

- **Establish that the process is in control.** As each out of control condition is identified and dealt with, this procedure is repeated until no alarms have been detected. When the process is in control (no alarms have been detected), the control limits are locked in place.

- **Continually survey the control charts for alarms (out of control conditions).** Data is gathered to monitor against the alarm mechanism (control limits) for changes in the conditions of the machine. When an out of control situation, or change, is detected the chart has done its job. The following tasks must be undertaken:
    - Search for the cause.
    - Alert management to the change.
    - Decide what to do.

Chapter Eight will now expand what we have already learned about SPC and control charts by adding knowledge about the remaining classic variable control charts. Each set was designed to monitor a particular situation. The remaining two classic charts are $\overline{X}$ and S and Individual charts.

Since all of the classic control charts are comprised of two control charts, our knowledge of the $\overline{X}$ and R charts and its similarity to the others will allow us to

expedite the explanation of how to construct the other charts. One chart monitors central tendency for any changes while the other control chart monitors for changes in the variability of the process.

	Central Tendency	Variability	Distribution
$\overline{X}$ and R	$\overline{X}$	R	Central Limit Theorem
$\overline{X}$ and S	$\overline{X}$	S	Central Limit Theorem
Individual	X	Moving Range	Histogram

The table above shows each chart monitoring its statistical element. The $\overline{X}$ and X control charts monitor central tendency and only the calculations are different. The R, S, and Moving Range all monitor variability for different situations using a specific calculation for the particular situation.

Remember, do not confuse control charts and control limits with a management chart to assess customer specifications. Control limits help us determine if a process is producing consistent output -- that is, whether its distribution is stable and the process is in control and not changing.

Now we must focus on the mechanics of the remaining charts. The remaining charts are continuations of the same approach we used to compute the $\overline{X}$ and R charts. Let's now focus on the control chart called $\overline{X}$ and S.

$\overline{X}$ AND S CHARTS

These charts should be used when the number of samples in the subgroup is large and the R value(from the $\overline{X}$ and R chart) is not precise. When the subgroup is small, the math associated with standard deviation adds no more precision than the R value because the number of samples in the subgroup is small. Either control chart ($\overline{X}$ and R or $\overline{X}$ and S) will function well in most situations.

Since the R chart is simpler than the S chart, the S chart is very seldom used. The S chart will be the tool of choice when the number of samples in the subgroup is large. Large is typically defined as greater than ten.

What does an $\overline{X}$ and S chart look like? Notice the $\overline{X}$ chart on the next page looks very much like the original chart we discussed in **Chapter Six**. Only the calculations have been slightly changed.

$\overline{X}$ chart is designed to monitor the movement or changes in the central tendency of the process. Throughout this book the term $\overline{X}$ will be used for average of the subgroup and $\overline{\overline{X}}$ for average of the averages.

The $\overline{X}$ chart is comprised of the following plot lines:

Monitor: $\overline{\overline{X}}$ is the benchmark of the central tendency of the process. $\mathbf{UCL_{Ave}}$ is the upper control limit that is three (3) standard errors above the mean. $\mathbf{LCL_{Ave}}$ is the lower control limit that is three (3) standard errors below the mean.

Data: $\overline{X}$ is the average of each subgroup and becomes the data point to be monitored.

$\overline{X}$ Chart

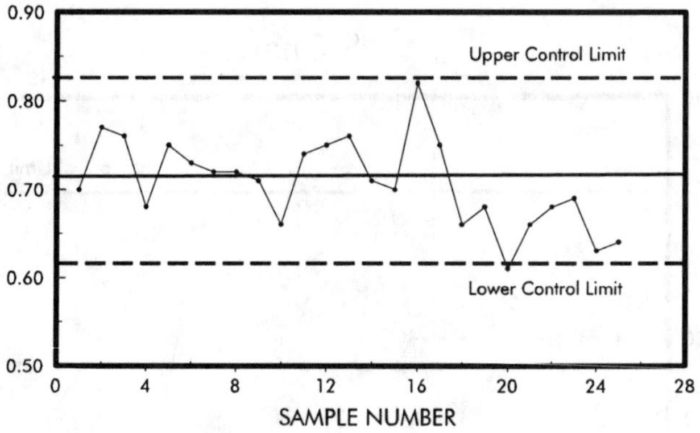

This chart is an example of an $\overline{X}$ chart used with S chart.

S Chart is designed to monitor the movement or changes in the variability of the process. This chart will track exactly like the R chart that has already been discussed. The S chart uses the standard deviation as the monitor while the R chart uses the range. Only the math is different. The S chart is more precise if the number of samples in a subgroup is large. A large subgroup sample is very rare, thus making the S chart a rarity in actual practice.

The S Chart is comprised of the following plot lines:

Monitor: $\bar{S}$ is the benchmark of the variability of the process. **UCL_s** is the upper control limit that is three (3) standard errors above the mean. **LCL_s** is the lower control limit that is three (3) standard errors below the mean.

Data: **S** is the standard deviation of each subgroup and becomes the data point to be monitored.

S Chart

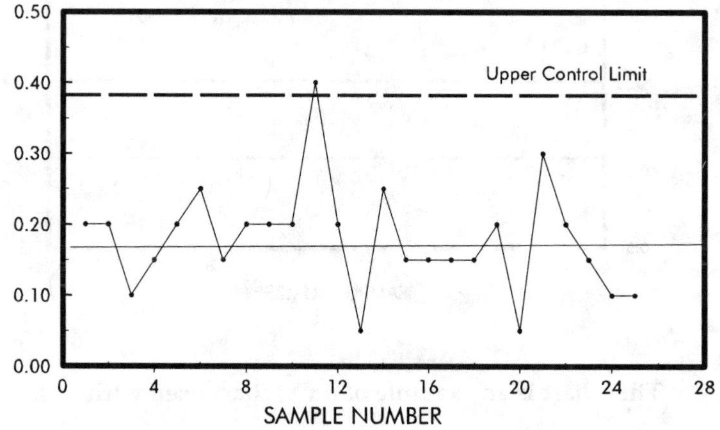

This chart is an example of an S chart. Note how similar this chart is to the R chart that we discussed earlier.

The next table is the data that we will use for our $\overline{X}$ and S example. The data is from one of our candy plant machines. Once again, to keep our example simple the data was pulled from 1:00 to 4:00. The preparation of actual control charts would follow the same method and need the same number of subgroupings that we covered in the $\overline{X}$ and R control charts.

Sample	1:00	2:00	3:00	4:00	5:00	6:00
1	10	14	10	10		
2	11	8	10	11		
3	13	10	9	9		
4	9	10	10	10		
5	10	9	10	10		
6	8	13	11	11		
7	9	12	12	12		
8	9	11	8	8		
9	12	9	7	9		
10	10	9	10	10		

$\overline{X}$ AND S CHART DATA

On the next page you will see the algebraic formulas that were used to compute subgroup control chart data points. They are used to derive the data to plot for the $\overline{X}$ and S charts. For the $\overline{X}$ chart, average data is used to provide a means to alert operators when a shift in the process' central tendency has occurred. For the S chart, standard deviation of the subgroup data is used to monitor shift in the process' variability. This should eliminate the potential for over adjusting control due to an overzealous alarm.

Remember, for control chart purposes the actual individual data is no longer of value and will not be used. These charts are tactical tools to assist the operator in the correct and consistent running of the machine.

Chart Data:

For our 1:00 through 4:00 data, the next few formulas are used to compute data that will be charted. The following shows the $\overline{X}$ data calculations for the 1:00 readings:

X_N is the data reading for the particular subgroup where N equals the size of the subgroup:

$$\overline{X} = \frac{X_1 + X_2 + X_3 + \ldots + X_N}{N}$$

where N equals the number of samples in the subgroup.

The actual 1:00 values are now inserted into the equation to compute the plotted 1:00 point for the control chart:

$$\overline{X} = \frac{10+11+13+9+10+8+9+9+12+10}{10}$$

$$= 10.1$$

The $\overline{X}$ value of 10.1 is now the 1:00 data point for plotting on the $\overline{X}$ chart. These calculations are then continued for all time frames. The actual individual data points are not used on the control charts.

Next the S value must be calculated for the 1:00 data points on the S chart. This standard deviation, or S, is the variability of the subgroup. We are contrasting each data point in the subgroup to the subgroup average. S for each subgroup will be used as the S chart's data.

$$S = \sqrt{\frac{\Sigma(\overline{X} - X_i)^2}{N-1}}$$

The 1:00 data points are inserted into this equation to give the following.

$$S = \sqrt{\frac{(10.1-10)^2 + (10.1-11)^2 + \ldots + (10.1-10)^2}{10-1}}$$

The table on the next page shows the detail calculations for the 1:00 S value reading. The calculations are the distance away from the subgroup mean, the squared distance, sum of squares, the variance, and the standard deviation. The first column is the subgroup sample number. The second column is the calculation of the distance each data point is away from the subgroup average.

This distance calculation is simply the data point less the subgroup average, or $\overline{X}$.

Samples	$\overline{X}-X_i$	Distance	Square of Distance
1	10.1 - 10	.1	0.0
2	10.1 - 11	-.9	.8
3	10.1 - 13	-2.9	8.4
4	10.1 - 9	1.1	1.2
5	10.1 - 10	.1	0.0
6	10.1 - 8	2.1	4.4
7	10.1 - 9	1.1	1.2
8	10.1 - 9	1.1	1.2
9	10.1 - 12	-1.9	3.6
10	10.1 - 10	.1	0.0

The last column of the table is the squared distance, rounded to one decimal place, for each data point in the 1:00 subgroup. These ten squared distance values are summed to give the sum of the squares which is 20.8. The formula for the sum of squares is:

$$\sum_{i=1}^{N}(\overline{X}-X_i)^2 = 20.8$$

Next, the number of samples for the 1:00 subgroup (ten) is subtracted by one to give a value of nine, called degrees of freedom. The sum of squares (20.8) is divided by the degrees of freedom (9) to calculate the variance of 2.3.

$$\text{Variance} = \frac{\sum_{i=1}^{N}(\overline{X}-X_i)^2}{N-1}$$

$$= \frac{20.8}{10-1}$$

$$= \frac{20.8}{9}$$

$$= 2.3$$

The square root of the variance is the standard deviation, or S value. Here, the variance is 2.3 so its square root is 1.5. This S value is the 1:00 data point for the S chart and is seen below:

$$S = 1.5$$

This set of calculations is repeated for each subgroup and is shown in the table. The next to last row of this table is the $\overline{X}$. $\overline{X}$ for each hour, or subgroup, is the data point for the $\overline{X}$ chart. The last row shows the S for each subgroup. The $\overline{X}$ and S for each hour are the data points that will be plotted on the $\overline{X}$ and S charts.

Subgroup	**1:00**	**2:00**	**3:00**	**4:00**	**5:00**	**6:00**
Sample						
1	10	14	10	10		
2	11	8	10	11		
3	13	10	9	9		
4	9	10	10	10		
5	10	9	10	10		
6	8	13	11	11		
7	9	12	12	12		
8	9	11	8	8		
9	12	9	7	9		
10	10	9	10	10		
$\overline{X}$ = Total / Samples	10.1	10.5	9.7	10.0		
S	1.5	2.0	1.4	1.2		

On a control chart the actual individual candy readings will not be used. From this point on in this chapter, no use of the individual readings will be made. Therefore, in the tables that follow, all of the individual readings have been eliminated. When we return in **Chapter Ten** to discuss capability studies, the individual readings will become significant again.

$\overline{X}$ CHART CALCULATIONS FOR $\overline{X}$ AND S

The following calculations are used to derive the control limits for the $\overline{X}$ chart of the $\overline{X}$ and S control chart. The following pages will show how our example uses these formulas.

X_N is the data reading for the particular sample where N equals the sample.

The calculated subgroup $\overline{X}$ value will become the data point on the $\overline{X}$ chart.

$$\overline{X} = \frac{X_1 + X_2 + X_3 + \ldots + X_N}{N}$$

where N equals the number of samples in the subgroup and K equals the number of subgroups.

$\overline{\overline{X}}$ is the monitor for the center of the $\overline{X}$ control chart.

$$\overline{\overline{X}} = \frac{\overline{X}_1 + \overline{X}_2 + \overline{X}_3 + \ldots + \overline{X}_K}{K}$$

where K equals the number of subgroups.

S is the monitor of variability for the subgroup.

$$S = \sqrt{\frac{\Sigma(\overline{X} - X_i)^2}{N - 1}}$$

$\overline{S}$ is the monitor for the center of the S control chart.

$$\overline{S} = \frac{S_1 + S_2 + S_3 + \ldots + S_K}{K}$$

The following are the formulas for the $\overline{X}$ control limits:

$$UCL_{Ave} = \overline{\overline{X}} + A_3 * \overline{S}$$

where $A_3 * \overline{S}$ is an approximation of three (3) standard errors.

$$LCL_{Ave} = \overline{\overline{X}} - A_3 * \overline{S}$$

where $A_3 * \overline{S}$ is an approximation of three (3) standard errors.

On the $\overline{X}$ and R charts a conversion factor of A_2 was used to approximate three standard errors. A detailed explanation of these conversion factor derivations was covered in **Chapter Six**. The **Chapter Six** derivation also applies, in principle, for the remaining variable data control charts. The A_3 conversion factor for the $\overline{X}$ and S control chart is similar in every aspect to the A_2 factor from the $\overline{X}$ and R charts.

The table below contains the conversion factors for the $\overline{X}$ and S control chart. The use of this table is exactly the same as how we used the $\overline{X}$ and R conversion table. The first column is used to look up the factor based on the size of the subgroup.

Subgroup Size	A_3	C_4	B_3	B_4
10	0.975	0.9727	0.284	1.716
11	0.927	0.9754	0.321	1.679
12	0.886	0.9776	0.354	1.646
13	0.850	0.9794	0.382	1.618
14	0.817	0.9810	0.406	1.594
15	0.789	0.9823	0.428	1.572
16	.763	.9835	.448	1.552
17	.739	.9845	.466	1.534
18	.718	.9854	.482	1.518
19	.698	.9862	.497	1.503
20	.680	.9869	.510	1.490
21	.663	.9876	.523	1.477
22	.647	.9882	.534	1.466
23	.633	.9887	.545	1.455
24	.619	.9892	.555	1.445
25	.606	.9896	.565	1.435

$\overline{X}$ & S Conversion Tables

A_3 is the conversion factor to arrive at three (3) standard errors for use in determining UCL and LCL of $\overline{X}$ chart.

CONTROL LIMIT CALCULATIONS FOR $\overline{X}$ EXAMPLE

First, the average of the averages and the average S values are calculated. The following formulas are completed below:

$$\overline{\overline{X}} = \frac{\overline{X}_1 + \overline{X}_2 + \overline{X}_3 + \ldots + \overline{X}_K}{K}$$

where K equals the number of subgroups.

$$\overline{S} = \frac{S_1 + S_2 + S_3 + \ldots + S_K}{K}$$

The following table shows our example calculations for $\overline{\overline{X}}$ and $\overline{S}$.

$\overline{\overline{X}} = \frac{10.1+10.5+9.7+10.0}{4} = \frac{40.3}{4} = 10.08$
$\overline{S} = \frac{1.5+2.0+1.4+1.2}{4} = \frac{6.1}{4} = 1.5$

Next, the averages are used to compute the control limits by using the following equations. The constant A_3 is obtained from the table at the top on the previous page. The subgroup size for our example is ten thus the A_3 constant that is used is 0.975.

$$UCL_{Ave} = \overline{\overline{X}} + A_3 * \overline{S}$$

where $A_3 * \overline{S}$ is an approximation of three (3) standard errors.

$$LCL_{Ave} + \overline{\overline{X}} - A_3 * \overline{S}$$

where $A_3 * \overline{S}$ is an approximation of three (3) standard errors.

$\overline{\overline{X}} = \frac{10.1+10.5+9.7+10.0}{4} = \frac{40.3}{4} = 10.08$
$\overline{S} = \frac{1.5+2.0+1.4+1.2}{4} = \frac{6.1}{4} = 1.5$
$UCL_{\overline{\overline{X}}} = \overline{\overline{X}} + A_3 * \overline{S} = 10.08 + .975 * (1.5) = 11.54$
$LCL_{\overline{\overline{X}}} = \overline{\overline{X}} - A_3 * \overline{S} = 10.08 - .975 * (1.5) = 8.62$

$\overline{X}$ CHART EXAMPLE

The table below shows all the details of the example.

Subgroup	1:00	2:00	3:00	4:00	5:00	6:00
Samples	10	10	10	10		
$\overline{X}$ = Total / Samples	10.1	10.5	9.7	10.0		
S	1.5	2.0	1.4	1.2		

$$\overline{\overline{X}} = \frac{10.1+10.5+9.7+10.0}{4} = \frac{40.3}{4} = 10.08$$

$$\overline{S} = \frac{1.5+2.0+1.4+1.2}{4} = \frac{6.1}{4} = 1.5$$

$$UCL_{\overline{\overline{X}}} = \overline{\overline{X}} + A_3 * \overline{S} = 10.08 + .975*(1.5) = 11.54$$

$$LCL_{\overline{\overline{X}}} = \overline{\overline{X}} - A_3 * \overline{S} = 10.08 - .975*(1.5) = 8.62$$

S CHART CALCULATIONS FOR $\overline{X}$ AND S

The following calculations are used to derive the data plots for the S Chart:

$$S = \sqrt{\frac{\Sigma(\overline{X} - X_i)^2}{N - 1}}$$

$$\overline{S} = \frac{S_1 + S_2 + S_3 + \ldots + S_K}{K}$$

where K equals the number of subgroups.

$$UCL_S = B_4 * \overline{S}$$

where $B_4 * \overline{S}$ is an approximation of three (3) standard errors above the mean.

$$LCL_S = B_3 * \overline{S}$$

where $B_3 * \overline{S}$ is an approximation of three (3) standard errors below the mean.

The **S Chart** is designed to monitor the movement or changes in the variability of the process. The S chart is comprised of the following plot lines:

Monitor: $\overline{S}$ is the benchmark of the center of the variability of the metric. **UCL_S** is the upper control limit above the variability benchmark. **LCL_S** is the lower control limit below the variability benchmark.

Data: S_K is the variability monitor of the subgroup and becomes the data point to be plotted. $\overline{S}$, upper control limit, and lower control limit are the alarms, with S being the data.

Subgroup Size	A_3	C_4	B_3	B_4
10	0.975	0.9727	0.284	1.716
11	0.927	0.9754	0.321	1.679
12	0.886	0.9776	0.354	1.646
13	0.850	0.9794	0.382	1.618
14	0.817	0.9810	0.406	1.594
15	0.789	0.9823	0.428	1.572
16	.763	.9835	.448	1.552
17	.739	.9845	.466	1.534
18	.718	.9854	.482	1.518
19	.698	.9862	.497	1.503
20	.680	.9869	.510	1.490
21	.663	.9876	.523	1.477
22	.647	.9882	.534	1.466
23	.633	.9887	.545	1.455
24	.619	.9892	.555	1.445
25	.606	.9896	.565	1.435

$\bar{X}$ and S Conversion Chart

B_3 is the conversion factor to arrive at three (3) standard errors for use in determining LCL of S chart.

B_4 is the conversion factor to arrive at three (3) standard errors for use in determining UCL of S chart.

S CHART EXAMPLE

As you did earlier, plot your results and compare them to the graphs later in this chapter.

Subgroup	1:00	2:00	3:00	4:00	5:00	6:00
Samples	10	10	10	10		
S	1.5	2.0	1.4	1.2		

$$\bar{S} = \frac{1.5 + 2.0 + 1.4 + 1.2}{4} = \frac{6.1}{4} = 1.5$$

$$UCL_S = B_4 * \bar{S} = (1.716) * (1.5) = 2.57$$

$$LCL_S = B_3 * \bar{S} = (0.284) * (1.5) = .43$$

The $\overline{X}$ and S charts from our example have been calculated. The $\overline{X}$ chart below is the completed graph for our example.

$\overline{X}$ Chart Example

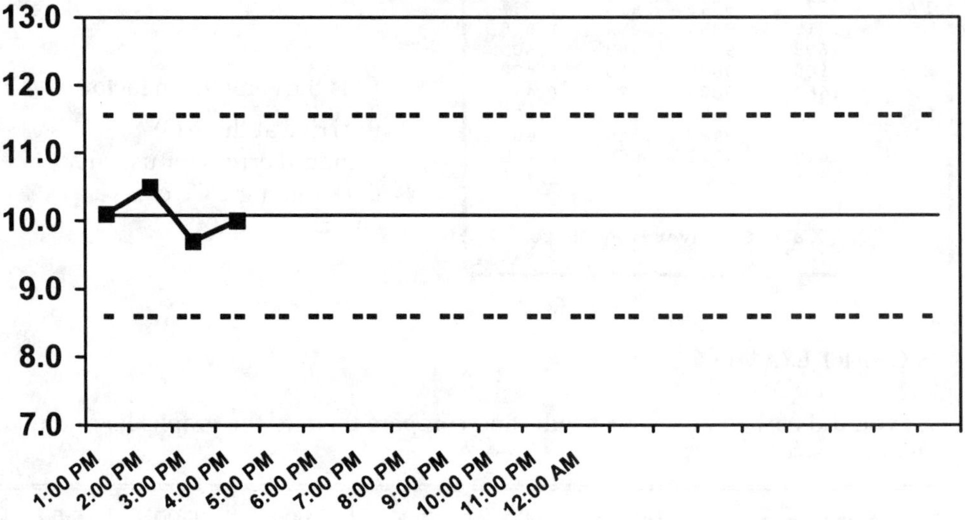

The S chart below is the completed graph for our example.

S Chart Example

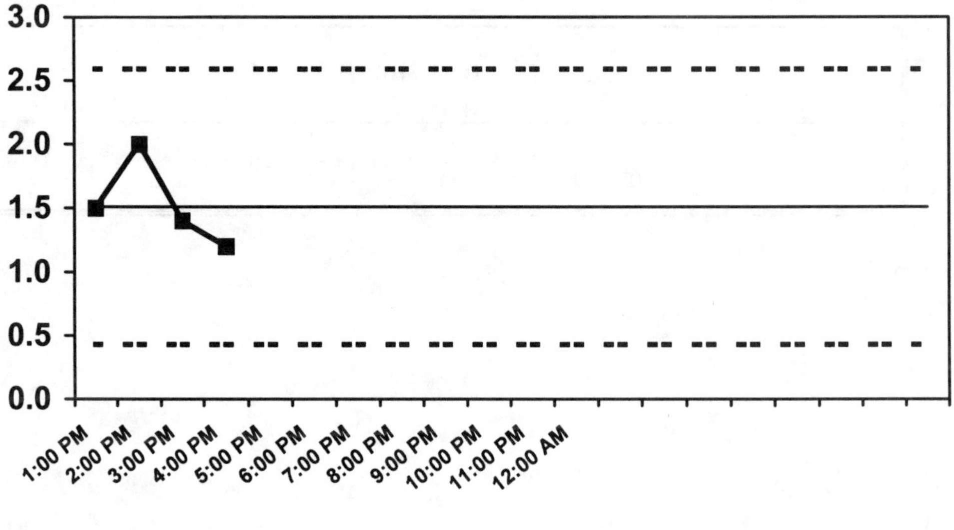

INDIVIDUAL CHART

Individual charts are used when we are able to take only one (1) sample. Individual charts are also used when multiple tests in a subgroup yield the exact same reading. Examples of this situation would include chemical processes, expensive products, low volumes of product, or homogeneous readings. The individual control charts are comprised of an Individual control chart for monitoring central tendency and a Moving Range chart for monitoring variability.

Individual Control Chart, sometimes referred to as the X chart, is designed to monitor the movement or changes in the central tendency of the process. The X chart is comprised of the following plot lines:

Monitor: $\overline{X}$ is the benchmark of the central tendency of the process. **UCL_{Ave}** is the upper control limit that is three (3) standard errors above the mean. **LCL_{Ave}** is the lower control limit that is three (3) standard errors below the mean.

Data: X is the data point to be monitored.

This is an example of the Individual or X control chart.

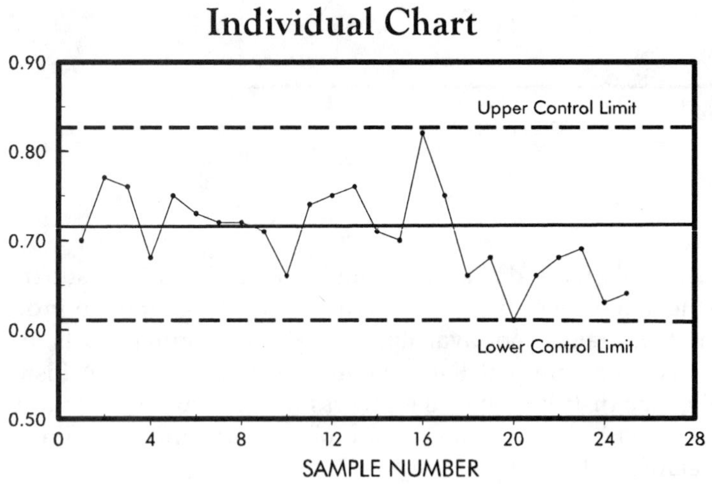

Moving Range Chart is designed to monitor the movement or changes in the variability of the process. The moving range chart is comprised of the following plot lines:

Monitor: $\overline{R}$ is the benchmark of the variability of the process. **UCL_R** is the upper control limit that is three (3) standard errors above the mean. **LCL_R** is the lower control limit that is three (3) standard errors below the mean.

Data: R is the moving range between the current and last reading and becomes the data point to be monitored.

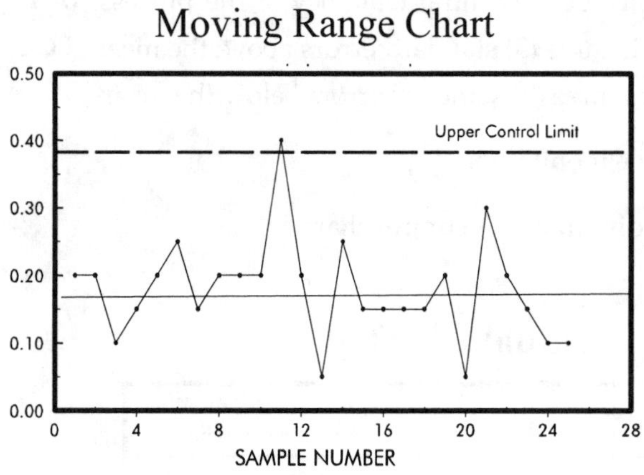

This is an example of a Moving Range control chart.

Since the Individual charts do not have multiple readings in a subgroup, the central limit theorem cannot be invoked. The normality guarantee provided by the central limit theorem is not available with the Individual charts; normality tests are required to assure that the standard alarms are valid. A histogram is used to monitor the distribution of the process in order to assure that it is truly normal. Failing the normality test is not a problem but simply requires revision to our interpretation rules.

Many people, in their desire to please or to take short cuts, omit variability control charts. Always include control charts for both central tendency **and** variability.

X CHART EXAMPLE

The data for the X chart of the Individual chart will be the individual values. For the variability of the data a moving range will be used which compares the current and prior value to compute the distance between the values.

The table below shows the 1:00, 2:00, 3:00, 4:00, and 5:00 readings. Our candy plant has a chocolate vat. Every hour the chocolate viscosity is measured. The readings below are our 1:00 through 4:00 chocolate viscosity readings from vat fourteen. These readings will be plotted on the individual chart as data.

Subgroup Sample	**1:00**	**2:00**	**3:00**	**4:00**	**5:00**	**6:00**
1	10	12	14	15	13	

The moving range value is now computed for each time period for monitoring the variability of the values. The 1:00 reading has no prior reading so no moving range can be computed. Our first moving range is computed for the 2:00 reading, where the 2:00 data of twelve is compared to 1:00 reading of ten. The moving range at 2:00 is two; it is plotted on the Moving Range chart. The formula for the 2:00 moving range is shown below:

$$R = \left| X_{\text{Current}} - X_{\text{Prior}} \right|$$

$$= |12 - 10|$$

$$= 2$$

Notice that the absolute value or positive value of the range is always used. This keeps the distance, whether moving up or down, relative. The table below shows the individual data and the moving range for all the example data.

Subgroup Sample	**1:00**	**2:00**	**3:00**	**4:00**	**5:00**	**6:00**
1	10	12	14	15	13	
R		2	2	1	2	

The following calculations are used to derive the data plots for the X chart for Individual charts:

X_N is the data reading for the particular sample.

$$\overline{X} = \frac{X_1 + X_2 + X_3 \ldots + X_N}{N}$$

where N equals the number of samples.

$$R = \left| X_{Current} - X_{Prior} \right|$$

$$\overline{R} = \frac{R_1 + R_2 + R_3 + \ldots + R_K}{K}$$

where K equals the number of subgroups.

Remember, even though this is an individual chart, we are still using standard error for our computations of control limits.

$$UCL_{Ave} = \overline{X} + 2.660 * \overline{R}$$

$$LCL_{Ave} = \overline{X} - 2.660 * \overline{R}$$

These formulas are used to calculate the data and the alarm system. (See page 241 for the conversion factors for determining UCL and LCL for the Individual chart.) Now let's take our example from the prior page and compute the control limit alarm.

Now we must take our individual values and compute the Individual control chart alarm system.

Subgroup Sample	1:00	2:00	3:00	4:00	5:00	6:00
1	10	12	14	15	13	
R		2	2	1	2	

As we have done in all our other control charts, we first must compute the average of both the Individuals and the average of the range using the following formula:

$$\overline{X} = \frac{X_1 + X_2 + X_3 \ldots + X_N}{N}$$

where N equals the number of samples.

$$\overline{X} = \frac{10+12+14+15+13}{5}$$

$$= \frac{64}{5}$$

$$= 12.8$$

$$R = \left| X_{Current} - X_{Prior} \right|$$

Now we compute the $\overline{R}$ value:

$$\overline{R} = \frac{R_1 + R_2 + R_3 + \ldots + R_K}{K}$$

where K equals the number of subgroups.

$$\overline{R} = \frac{2+2+1+2}{4}$$

$$= \frac{7}{4}$$

$$= 1.75$$

The table below summarizes our calculations for the center point of the Individual and Moving Range charts.

$\overline{X} = \frac{10+12+14+15+13}{5} = \frac{64}{5} = 12.8$
$\overline{R} = \frac{2+2+1+2}{4} = \frac{7}{4} = 1.75$

With the averages computed, control limits can now be computed. The Individual chart, like all other control charts, uses standard error for computing the control limits. Since the moving range average uses two values, current and prior reading, the sample size of the subgroup is two. To simplify the calculations the following factors and formulas are used:

$$UCL_{Ave} = \overline{X} + 2.660 * \overline{R}$$

Inserting our $\overline{X}$ value of 12.8 and $\overline{R}$ of 1.75 yields the following equation for the upper control limits:

$$UCL_{Ave} = 12.8 + 2.660 * 1.75$$

$$= 12.8 + 4.66$$

$$= 17.46$$

Next we compute lower control limits:

$$LCL_{Ave} = \overline{X} - 2.660 * \overline{R}$$

$$LCL_{Ave} = 12.8 - 2.660 * 1.75$$

$$= 12.8 - 4.66$$

$$= 8.14$$

The table below summarizes our Individual chart calculations.

$\overline{X} = \frac{10+12+14+15+13}{5} = \frac{64}{5} = 12.8$
$\overline{R} = \frac{2+2+1+2}{4} = \frac{7}{4} = 1.75$
$UCL_{\overline{X}} = \overline{X} + 2.660 * \overline{R} = 12.8 + (2.66)*(1.75) = 17.46$
$LCL_{\overline{X}} = \overline{X} - 2.660 * \overline{R} = 12.8 - (2.66)*(1.75) = 8.14$

The Individual control chart can now be plotted.

Subgroup Sample	1:00	2:00	3:00	4:00	5:00	6:00
1	10	12	14	15	13	
R		2	2	1	2	

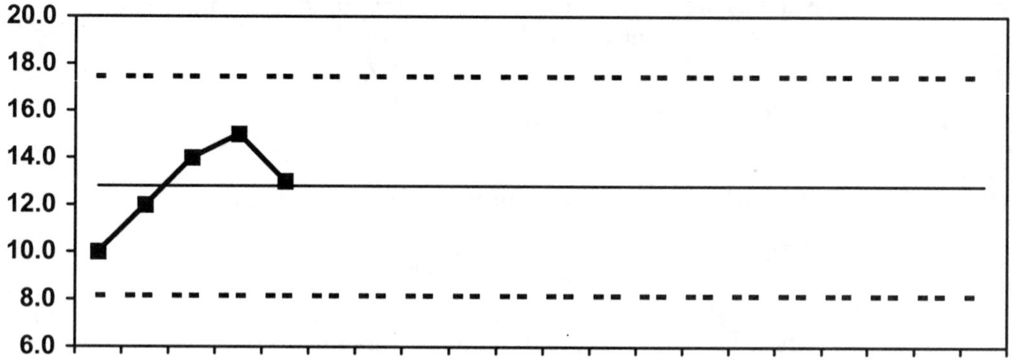

SPECIAL CALCULATIONS FOR INDIVIDUAL CHARTS

In the previous example, the moving range was calculated based on the present and previous readings (a "range frequency" of two data points). Special cases call for a moving range to be figured based on three or even more data points. The formulas below are for calculating Individual chart alarms for the generalized case of range subgroup frequency. If the moving range is based on a range subgroup frequency of more than two, then chart alarms should be calculated by using these formulas and constants.

The following calculations are used to derive the data plots for the Individual chart:

X_N is the data reading for the particular sample.

$$\overline{X} = \frac{X_1 + X_2 + X_3 \ldots + X_N}{N}$$

where N equals the number of samples.

$$R_K = \left| X_i - X_j \right|$$

where i is the maximum reading and j is the minimum reading; we are contrasting the K subgroup.

$$\overline{R} = \frac{R_1 + R_2 + R_3 + \ldots + R_K}{K}$$

where K equals the number of subgroups.

$$UCL_{Ave} = \overline{X} + E_2 * \overline{R}$$

where $E_2 * \overline{R}$ is an approximation of 3 standard errors.

$$LCL_{Ave} = \overline{X} - E_2 * \overline{R}$$

where $E_2 * \overline{R}$ is an approximation of 3 standard errors.

The range subgroup frequency is now used to look up the correct table constant. We find the range subgroup frequency in the table under subgroup frequency.

Subgroup Freq	E_2	d_2	D_3	D_4
2	2.660	1.128	-	3.267
3	1.772	1.693	-	2.574
4	1.457	2.059	-	2.282
5	1.290	2.326	-	2.114
6	1.184	2.534	-	2.004
7	1.109	2.704	0.076	1.924
8	1.054	2.847	0.136	1.864
9	1.010	2.970	0.184	1.816
10	0.975	3.078	0.223	1.777

Individual Chart Conversion

E_2 is the conversion factor to arrive at three (3) standard errors for use in determining UCL and LCL for Individual charts.

Note how the E_2 value decreases as the subgroup frequency increases. The logic for changing the E_2 is the same as for the A_2 constant of the $\overline{X}$ and R charts, covered in **Chapter Six**.

MOVING R CHART CALCULATIONS

The following calculations are used to derive the data plots for the Moving Range chart. Since most Individual charts are based on the current and prior values, then:

$$R_K = |X_{Current} - X_{Prior}|$$

where K equals the subgroup number.

$$\overline{R} = \frac{R_1 + R_2 + R_3 + \ldots + R_K}{K}$$

where K equals the subgroup number.

$$UCL_R = 3.267 * \overline{R}$$

$$LCL_R = 0$$

Upper and lower control limits are derived from constants called D_4 and D_3 respectively. These will be covered in more depth later in this chapter.

R Chart is designed to monitor the movement or changes in the variability of the process.

Monitors: $\overline{R}$ is the benchmark of the variability. R_K is the variability of the subgroup. UCL_R is the upper control limit above the benchmark variability. LCL_R is the lower control limit below the benchmark variability.

MOVING RANGE DATA

The Moving Range control chart limits can now be calculated for our example.

Subgroup Sample	1:00	2:00	3:00	4:00	5:00	6:00
1	10	12	14	15	13	
R		2	2	1	2	

The following are formulas for computing the alarm system for the Moving Range control chart. Now we will insert our example's data with the $\overline{R}$ of 1.75:

$$UCL_R = D_4 * \overline{R}$$

where $D_4 * \overline{R}$ is an approximation of three (3) standard errors.

$$UCL_R = D_4 * \overline{R}$$
$$= 3.267 * 1.75$$
$$= 5.72$$

$$LCL_R = D_3 * \overline{R}$$

where $D_3 * \overline{R}$ is an approximation of three (3) standard errors.

$$LCL_R = D_3 * \overline{R}$$
$$= 0$$

The following table shows the results of our calculations:

$\overline{R} = \frac{2+2+1+2}{4} = \frac{7}{4} = 1.75$
$UCL_R = 3.267 * \overline{R} = 3.267 * 1.75 = 5.72$
$LCL_R = 0$

Now we can plot our example and see the results.

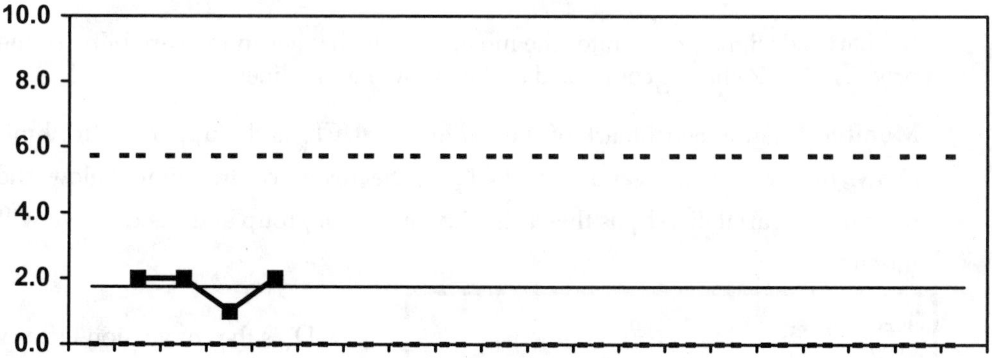

The following are the generalized calculations for varying range frequency. If the moving range is based on a range frequency of more than two, then chart alarms should be calculated by using the following formulas and constants. The following calculations are used to derive the data plots for the R chart:

$$R_K = \left| X_i - X_j \right|$$

where i is the maximum reading and j is the minimum reading we are contrasting for the K subgroup.

$\overline{R}$ is the center alarm formula for the Moving Range chart:

$$\overline{R} = \frac{R_1 + R_2 + R_3 + \ldots + R_K}{K}$$

where K equals the number of the subgroups.

UCL_R is the upper control limit formula for the Range chart:

$$UCL_R = D_4 * \overline{R}$$

where $D_4 * \overline{R}$ is an approximation of three (3) standard errors.

LCL_R is the lower control limit formula for the moving range chart:

$$LCL_R = D_3 * \overline{R}$$

where $D_3 * \overline{R}$ is an approximation of three (3) standard errors.

R Chart is designed to monitor the movement or changes in the variability of the process. The R chart is comprised of the following plot lines:

Monitor: R is the benchmark of the variability. **UCL_R** is the upper control limit above the benchmark variability. **LCL_R** is the lower control limit below the benchmark variability. **R_K** is the variability of the subgroup and the data we will monitor.

Subgroup Freq	E_2	d_2	D_3	D_4
2	2.660	1.128	-	3.267
3	1.772	1.693	-	2.574
4	1.457	2.059	-	2.282
5	1.290	2.326	-	2.114
6	1.184	2.534	-	2.004
7	1.109	2.704	0.076	1.924
8	1.054	2.847	0.136	1.864
9	1.010	2.970	0.184	1.816
10	0.975	3.078	0.223	1.777

Individual Chart Conversion

D_3 is the conversion factor to arrive at three (3) standard errors for use in determining LCL of R chart.

D_4 is the conversion factor to arrive at three (3) standard errors for use in determining UCL of R chart.

INDIVIDUAL CONTROL CHARTS

The charts below reflect the data in our simple example. The Individual chart is designed to monitor the movement or changes in the central tendency of the process. The Individual chart is comprised of the following plot lines: $\overline{X}$, the upper control limit, lower control limit, and data. The following chart shows our solved example:

Individual Chart Example

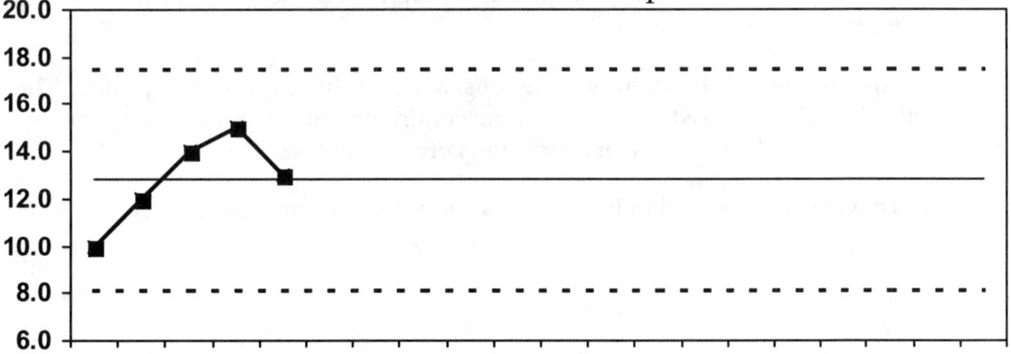

Moving Range Chart is designed to monitor the movement or changes in the variability of the process. The Moving Range chart is comprised of the following plot lines: $\overline{R}$, upper control limit, lower control limit, and R data. The following chart shows our solved problem:

Moving Range Chart Example

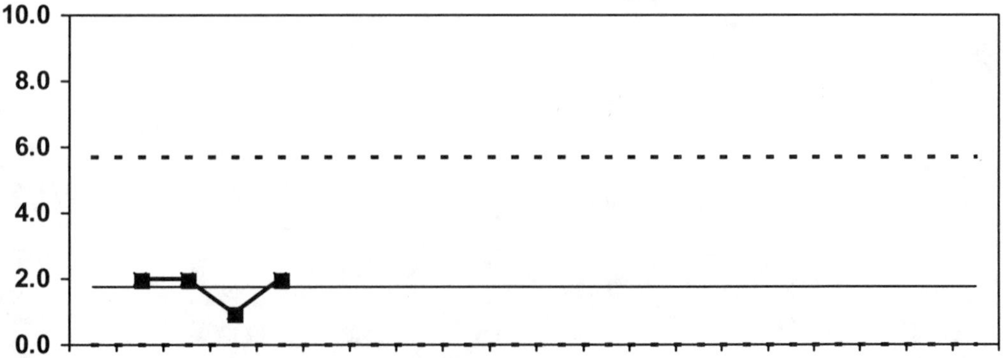

WHEN TO USE WHICH CHART

Now that we have covered the classic variable charts, let's recap where the different charts are to be used. Each chart was designed for a particular situation, and all detect a shift in the metric that they are monitoring.

The $\overline{X}$ and R chart is designed for a high volume operation and is the most commonly used chart. The $\overline{X}$ and R chart is used for high volume discrete product metrics or discrete process metrics.

The $\overline{X}$ and S chart takes care of the case where large samples are pulled for each subgroup. The $\overline{X}$ and S is typically used for high volume discrete product where the subgroup sample is large.

The Individual chart monitors situations where only one point is pulled. The individual chart is used for high volume continuous product metrics, expensive destructive product metrics, or continuous process metrics.

Let's cover some special kinds of metrics and which control chart to use.

The chart below summarizes our variable control charts and the situations that require their use. The last three columns show the three classic variable control charts. The first column shows the type of metric and the planned use. When an X appears at an intersection, it flags a general suggestion of which of the three charts to use.

	$\overline{X}$ and R	**$\overline{X}$ and S**	**Individual**
Product Metrics: • High volume • Discrete product	X		
Product Metrics: • High volume • Continuous product			X
Product Metrics: • High volume • Discrete product • Large samples in a subgroup		X	
Product Metrics: • Low volume			X
Product Metrics: • Expensive product with destructive test			X
Process Metrics: • Continuous			X
Process Metrics: • Discrete	X		

This chart provides some guidelines for selecting the proper control chart to use for a particular situation. This should provide you with a starting point for the monitoring effort.

CHAPTER SUMMARY

$\overline{X}$ and S Charts

$$\overline{\overline{X}} = \frac{\overline{X}_1 + \overline{X}_2 + \overline{X}_3 + \ldots + \overline{X}_K}{N}$$

$$S = \sqrt{\frac{\sum^{N} (\overline{X} - X_i)^2}{N-1}}$$

$$\overline{S} = \frac{S_1 + S_2 + S_3 + \ldots + S_K}{K}$$

Subgroup Size	A_3	C_4	B_3	B_4
10	0.975	0.9727	0.284	1.716
11	0.927	0.9754	0.321	1.679
12	0.886	0.9776	0.354	1.646
13	0.850	0.9794	0.382	1.618
14	0.817	0.9810	0.406	1.594
15	0.789	0.9823	0.428	1.572
16	.763	.9835	.448	1.552
17	.739	.9845	.466	1.534
18	.718	.9854	.482	1.518
19	.698	.9862	.497	1.503
20	.680	.9869	.510	1.490
21	.663	.9876	.523	1.477
22	.647	.9882	.534	1.466
23	.633	.9887	.545	1.455
24	.619	.9892	.555	1.445
25	.606	.9896	.565	1.435

A_3 is the conversion factor to arrive at three (3) standard errors for use in determining UCL and LCL of $\overline{X}$ chart where $A_3 * \overline{S}$ is an approximation of three (3) standard errors.

B_3 is the conversion factor for the approximation of three (3) standard errors used as the LCL on the S chart.

B_4 is the conversion factor for the approximation of three (3) standard errors used as the UCL limit on the S chart.

$\overline{X}$ chart control limits

$$UCL_{Ave} = \overline{\overline{X}} + A_3 * \overline{S}$$

$$LCL_{Ave} + \overline{\overline{X}} - A_3 * \overline{S}$$

S chart control limits

$$UCL_S = B_4 * \overline{S}$$

$$LCL_S = B_3 * \overline{S}$$

Individual chart

$$\overline{X} = \frac{X_1 + X_2 + X_3 + \ldots + X_N}{N}$$

$$R_K = \left| X_i - X_j \right|$$

$$\overline{R} = \frac{R_1 + R_2 + R_3 + \ldots + R_K}{K}$$

where K equals the number of subgroups.

Subgroup Freq	E_2	d_2	D_3	D_4
2	2.660	1.128	-	3.267
3	1.772	1.693	-	2.574
4	1.457	2.059	-	2.282
5	1.290	2.326	-	2.114
6	1.184	2.534	-	2.004
7	1.109	2.704	0.076	1.924
8	1.054	2.847	0.136	1.864
9	1.010	2.970	0.184	1.816
10	0.975	3.078	0.223	1.777

Individual Chart Conversion

E_2 is the conversion factor to arrive at three (3) standard errors for use in determining UCL and LCL of the Individual chart.

D_3 is the conversion factor to arrive at three (3) standard errors for use in determining LCL of the R chart.

D_4 is the conversion factor to arrive at three (3) standard errors for use in determining UCL of the R chart.

$\overline{X}$ chart control limits

$$UCL_{Ave} = \overline{X} + E_2 * \overline{R}$$

$$LCL_{Ave} = \overline{X} - E_2 * \overline{R}$$

Moving Range control limits

$$UCL_R = D_4 * \overline{R}$$

$$LCL_R = D_3 * \overline{R}$$

Remember, all the variable charts are based on a normal distribution and use the same interpretation rules. We have covered the construction of the variable control charts and are now ready to move to **Chapter Nine** to show you how to construct attribute charts.

Chapter Nine: Attribute Control Charts

In **Chapter Five: Where Do We Start?**, the two types of metric measurements of variable and attribute data were covered. In **Chapters Six** and **Eight**, the Variable measurement control charts were constructed and covered in depth. Now we must move on to Attribute control charts. The same interpretation from **Chapter Seven** will be used here for our Attribute control charts.

Remember that a control chart is the operator's tool to monitor the workings of a particular machine or system in chronological order. Attribute control charts are often confused with management reports, but like all other control charts, they are still a tactical tool. Attribute control charts include an alarm system with a mechanism for detecting any type of shift or change. This alarm must be dynamically recalibrated to reflect the current status.

The attribute metric measurement type of data is generally thought of as the acceptance (or rejection) of a part. Even though this type of data is pass/fail, we can count the frequency of occurrence. Attribute (categorical) data is "yes" or "no"; "good" or "bad"; "go" or "no go"; or "it is" or "it is not."

THE ATTRIBUTE CONTROL CHARTS

Variable control charts come in three varieties to take care of unique situations. Attribute control charts are like Variable control charts in that four charts are available and each takes care of a different situation. The four Attribute control charts are NP, P, C, and U. The following gives a brief description of each Attribute control chart.

NP Charts measure the frequency of nonconforming parts. The inspection sample sizes (N) for this chart must be equal.

P Charts measure the proportion of nonconforming units.

C Charts measure the frequency or number of nonconformities (defects) where C equals the number of defects.

U Charts measure the proportion of defects by counting the number of nonconformities, C (defects), and dividing by the sample size N.

The Attribute control charts' objective is to detect product or process change. The demonstrated effectiveness of a control chart is attributable to its objective and systematic analytical methods. The methods for effective control of attribute data are the same as all the other control charts and include the following steps:

- Calculate the initial control limits.
- Establish that the process is in control.
- Continually survey the control charts for alarms (out of control conditions).
- Assess the capability of the in control process.

CALCULATING INITIAL CONTROL LIMITS

To set the initial control limits, data must be gathered. As a guideline, thirty sets of values are captured to calculate and post on the charts. Remember, since a control chart is for one particular machine, the data must come from that one machine. Different control alarms for each machine would not be surprising. These same thirty subgroups are used to compute trial control limits. The subgroup reading and the alarms are then posted on the chart for statistical control interpretation. This chapter will explain the mechanics and calculations for control limits for Attribute control charts.

Chapter Seven covered the interpretation, reading, and the use of control charts. These details of control chart interpretation tasks are used now for attribute data. In **Chapter Seven**, the following was explained and can be used for all our Attribute charts because these charts use a special type of normal distribution:

- **Establish that the process is in control.** As each out of control condition is identified and dealt with, this procedure is repeated until no alarms have been detected. When the process is in control (no alarms have been detected), the control limits are locked in place. **Chapter Seven** explained the reading and interpretation of the control charts.

- **Continually survey control charts for alarms (out of control conditions).** Data is gathered to monitor against the alarm mechanism (control limits) for changes in the conditions of the machine. When an out of control situation or change is detected, the chart has done its job. The following tasks must then be undertaken:

    - Search for the cause.
    - Alert management to the change.
    - Decide what to do.

ATTRIBUTE DATA

Many situations require Attribute control charts. These situations are still for a continuous operation like all the other control charts. All of these tactical tools must be used to monitor a continuous operation.

Attribute data can be gathered from many sources such as textile rolls of fabric, the communications and information industries, the maintenance of a manufacturing plant, environmental information, transportation and traffic information, safety information, maintenance work orders for manufacturing and service industries, and the scrap rate for a manufacturing machine.

I, like most other business professionals today, must travel extensively. Almost all the stories I tell about my travels would make a good comedy, but my best stories have occurred at the airport or on a commercial airliner. Over the years I have learned to accept the inconvenience of commercial air travel. Maybe rather than accept this, I should encourage the airlines to use Statistical Process Control (SPC) to improve their processes!

The baggage handling and claim process, depicted to the right, will be the example that we will use for our Attribute control chart exercises. If you have flown on a commercial airline, you already know that your baggage does not always arrive at your destination with you.

Let's focus our attention on the details dealing with the construction requirements for Attribute charts. Our first Attribute control chart is the NP chart. We will use the airline example to explain the Attribute charts.

The baggage handling problem of monitoring the consistency of lost bags will be our first example. Each day on the 3:00 PM flight from Nashville, Tennessee to Orlando, Florida, 200 bags are processed. The following table shows the number of lost bags each day. On Monday two bags were lost, on Tuesday three bags were lost, on Wednesday four bags were mishandled, on Thursday there were three misplaced bags, and on Friday another three bags were lost.

Subgroup	Mon	Tues	Wed	Thurs	Fri	Sat
NP	2	3	4	3	3	

Our reason for monitoring the bags with a control chart is to determine how consistent the airline's baggage handling system really is. This control chart is an operational tool for monitoring the consistency of the baggage lost and to detect any changes in the consistency of the baggage handling system.

Since the total number of bags handled each day is the same (200 bags each day), then the NP control chart can be used as our monitoring system.

THE NP CHART

An NP chart is an operator's tool to monitor the consistency of counts where the size in each group is the same. This chart, like all other control charts, is intended to detect change for investigation. NP charts will have the same alarm system of calculated values that make up all control charts. This alarm system is calculated from past history to provide the center point and the control limits. The chart below is an example of an NP chart:

NP Chart

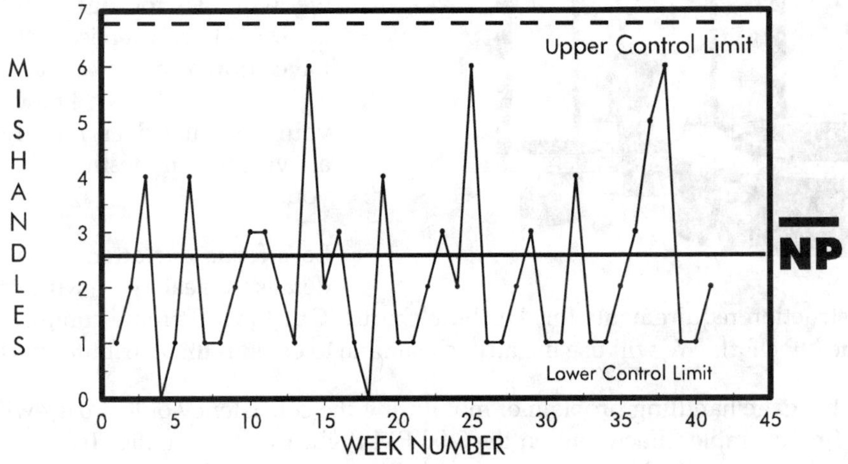

NP CHARTS

When do we use the NP chart? NP charts measure the frequency of the nonconforming parts. The inspection sample size (N) for this chart must be equal for each reading.

The following shows the formula for computing the control limits for NP charts.

Data:

NP equals the number of nonconforming parts.

N equals the subgroup sample size, and for an NP chart, the N value (size of the subgroup) must always be the same from group to group.

Alarms

The following formulas are used to compute the alarm system for both the center point and the control limits. The control limits for the NP chart are used and read like all the other control charts. Only .1% of the value should fall above the control limits or .1% should fall below the control limits. Like all control charts, any value outside the control limits should come as a shock requiring a detailed investigation to determine the cause.

$$\overline{NP} = \frac{NP_1 + NP_2 + NP_3 + \ldots + NP_K}{K}$$

where K equals the number of subgroups.

The upper and lower control limit formulas are shown below:

$$UCL_{NP} = \overline{NP} + 3 * \sqrt{\overline{NP} * \left(1 - \frac{\overline{NP}}{N}\right)}$$

$$LCL_{NP} = \overline{NP} - 3 * \sqrt{\overline{NP} * \left(1 - \frac{\overline{NP}}{N}\right)}$$

Remember, the NP chart can be used only when the sample size is equal for all subgroups. Also, like all other control charts, when the process or product is stable, the alarm system is locked in place until a decision is made to recalibrate the alarms that were identified from a shift in the process.

Let's take our airline baggage problem and see how the completed NP chart looks.

NP CHART EXERCISE

The NP values equal the number of nonconforming parts or lost bags for each day.

Subgroup	Mon	Tues	Wed	Thurs	Fri	Sat
NP	2	3	4	3	3	

The monitoring system for the NP chart for the 3:00 PM flight is shown below. N equals the subgroup sample size and must be present for the NP chart to perform correctly. For the airline example, the total number of bags, or N, is 200 each day.

$$\overline{NP} = \frac{NP_1 + NP_2 + NP_3 + \ldots + NP_K}{K}$$

$$= \frac{2+3+4+3+3}{5}$$

$$= \frac{15}{5}$$

$$= 3$$

where K equals the number of subgroups.

The formula for computing the upper control limits is shown below:

$$UCL_{NP} = \overline{NP} + 3 * \sqrt{\overline{NP} * \left(1 - \frac{\overline{NP}}{N}\right)}$$

The upper control limit calculations and results of the exercise are shown next:

$$UCL_{NP} = 3 + 3 * \sqrt{3 * \left(1 - \frac{3}{200}\right)}$$

$$= 3 + 3 * \sqrt{3 * (1 - .015)}$$

$$= 3 + 3 * \sqrt{3 * (.985)}$$

$$= 3 + 3 * 1.719$$

Continuing to solve the equation we see the following results:

$$UCL_{NP} = 3 + 3 * 1.719$$

$$= 3 + 5.157$$

$$= 8.157$$

Finally, the upper control limit for our exercise is 8.157. Let's move onto the calculations for lower control limit.

The lower control limit calculations are shown below. For the lower control limit we have shortened the steps to the result.

$$LCL_{NP} = \overline{NP} - 3 * \sqrt{\overline{NP} * (1 - \frac{\overline{NP}}{N})}$$

$$= 3 - 3 * \sqrt{3 * (1 - \frac{3}{200})}$$

$$= 3 - 5.157$$

$$= 0$$

The NP average, upper control limit, and lower control limit form an alarm system for detecting change and shifts.

Our exercise is now complete and the results are shown in the table below. Remember the NP chart is used as a monitor for detecting a change and shift for our airline bag handling exercise. This chart is not intended to assess whether the change is good or bad but simply that a change has occurred.

Subgroup	Mon	Tues	Wed	Thurs	Fri	Sat
NP	2	3	4	3	3	
$\overline{NP} = 3$						
UCL = 8.157						
LCL = 0						

Now the completed NP chart for our example is shown below:

NP Chart Example

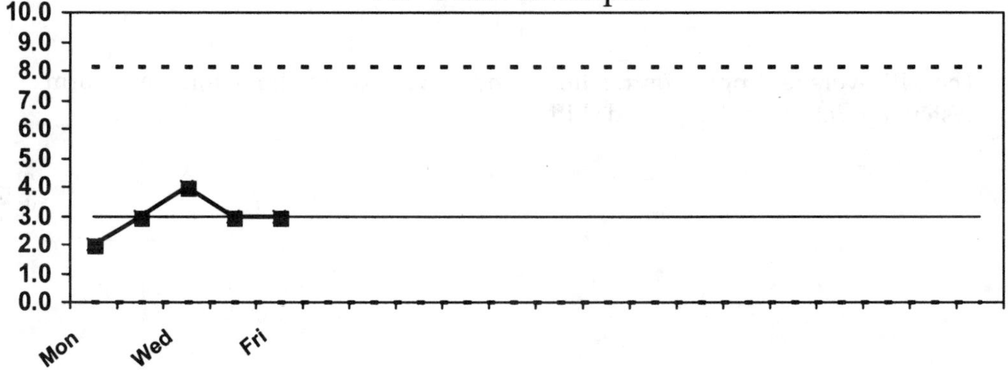

The interpretation rules for the NP chart are the same rules that were covered in **Chapter Seven**; for a detailed explanation of those rules see that chapter. The explanation for why these interpretation rules work will be covered later in this chapter.

SAMPLE SIZE VARIATION

The NP chart can only be used when the sample size is equal for each subgroup. Therefore, the NP chart is a wonderful tool, but it is limited by the requirement for subgroup size equality.

For most airline flights from Nashville to Orlando, the total number of bags handled usually will not be the same from day to day. A more realistic problem is shown below where the total number of bags varies by day.

200 bags are handled on Monday, 200 on Tuesday, 200 on Wednesday, 150 on Thursday, and 150 bags on Friday.

The total number of bags handled each day is shown below:

Subgroup	Mon	Tues	Wed	Thurs	Fri	Sat
N	200	200	200	150	150	

When the number of bags handled varies, monitoring only lost bags give a false picture. If one day 500 bags are processed and one bag is lost, and on a second day 200 bags are processed and one bag is lost, the monitor says that both days are the same when in reality, each day is very different.

To resolve the unequal number of samples in the subgroup a new control chart is required. This new control chart is called the P chart and is designed to resolve the unequal sample size issue. The P stands for proportion or percentage where the number of nonconforming items is a rate of the total number of samples.

HOW DOES A P CHART LOOK

The P chart uses the proportion of the count divided by the number of samples as a means of computing the data to plot. This ratio gives equal weight when the sample size changes. This P data point's equal weight removes the equality of the sample size required by the NP chart. The equal weight makes the P chart a more versatile chart.

The next chart is an example of a P chart. This chart is also a tactical tool for detecting change.

P CHART

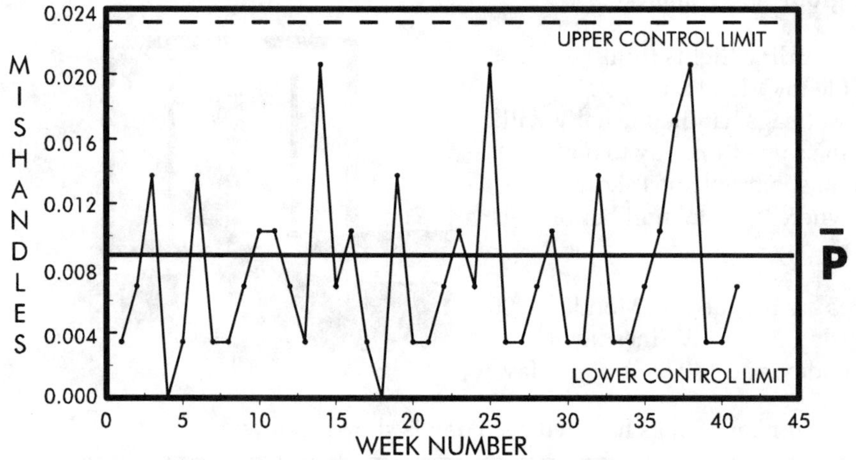

The P chart uses the P values (the ratios, proportions, or percentages) as the data. The P value resolves the unequal subgroup size problem. This historical data is then used to compute the alarm system for the center point and the control limits.

The control limits are the points outside of which we would be surprised to see a data point (P) fall. The P control limits use the same mathematical principles that the other control charts use.

P CHARTS

P Charts measure the proportion of nonconforming units. By using proportion or ratios, rather than the NP counts, having unequal samples from the subgroups will not matter.

The data for the P chart is calculated by computing the ratio of the number of nonconforming items divided by the number of samples in the subgroup. This formula is shown below:

$$P = \frac{NP}{N}$$

where N equals number of items checked, and NP equals the number of items failing or nonconforming.

MONITOR

The value and formula below is the center point at which, when the process is run correctly and consistently, the P values should be half on one side and half on the other.

$$\overline{P} = \frac{NP_1 + NP_2 + NP_3 + \ldots + NP_K}{N_1 + N_2 + N_3 + \ldots + N_K}$$

where K is the number of subgroups studied.

The average sample size is needed for our calculation of variability.

$$\overline{N} = \frac{N_1 + N_2 + N_3 + \ldots + N_K}{K}$$

UPPER AND LOWER CONTROL LIMIT CALCULATION

The upper and lower control limit formulas below are the points where a value falling outside is a rarity. Remember, like all other control charts, the P chart's upper and lower control limits are three standard errors around the mean.

$$UCL_P = \overline{P} + 3 * \frac{\sqrt{\overline{P} * (1 - \overline{P})}}{\sqrt{\overline{N}}}$$

$$LCL_P = \overline{P} - 3 * \frac{\sqrt{\overline{P} * (1 - \overline{P})}}{\sqrt{\overline{N}}}$$

Don't forget, the P chart is used to detect change. When the process or product is stable, the alarm system is locked in place until a decision is made to recalibrate the alarms based on a change in the process.

P CHART DATA

The NP chart works when the sample size is equal from subgroup to subgroup, but the total number of bags handled in the example below varies from day to day. This varying size is really a more typical life situation. Because of the typical shifting of the size, the P chart is used much more often than the NP chart.

To have a relative number that is comparable from day to day, the number of bags lost must be made relative to the total number of bags processed. Notice that three bags were lost on both Tuesday and Thursday. However, 200 bags were processed on Tuesday while only 150 bags were processed on Thursday. Therefore, a simple comparison of the lost bags will give an incorrect picture.

Subgroup	Mon	Tues	Wed	Thurs	Fri	Sat
NP	2	3	4	3	3	
N	200	200	200	150	150	

By making the lost bags a function of the total bags (NP/N), the relationship between the days is much clearer. Tuesday's ratio or P value is .015 and Thursday's ratio or P value is .02. The table below shows the computed results of the P values for each day:

Subgroup	Mon.	Tues.	Wed.	Thurs.	Fri.	Sat.
NP	2	3	4	3	3	
N	200	200	200	150	150	
P Calculations	$\frac{2}{200}$	$\frac{3}{200}$	$\frac{4}{200}$	$\frac{3}{150}$	$\frac{3}{150}$	
P	.01	.015	.02	.02	.02	

Now the calculation and establishment of the control limits are required. We will take the $\overline{P}$ and control limit formulas and insert our example data.

P CHART EXAMPLE CONTROL LIMITS

The table below shows the calculations for our baggage example. The table shows each day's P value.

Subgroup	Mon	Tues	Wed	Thurs	Fri	Sat
NP	2	3	4	3	3	
N	200	200	200	150	150	
P	.01	.015	.02	.02	.02	

The P chart alarm system for the 3:00 PM flight is shown below.

$$\overline{P} = \frac{NP_1 + NP_2 + NP_3 + ... + NP_K}{N_1 + N_2 + N_3 + ... + N_K}.$$

$$= \frac{2+3+4+3+3}{200+200+200+150+150}$$

$$= \frac{15}{900}$$

$$= .017$$

Our control limit calculations require the average sample size of our data. For the 3:00 PM flight data, the calculations are shown below.

$$\overline{N} = \frac{N_1 + N_2 + N_3 + ... + N_K}{K}$$

$$= \frac{200+200+200+150+150}{5}$$

$$= \frac{900}{5}$$

$$= 180$$

The formula for computing the upper control limit for the P chart is shown below.

$$UCL_P = \overline{P} + 3 * \frac{\sqrt{\overline{P} * (1 - \overline{P})}}{\sqrt{\overline{N}}}$$

Now we can use our 3:00 PM flight data for $\overline{P}$ which is .017 and $\overline{N}$ which is 180. These values can now be inserted in our upper control limit calculation.

$$UCL_P = .017 + 3 * \frac{\sqrt{.017 * (1 - .017)}}{\sqrt{180}}$$

Next we solve the equation.

$$UCL_P = .017 + 3 * \frac{\sqrt{.017 * .983}}{\sqrt{180}}$$

$$= .017 + 3 * \frac{.1293}{13.416}$$

$$= .017 + .029$$

$$= .046$$

The formula for the lower control limit is:

$$LCL_P = \overline{P} - 3 * \frac{\sqrt{\overline{P} * (1 - \overline{P})}}{\sqrt{\overline{N}}}$$

When solved with our $\overline{P}$ and $\overline{N}$ values, this formula will yield:

$$LCL_P = .017 - .029$$

Since negative lost bags are impossible, our lower control limit for the P chart will be zero.

The next table shows the $\overline{P}$ upper control limit and lower control limit calculations and results:

$\overline{P} = \frac{2+3+4+3+3}{200+200+200+150+150} = \frac{15}{900} = .017$
$UCL = .017+3*\frac{\sqrt{(.017)*(1-.017)}}{\sqrt{900/5}} = .017+\frac{3*(.1293)}{13.416} = .017+.029 = .046$
$LCL = .017-3*\frac{\sqrt{(.017)*(1-.017)}}{\sqrt{900/5}} = .017-.029 = 0$

The completed P chart for our example is shown below:

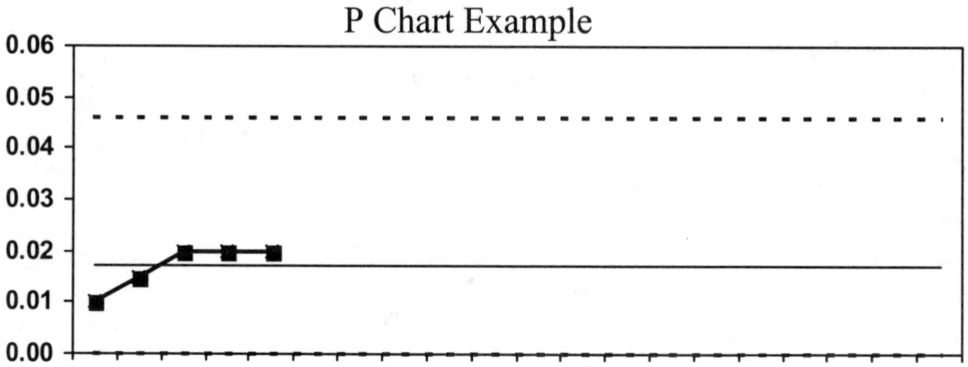

With this baggage P chart, we would begin to monitor the consistency of the 3:00 Nashville to Orlando flight. Now let's see how we can use the same interpretation rules that we used for Variable control charts.

ATTRIBUTE DISTRIBUTION

Revisiting our good friend the normal distribution gives us a starting point for discussing the distribution for attributes. The following is the earlier description of the normal or bell-shaped distribution where the average is the central point of the measurements and the standard deviation is the variability of the measurements. The distribution is symmetrical around its average. Fifty percent of the data points are above the average and fifty percent of the measurements are below the average. The frequency of occurrence drops rapidly as we get farther and farther away from the center. This characteristic is for both above and below the average. The frequency of occurrence above and below the average is symmetrical.

As we move farther and farther away from the average, the number of occurrences drops at a rapid rate. This tendency toward the normal is in both directions from the average.

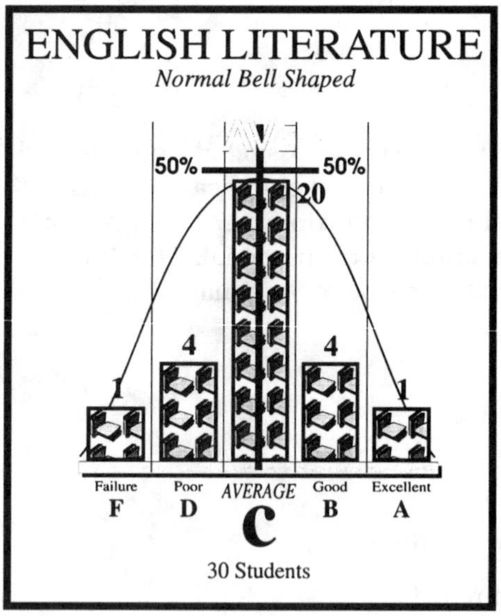

The chart to the left is used to depict how a process, with its measurements, will look. The chart shows the spread of grades from the English literature class of thirty students covered in **Chapter One**. When the score measurements are converted to letter grades, the histogram of the process is well represented by a normal distribution. The perfect normal does not have the steps of a histogram but is a smooth curve. A very clear pattern is formed for the probabilities of the normal distribution. These probabilities were used for the alarms associated with variable data.

SPECIAL NORMAL DISTRIBUTION – BINOMIALS

Having data that is well represented by a normal distribution allows us to predict using the probabilities of the normal. A good understanding of these probabilities was an essential part of the alarms for the Variable control charts. How does the knowledge of the normal help us with the alarms for attribute data?

Attribute charts are based on a kind of distribution called a binomial. The binomial is really a special kind of normal distribution. Let's discuss this binomial distribution.

We need to develop a methodology or distribution to handle attribute data. The type of data we will analyze is an either/or condition similar to a true/false condition. The airline example of lost bags fits this category. The bag arrives with you and your flight (true) or the bag does not arrive with you and your flight (false). We will come back to our airline problem but first let's take a simpler example to clarify the binomial.

The example we will use is the tossing of a quarter and determining the rate of occurrence of heads or tails. The probability of heads occurring is 1/2. Flipping a coin is a perfect example of the binomial. Heads is the true and tails is the false side of the equation.

The binomial distribution has the following conditions:

- A fixed number, N, of objects is examined.
- The probability of occurrence is the same for each test.
- Each test is independent.

For a binomial where N equals the number of items and P equals the probability of occurrence, the mean equals $\overline{P}$ and the standard deviation equals $\sqrt{N * \overline{P} * (1 - \overline{P})}$.

We will flip our quarter twenty times to fulfill the condition of a fixed number of trials.

Thus, our coin toss meets the three criteria of the binomial. We will flip the quarter twenty times to meet the first condition. The chance of our coin landing heads up when flipped is always fifty percent. This meets the second condition. Lastly, the fact that each flip is independent of all prior flips meets the last condition.

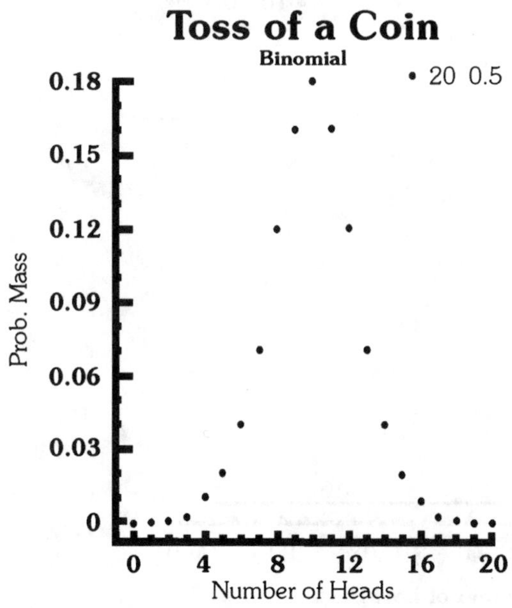

Most people, when asked how many heads they would expect, say "ten out of the twenty." What they mean is that they expect *about* ten; they really don't expect *exactly* ten heads each time. What comes as a surprise is that the *variation* from ten follows a bell shaped curve.

Looking at the chart of the binomial associated with our quarter flipping, the distribution looks very similar to the normal distribution. The binomial distribution is just a special kind of normal to take care of proportions, ratios, and percentages.

The idea that "ten out of twenty" occurs only eighteen percent of the time is a surprise to most people. This understanding of the binomial allows us to better interpret percentages and proportions, and to not be surprised when they are not exact.

Revisiting our airline baggage problem, we see that lost bags are very similar to our tossing tails on a coin and that the properly arriving bag is like the flip being heads. The biggest difference is that the starting percentage of lost baggage will be different from the flip of our quarter.

Like the P chart, the NP attribute control chart also uses the binomial distribution as the basis for its assumptions.

The binomial is a special kind of normal distribution and the normal distribution is used to develop the interpretation rules for variable data. Thus, the out of control points for attribute and variable data are found using the same interpretation rules.

Below is an illustration of the airline's lost bag problem. The illustration shows how the lost bags' distribution would look which is the same as how the binomial distribution will appear.

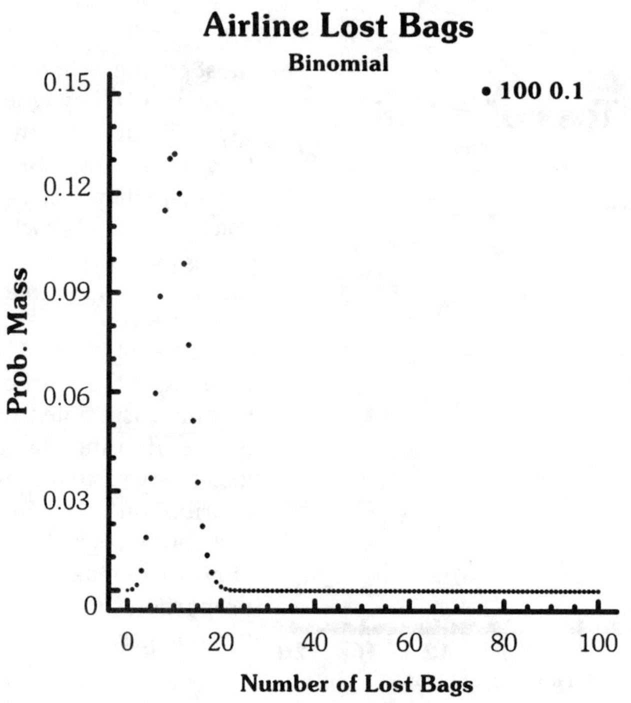

An appreciation of the binomial makes our understanding of the variability of the lost bags on our airline flight very clear.

P CHART STANDARD DEVIATION DERIVATION

From our explanation of the binomial, the standard deviation formula is $\sqrt{N * \overline{P} * (1 - \overline{P})}$. This formula is designed to show the variability of the number of occurrences. The result of this formula yields a count or number of occurrences. This formula must be rearranged for use in a P chart with proportions, ratios, and percentages. This will be accomplished by dividing the standard deviation of the count by the number of samples in the group.

Standard deviation of the percentage defective is required and is calculated as follows:

$$\frac{\text{Standard Deviation of Number Defective}}{\text{Sample Size}}$$

The actual symbols are now inserted in this formula as follows:

$$= \frac{\sqrt{N * \bar{P} * (1 - \bar{P})}}{N}$$

The N is then replaced by the square root of N multiplied by the square root of N. This replacement simply results in the same number.

$$= \frac{\sqrt{N * \bar{P} * (1 - \bar{P})}}{\sqrt{N} * \sqrt{N}}$$

Next, the square root of N is rearranged in the top portion of the formula.

$$= \frac{\sqrt{N} * \sqrt{\bar{P} * (1 - \bar{P})}}{\sqrt{N} * \sqrt{N}}$$

The top square root of N is divided by the bottom square root of N resulting in one that allows both to be dropped.

$$= \frac{\sqrt{\bar{P} * (1 - \bar{P})}}{\sqrt{N}}$$

Thus, the P Chart uses $\dfrac{\sqrt{\bar{P} * (1 - \bar{P})}}{\sqrt{N}}$.

Notice the formula here uses the square root of N where in our first P chart the formula used the square root of the average of N. The average technique is allowed as long as the difference between the sizes of the groups is small. If the difference between the sizes is more than twenty to twenty-five percent, then the exact formula should be used as shown above.

LARGE SAMPLE SIZE DIFFERENCES IN SUBGROUPS

If the sizes of the samples in the subgroups vary significantly, then the control limits must be adjusted for each different subgroup. A subgroup size variation of twenty to twenty-five percent from one subgroup to another is considered large.

When the control limits are adjusted from group to group, they shrink as the size increases because our precision increases as the number of data points increases.

Note in the chart below that the control limits spread and shrink. The spreading control limits are from fewer samples in the subgroup because we are less certain of the precision of the subgroup's P value. The collapsing control limits are from increasing the number of samples in the subgroup and the resulting increased P value precision.

P Chart

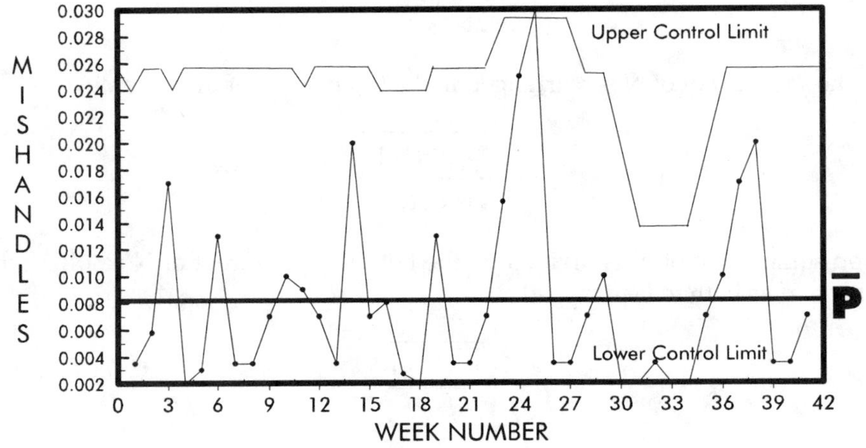

Let's return to our airline problem and see how a large shift impacts the control limit calculations. The control limits for the changing sample size in the subgroup are shown for our airline baggage problem.

Should the total number of bags handled from day to day vary as in the example below, then the control limits will have to be adjusted to reflect the radically changing sample size. Notice how the Saturday flight's total number of bags has jumped to 500. This jump is well above our twenty to twenty-five percent threshold so the control limits must be adjusted. This adjustment is not a recalibration of the control limits, but simply a reflection of more precision.

Subgroup	Mon	Tues	Wed	Thurs	Fri	Sat
NP	2	3	4	3	3	3
N	200	200	200	150	150	500

Our P values will still be calculated using the same formula.

Subgroup	Mon	Tues	Wed	Thurs	Fri	Sat
NP	2	3	4	3	3	3
N	200	200	200	150	150	500
P	.01	.015	.02	.02	.02	.006

Our change comes in the control limit calculation. Let's take a look at these slightly enhanced formulas.

P CHARTS

P Charts measure the proportion of units nonconforming. The P chart is a special case of the NP chart.

Data:

$$P = \frac{NP}{N}$$

where N equals number of items checked and NP equals the number of items failing.

Monitor:

$$\bar{P} = \frac{NP_1 + NP_2 + NP_3 + \ldots + NP_K}{N_1 + N_2 + N_3 + \ldots + NP_K}$$

where K is the number of subgroups studied.

The following control limit formulas have incorporated the actual N to replace the average sample size used earlier.

$$UCL_P = \bar{P} + 3 * \frac{\sqrt{\bar{P} * (1 - \bar{P})}}{\sqrt{N}}$$

$$LCL_P = \bar{P} - 3 * \frac{\sqrt{\bar{P} * (1 - \bar{P})}}{\sqrt{N}}$$

Theoretically, when the sample size changes the control limits should be recalculated. When the N value varies within a range of ±20-25% the use of $\bar{N}$, or the average sample size, is adequate for our purposes.

Returning to our airline exercise, the variation of N is large. These large differences in sample size cause our P chart example to have varying control limits.

Subgroup	Mon	Tues	Wed	Thurs	Fri	Sat
NP	2	3	4	3	3	3
N	200	200	200	150	150	500
P	.01	.015	.02	.02	.02	.006

For the airline example, the control limit calculations follow. The first formula is the upper control limit.

Upper Control Limit

$$UCL_P = \overline{P} + 3 * \frac{\sqrt{\overline{P} * (1 - \overline{P})}}{\sqrt{N}}$$

The upper control limit formula now must be solved with our airline baggage data. The following allows us to compare the two methods for computing the P control limits.

With $\overline{N}$:

Our first solution is achieved by using the average N.

$$UCL = .0129 + 3 * \frac{\sqrt{(.0219) * (1 - .0129)}}{\sqrt{1400/6}}$$

$$= .0129 + \frac{3 * (.1128)}{15.3}$$

$$= .0129 + .022$$

$$= .035$$

With N:

The second solution is computed by using the N for each subgroup. This example uses the N of 500 bags for Saturday.

$$UCL = .0129 + 3 * \frac{\sqrt{(.0129) * (1 - .0129)}}{\sqrt{500}}$$

$$= .0129 + \frac{3 * (.1128)}{22.4}$$

$$= .0129 + .0151$$

$$= .0280$$

Notice how the upper control limit, calculated with the actual Saturday N of 500 is .0280. This control limit is tighter than the control limit calculated with the average N.

Lower Control Limit

The next formula computes the lower limit for our example.

$$LCL_P = \bar{P} - 3 * \frac{\sqrt{\bar{P} * (1 - \bar{P})}}{\sqrt{N}}$$

The lower control limit formula now must be solved using our airline baggage data.

With $\overline{N}$:

Our first solution is achieved by using the average N.

$$LCL = .0129 - 3 * \frac{\sqrt{(.0129) * (1 - .0129)}}{\sqrt{1400 / 6}} = .0129 - \frac{3 * (.1128)}{15.3}$$

$$= .0129 - .022$$

$$= .0$$

With N:

The second solution is computed by using the N for each subgroup. This example uses the N of 500 bags for Saturday.

$$\text{LCL} = .0129 - 3 * \frac{\sqrt{(.0129)*(1-.0129)}}{\sqrt{500}}$$

$$= .0129 - \frac{3*(.1128)}{22.4}$$

$$= .0129 - .0151$$

$$= .0$$

The table below shows the results of the P chart. This table shows how the control limits will change as the number of samples changes from subgroup to subgroup.

Subgroup	**Mon**	**Tues**	**Wed**	**Thurs**	**Fri**	**Sat**
NP	2	3	4	3	3	3
N	200	200	200	150	150	500
P	.01	.015	.02	.02	.02	.006
Lower Control Limit	**0**	**0**	**0**	**0**	**0**	**0**
Upper Control Limit	**.037**	**.037**	**.037**	**.041**	**.041**	**.028**

Notice that an extremely large number of bags are processed on Saturday as compared to the other days. Therefore, the control limits are radically tighter for Saturday as compared to Monday through Friday. Saturday's upper control limit is .028 for 500 bags while Monday through Wednesday's sample size each day is 200, giving a wider control limit of .037. On Thursday and Friday the sample size is 150 bags which yields an even wider control limit of .041. As we would expect, fewer samples give less precision and wider control limits.

Now the completed P chart for our example:

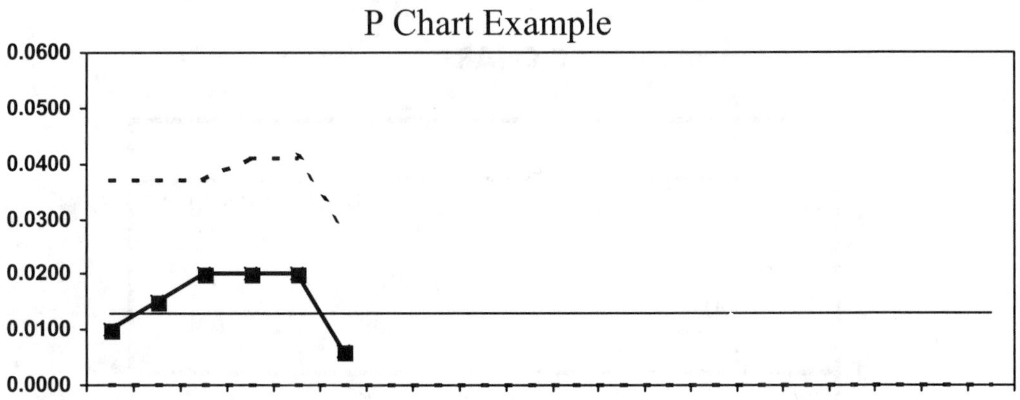

Note how the control limits expand and contract as the sample size decreases and increases respectively.

TWO DIFFICULT SITUATIONS FOR A P CHART

When the probability is low and the opportunities are high, the P chart alarm system becomes unworkable. The problem is caused by the standard deviation calculation. Let's take a look at the calculation that follows: $\frac{\sqrt{\bar{P}*(1-\bar{P})}}{\sqrt{N}}$.

When N is very large, it may be unknown. (How many opportunities are there for pinholes in a sheet of paper?) $\bar{P}$ may be impossible to calculate. (What is the ratio of actual pinholes to possible pinholes?)

The solution is an approximation that simplifies the standard deviation formula above. If $\bar{P}$ is almost zero, then $(1-\bar{P})$ is almost (1-0). The formula collapses to $\sqrt{N\bar{P}} - \sqrt{\text{average number defective}}$ (not percentage defective). In other words, if $\bar{P}$ is very small and N is uncountably large, then a simpler formula can be used which requires neither $\bar{P}$ nor N.

A second problem occurs with a tiny $\bar{P}$ and small sample sizes. The probability of a defect is so small that our expectation is "zero defects" each time we sample. A single defect represents change: an out of control situation. In these cases,

either the SPC is reduced to "Checkmark" SPC or an alternative chart must be devised.

The solution to both of these problems is called a C chart.

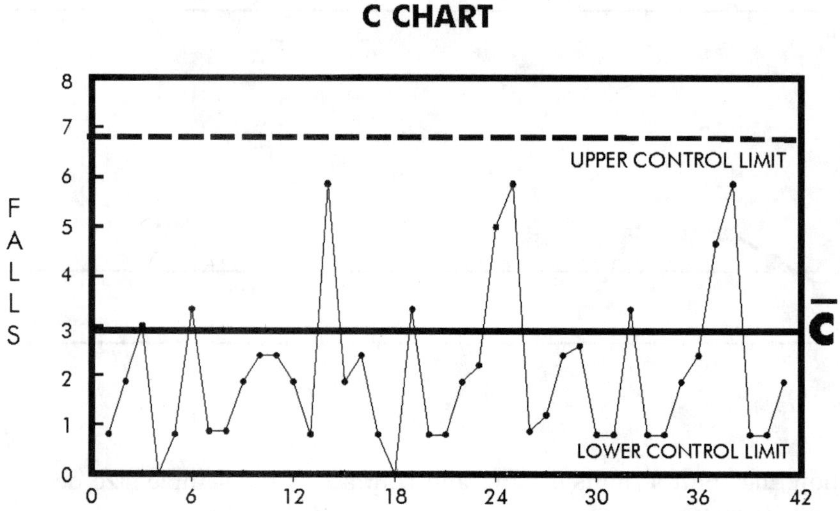

The chart above is an example of a C chart. Now let's discuss the calculations that will be used in the C chart.

C CHARTS

The C Chart is a special case of the P chart to take care of the following conditions:

1. The probability is low.
2. The number of opportunities is high.

C charts measure the frequency or number of non-conformities (for example, defects) where C equals the number of defects. C equals a count of the number of occurrences for each subgroup. For a C chart the alarms are the average and control limits that all control charts use. The following show the special calculations that C chart alarms use.

$$\overline{C} = \frac{C_1 + C_2 + C_3 + \ldots + C_K}{K}$$

where K equals the number of subgroups.

The standard deviation for a C chart is the square root of the average count.

$$UCL_C = \overline{C} + 3 * \sqrt{\overline{C}}$$

$$LCL_C = \overline{C} - 3 * \sqrt{\overline{C}}$$

Let's continue our airline example on a trip from Nashville to Orlando by monitoring another metric. Over the years, the passengers have changed their baggage carrying habits due to lost bags and delays in baggage claim at the final destination. To compensate for these failures, many passengers carry their bags onto the plane.

A new problem arises with bags falling out of the overhead compartment. The probability of this happening is really quite low, but the number of opportunities for the bag to fall is high. The number of bags falling from the overhead is our count and C value.

C CHART EXERCISE

C Chart Data - Number of fallen bags per flight

Subgroup	Mon	Tues	Wed	Thurs	Fri	Sat
C	3	2	1	4	3	

The above counts are now used to compute the control limits for the situation in which the number of falling bags is changing.

$\overline{C} = \frac{3+2+1+4+3}{5} = \frac{13}{5} = 2.6$
$UCL = 2.6 + 3 * \sqrt{2.6} = 7.4$
$LCL = 2.6 - 3 * \sqrt{2.6} = 0$

Now take these C values and control limits, and build the C control chart for the Nashville to Orlando falling bags. The completed C chart for our example is shown below:

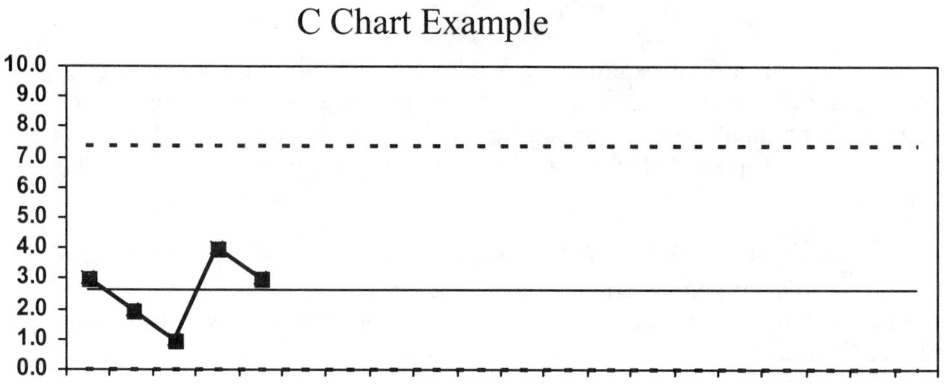

The C chart is read and used like all the other control charts. The alarms from **Chapter Seven** will be used to interpret shifts and changes. You are probably asking yourself why the C chart uses the same alarms as Variable charts and P charts.

When we discussed the Variable chart, the alarms were based on the normal distribution. The Variable chart alarms use the probabilities of the normal. Most of the values are clustered around the average, with virtually no values falling outside the control limits. The odds of having a value outside the control limits are 0.1%.

The P chart, discussed earlier in this chapter, uses a special case of the normal called the binomial distribution. The binomial allows the same variable chart alarms to be used to drive the P system.

Now we must discuss the C chart alarm system. The distribution for the C chart is the Poisson distribution. The Poisson is a special case of the binomial. The Poisson is for the situation in which the counts are low and the number of opportunities is great.

POISSON DISTRIBUTION

The Attribute control charts also use the Poisson distribution as the basis for their assumptions of the U chart and the C chart. By using the Poisson, which is a special case of the binomial, (remember that the binomial is a special case of

the normal) all the control charts use the same fundamental alarm system. All control charts are based around some type of normal distribution.

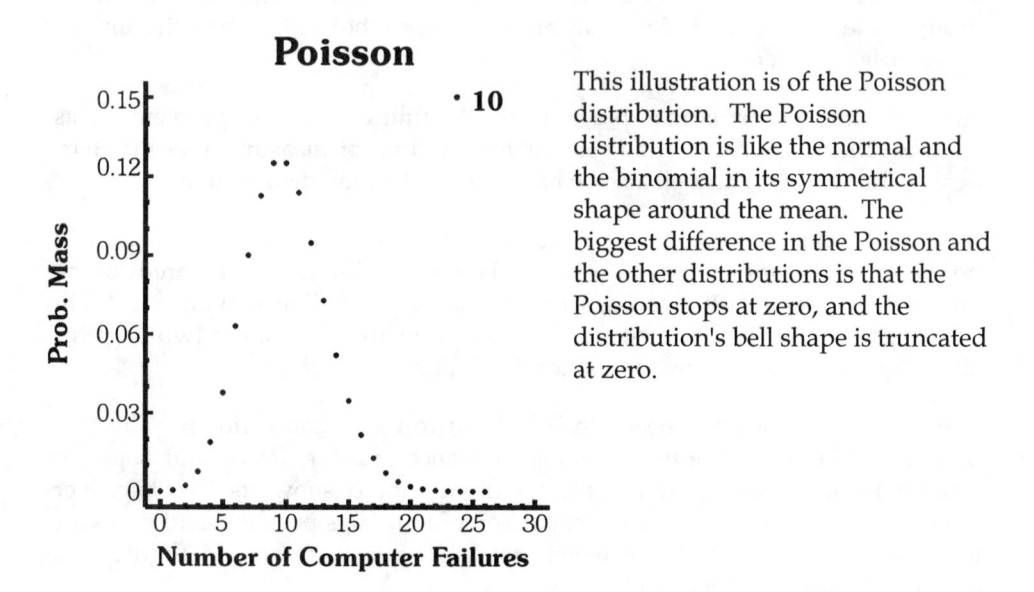

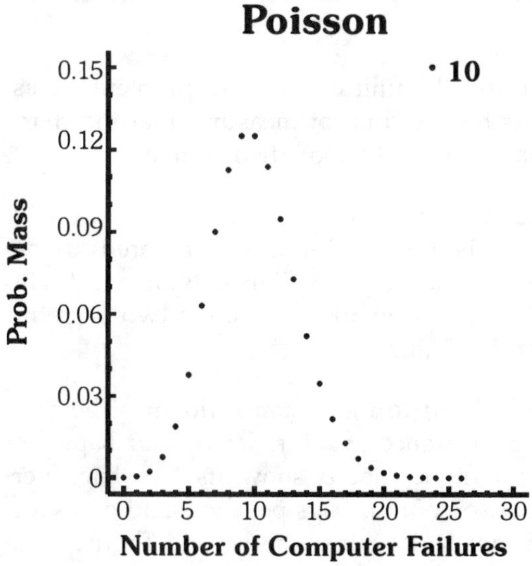

This illustration is of the Poisson distribution. The Poisson distribution is like the normal and the binomial in its symmetrical shape around the mean. The biggest difference in the Poisson and the other distributions is that the Poisson stops at zero, and the distribution's bell shape is truncated at zero.

The Poisson, being a special case of the normal distribution, allows us to use the same assumptions and alarms that we use for variable data. The formula for the standard deviation is the main difference:

Standard Deviation = Square root of the count mean

$$=\sqrt{\bar{C}}$$

Thus, the out of control points of attribute data are also the following equations:

Upper Control Limit = mean + three standard deviation

$$=\bar{C}+3*\sqrt{\bar{C}}$$

Lower Control Limit = mean - three standard deviation

$$=\bar{C}-3*\sqrt{\bar{C}}$$

This standard deviation and the Poisson distributions are the base for the C chart. Now we have covered three of our attribute charts: NP, P, and C.

The C chart will serve us well as long as the unit of measure for each subgroup remains equal.

UNIT OF MEASURE VARIATIONS

The C chart is a wonderful tool for monitoring the shifts of counts. A problem arises though when the unit of measure of the C chart varies from group to group. The C chart is designed to monitor counts but only when the unit of measure is consistent.

Another control chart is required to offset the unit of measure problem. This chart is called a U chart. The U stands for the "unit of measure" that the chart deals with. This U chart will also be based on the Poisson distribution.

If the flight course is changed and the mileage varies, our unit of measure will not be consistent for each count. Thus, the flights cannot be compared to one another consistently. If two bags fall in each of two flights, with one flight covering 500 miles and the second flight covering 1000 miles, the two bags for both flights is not a fair way to monitor the flights.

The count of falling bags needs to be related to the distance flown. The first flight should monitor the two bags for a distance of 500 miles or four bags per thousand miles flown, and the second flight should show its two bags per thousand miles flown. Thus the comparison of four bags per thousand miles for the first flight compares fairly when matched against the second flight's two bags per thousand miles flown.

The C indicates the number of bags falling from the overhead. The N represents the number of miles flown. The C and N values are then divided to compute a ratio. This ratio is called U. The chart below shows the airline flight information.

Subgroup	1	2	3	4	5	6
C (Falling Bags)	2	1	3	3		
N (Number Flight Miles)	200	200	200	300		

A new chart is required to fix our varying unit of measure problem. This new control chart is a special type of C chart; it is called U, which stands for the first letter of "unit of measure."

What does a U chart look like? The U chart, like all other control charts, has data and alarms. The alarms are the center average and the control limits. The chart below is an example of a U chart.

U Chart

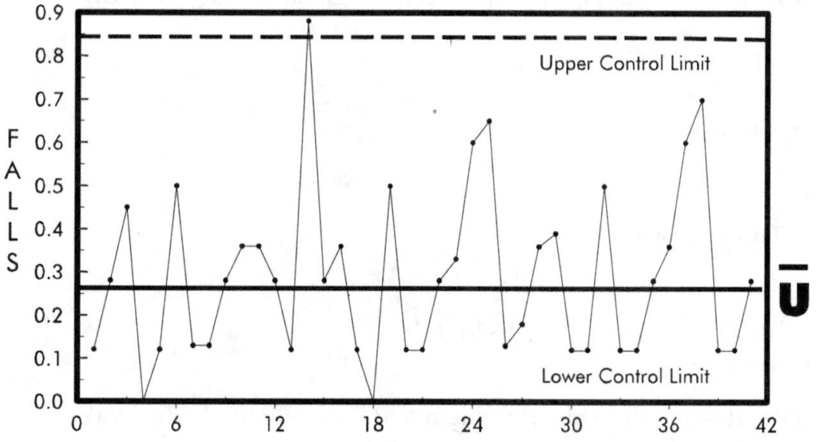

Falls Per Week

Since the U is a special kind of C, the U is like the C in that both use the Poisson distribution for our interpretation rules. Remember, the Poisson distribution is a special kind of binomial distribution and the binomial is a special kind of normal distribution. Thus, reading the U chart is like reading all the other control charts; readings are based on the rules derived from the normal distribution. The details of reading all control charts were covered in **Chapter Seven.**

U CHARTS

The U Chart is a special case of the C chart to take care of inconsistent units of measure.

U charts measure the proportion of defects by counting the number of nonconformities, C (defects), and divided by the sample size N.

C ... Counts of the number of nonconformities

N ... Number of samples

U ... Ratio of count of nonconformities to total pieces

$$U = \frac{C}{N}$$

Monitor

$$\overline{U} = \frac{C_1 + C_2 + C_3 + \ldots + C_K}{N_1 + N_2 + N_3 + \ldots + N_K}$$

The formulas for the upper and lower control limits are shown below:

Upper Control Limits

$$UCL_U = \overline{U} + 3 * \frac{\sqrt{\overline{U}}}{\sqrt{\overline{N}}}$$

Lower Control Limits

$$LCL_U = \overline{U} - 3 * \frac{\sqrt{\overline{U}}}{\sqrt{\overline{N}}}$$

Now let's return to the airline problem and compute the U data values for each day. The table below shows the U values for this example:

U CHART EXAMPLE CONTROL LIMITS

Subgroup	Mon	Tues	Wed	Thurs	Fri	Sat
C	2	1	3	3		
N	200	200	200	300		
U	.01	.005	.015	.01		

For our example the average sample, $\overline{N}$, is calculated below:

$$N = \frac{N_1 + N_2 + N_3 + \ldots + N_K}{K}$$

$$= \frac{200 + 200 + 200 + 300}{4}$$

$$= \frac{900}{4}$$

$$= 225$$

The alarm system is now calculated from the measurements above. These alarms are shown in the table below:

$\overline{U} = \frac{2+1+3+3}{200+200+200+300} = \frac{9}{900} = .01$
$UCL = .01+3*\frac{\sqrt{.01}}{\sqrt{225}} = .01+3*\frac{.1}{15} = .01+.02 = .03$
$LCL = .01-3*\frac{\sqrt{.01}}{\sqrt{225}} = .01-.02 = 0$

Now the completed U chart for our example is shown below:

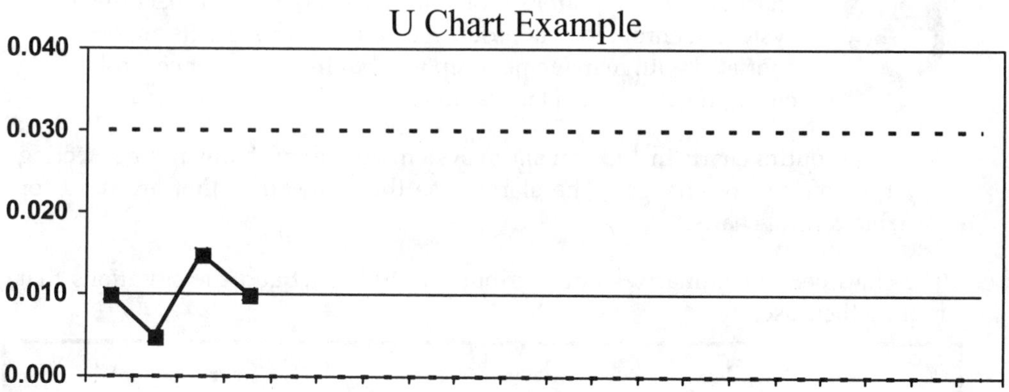

The U chart is used for situations like monitoring the safety record of a trucker, the environmental particles in water or air, holes in textile fabric, defects in electronics, or the accident record for a machine.

Now we have covered both Variable and Attribute charts. This chapter has detailed the computation for NP, P, C, and U control charts.

CHAPTER SUMMARY

This chapter covered the Attribute control charts. The calculations, where to use each chart, and the formulas were described.

NP Charts measure the frequency of the nonconforming parts. The inspection sample sizes (N) for this chart must be equal.

P Charts measure the proportion of units nonconforming.

C Charts measure the frequency or number of non-conformities (defects) where C equals the number of defects.

U Charts measure the proportion of defects by counting the number of non-conformities, C (defects), and dividing by the sample size N.

Remember, these Attribute control charts, like Variable control charts, are the operator's tool to monitor a particular machine or system in chronological order. Attribute control charts are often confused with management reports, but like all other control charts, they are still a tactical tool.

Attribute control charts include an alarm system with a mechanism for detecting any type of shift or change. The alarms use the same rules that are used for Variable control charts.

The chart below summarizes our Attribute control chart and the situations that require their use:

Use	Chart
Percentage or Proportions	**P Chart**
Counts: Use this chart when percents are low, and the N is large.	**C Chart**
Unit of Measure: Use this chart when the unit of measure changes from subgroup to subgroup.	**U Chart**

Now, let's move on to cover capability studies. The capability study is the companion of the control chart forming the Statistical Process Control (SPC) team. Both tools must be used brilliantly to provide tactical and strategic players with the information that they need.

CONTROL CHART SUMMARY

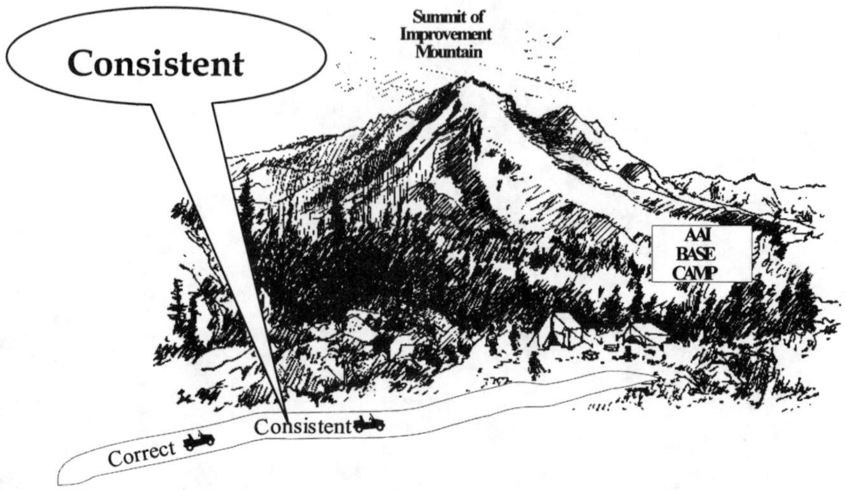

In **Chapter Four** the general concept of control charts was explained.

Chapter Six, **Chapter Eight**, and **Chapter Nine** have covered the setting up and construction of both Variable and Attribute control charts. This construction of the Variable charts, $\overline{X}$ and R, $\overline{X}$ and S, and Individual are clear. NP, P, C, and U have been covered such that we can now construct them.

Finally, in **Chapter Seven** we covered the reading and use of control charts. Now with our statistical tool called control charts we are ready to establish our second base-camp milestone: consistency.

Chapter Ten will take us to the third milestone of capability.

Chapter Ten: Capability Analysis

SPC NOW SUPPORTS STRATEGIC DECISION-MAKING

Throughout this book we have discussed the importance of Division of Labor for decision-making, goal setting, and proper analysis. This Division of Labor clarifies the difference between strategic and tactical issues. Let's briefly revisit these issues prior to discussing our strategic analysis called capability studies.

Tactical execution is required for strategic decisions to be effective. If operations fail to correctly run the facility, no strategy will work. Our strategic decision-makers must count on our tactical decision-makers to do their job, for only then can the strategic decisions be effective. Many strategic options are available, but they will work only if the operation can run smoothly.

To repeat, management can make decisions only when operations is correctly and consistently running the facility. When this is the case, many options are available to management. When the plant is run incorrectly, we have no way of making a strategic decision that is based on sound logic.

The prediction intervals and confidence intervals become the eyes and ears for effective decisions. The correct set of books must be selected to provide the appropriate information to support the type of decision being made. The correct presentation of information is essential to good, sound decisions. Failure to provide or choose the correct set of books and the correct analysis tool will yield incorrect information.

When strategic and tactical personnel both do their jobs, they form a team. Operations is in deep trouble when management does not do its decision-making job of providing the facility. If the facility (available means) is not capable, we are doomed to having dissatisfied customers and stockholders. If operations does not perform its role of running the facility (available means) correctly and consistently, then how can management assess the impact to the customer?

The correct selection of the analytical tool then becomes of paramount importance so that the tactician and the strategist can work together. Just as strategic and tactical decisions form a team, confidence and prediction intervals also form an essential team for properly prepared information. Both the decision-makers and the proper support information must come together to build a finely honed partnership that allows for good, effective, clear decisions.

In **Chapter Two,** we discussed support for both tactical and strategic decisions and goal setting. Two sets of analysis tools are provided: one for strategic decisions and the other for tactical decisions. The following table summarizes the analytical tools to support tactical and strategic decision-making and goal setting.

	Tactical	**Strategic**
	Operations ↓ Detect Change ↓ Averages	Management/Customers/Sales ↓ Assess Capability ↓ Individuals
Central Tendency	$Ave_{Ave} = Ave_{Ind}$	
Variability	Std_{Ave}	Std_{Ind}
	$Std_{Ave} = \frac{Std_{Ind}}{\sqrt{N}}$ Where N = subgroup size	
Distribution	Central Limit Theorem Normalizes Data	Histogram
	Confidence Intervals $X_i = X_{Ave} \pm Z * \frac{Std_{Ind}}{\sqrt{N}}$	**Prediction Intervals** $X_i = X_{Ave} \pm Z * Std_{Ind}$

All reports must assure that the proper set of books matches the proper decision type - either strategic or tactical. No one analysis tool can support both types. Both sets of books must complement each other and work as a team. Since this chapter deals with capability studies (strategic analysis) then prediction intervals or individual readings must be used.

Throughout this book, the methods to effectively control a process and product have been discussed. As a review, the following are the steps:

- Calculate the initial control limits.
- Establish that the process is in control.
- Continually survey the control charts for alarms (out of control conditions).

As the drawing illustrates, the first essential component is establishing a consistent pattern. My favorite sport as a boy was playing third base in baseball. My skills with the glove were always flawless. My teammates called me "the vacuum cleaner" because nothing ever went past me. However, this didn't guarantee an out for our team because I had a shotgun arm to make the throw to first base. To explain my problem a little, when I made my throw, the first baseman and I were always in a panic. We both knew that with my release, the ball would have tremendous speed, but nobody, including me, knew where the ball was going. Sometimes it sailed perfectly to first for the out, at other times it landed in the dirt half way to first, and sometimes it flew straight into the stands. You can see the importance of consistency.

Now with the process in control we are ready to discuss the methods to effectively assess the capability of the process and product. Once again our initial steps are the following:

- Calculate the initial control limits.
- Establish that the process is in control.
- Continually survey the control charts for alarms (out of control conditions).

And now we're ready to begin the final step of assessing the capability of the in control process. Our final step allows the strategic decision-makers to assure that the facility is truly capable of making the product the customer wants.

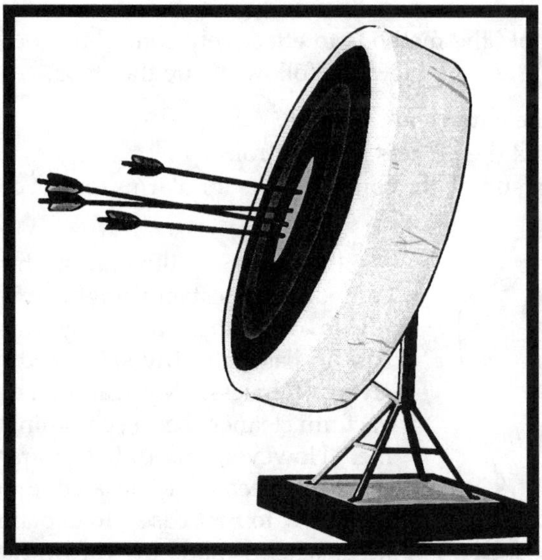

Continuing Improvement ... through Control and Capability

As in the drawing, a consistent product and a capability study show us what and where the improvements to our product and process must be made. The strategic decision-makers can now use this knowledge to achieve a bull's-eye every time. This bull's-eye will equate to improved products and processes.

Since consistency is so crucial for capability, let's recap the control charts and see how they must work to make the capability study accurate.

HOW DOES CONTROL FIT WITH CAPABILITY?

For a proper capability study, your homework must be completed. This homework is the proper building and grouping of your data and is fundamental to obtaining a proper understanding of the capability of your machine or process. In baseball, much hard work is expended before the first game is played. Spring training and practice sessions must be complete so that the season can begin and we can achieve the results that a baseball team desires: WINS!! In a continuous process, our homework is tactical execution that must be monitored and pushed to a level of brilliance.

The tactical tools we use to assess that the fundamentals are performed correctly are the control chart and the *Walkabout ™* Dependency Diagram. The control chart is the tool to evaluate the consistency of the product or process. The *Walkabout ™* is the tool to monitor the correct running of the machine. The *Walkabout ™* and the control charts must work together to state that the machine is running correctly and consistently. These are the tactical tools used by the operator to assure the strategic decision-makers that all is ready for our

capability study. These tactical tools have been covered in depth in the prior chapters of this book.

Now we are ready to begin. Then and only then, after the tactical force's job is complete, can we state that we are ready to assess the capability of the process. Now our strategic decision-makers can take over.

The tactical and strategic forces must work together as a team to provide good information just as a pitcher and a catcher must work together. The catcher calls a good mix of pitches to keep the batter off guard, and the pitcher then must deliver these pitches where the catcher calls for them. Finally, the catcher must catch the pitch that is delivered.

If either player works out of harmony with the other, then disaster is brewing. Should the pitcher ignore the catcher's call for a fast ball and deliver a curve ball, the ball is a very likely to get away from the catcher. Even if the pitch is a strike leading to a strikeout, the batter can still get to first because of the wild pitch.

For comparison's sake, the control chart is the tactical tool that monitors execution of the plan, just as the pitcher is the tactical person that must deliver the correct pitches in the called for location.

WHAT CONTROL MEANS

Control means consistency. When I was younger and lived in the small town of Alexander City, Alabama, I coached a youth baseball team. My coaching approach was unique in that we built a team of very specialized players. Early on in my first player draft (you can see we took this very seriously) one very young kid named Greg wanted to be a pitcher but was being overlooked by the other teams. When this kid pitched, he wasn't the fastest or the most overpowering. He didn't have the sharpest curve ball or the largest selection of pitches. What this kid had was consistency - every pitch was exactly a strike!

I drafted him and planned to use him as our relief pitcher. We worked with him to assure that he made a strike on every pitch. As the team played together, Greg knew his role and was never disappointed because he didn't start. He knew he would be there when the team needed him.

When our team was in trouble and needed to stop an opposing team's rally, we knew who our relief pitcher was. When my players saw Greg warm up, they would cheer because they knew we were about throw cold water on the other team. In fact, they began to call him "the fireman." We all learned that Greg was consistent and always threw strikes that put pressure on the opposing team.

This predictability won many a game for our team. In baseball, this type of pitcher is called a control pitcher. He knows where the ball is going to be placed and positioned each time he throws the ball.

Consistency means predictability, and consistency and predictability are synonyms for the word control. Capability says we are predicting the future from the past. Should we attempt to make a prediction from something that is unpredictable, then we must question our results.

Out of control means the process is not consistent and is unpredictable. If the process is capable but is out of control, the future is not predictable or well represented based on the past and present data. Similarly, if the process is not capable and is out of control, bad product is not necessarily inevitable.

In control means the process is consistent and predictable. If the process is capable and is in control, the future is predictable because of the consistent

nature of the past. Our capability is well represented based on this past and present information. Similarly, if the process is not capable and is in control, bad product is definitely coming our way.

PROCESS METRICS

Don't forget the basics from the first Process Management Principle. The first Principle says the process must be improved for the product to improve. We must not forget that the P in SPC stands for process. Time and time again people do SPC as if the name stood for "statistical product control" - they completely forget the process component! The process metrics must be run correctly and consistently.

The maintenance and compliance of the facility (housekeeping) is fundamental to the correct and consistent running of the facility. No statistics, analysis, expert systems, experimentation, automation, or computerized system can overcome housekeeping lapses. An automated facility that is not maintained will produce huge problems, inefficiencies, and defects. Automation demands good housekeeping and manufacturing practices. Housekeeping demands a continuous and ongoing dedication to the maintenance of the facility. Good housekeeping is an absolute must to achieve improvement. A clear understanding of the linkage between the Principles of Process Management, improvement, quality, customer satisfaction, and the long-term viability of the facility must be understood.

Walkabouts ™ are the focal point for assessing the compliance of the housekeeping effort. The *Walkabout ™* provides an easy way for an operator to document one machine's running parameters.

Both product and process metrics are critical to housekeeping. No one parameter is more or less important than any other because the one metric that goes lacking for proper attention may be the one metric that keeps us from good product and improvement. Sometimes, in our rush to do a product capability study, the process metrics are forgotten. **All process metrics must be run both correctly and consistently for the product capability study to be valid.**

All associates must understand what we are trying to achieve through the *Walkabout ™*, and they must use the *Walkabout ™* to run the machine. We will expect to have a *Walkabout ™* for ***each*** machine and product. The *Walkabout ™* gives us a tool to not only run the facility but to assess compliance as well.

KEEPING THE FACILITY RUNNING CORRECTLY

The *Walkabout ™* is the tool that provides a clear documentation of the process. It must be a dynamic tool that is used by all associates. The *Walkabout ™* gives us a benchmark to begin our changes and allows all associates to understand the process. Good housekeeping is of prime importance to all associates. When we deviate, we have a clear procedure for documenting change. Depending on the magnitude and impact of the change, we will need to report the change up and down the decision ladder.

Grandma used the *Walkabout ™* to explain southern biscuit-making, step by step, to my mother. The *Walkabout ™* first became a tool to document how Grandma made the biscuits. Then Grandma used the completed *Walkabout ™* to teach my mother how to make the biscuits. Finally, the *Walkabout ™* became Mama's tool to check to see that everything was done properly. Grandma and Mama both kept good housekeeping practices.

The *Walkabout ™* is the operational tool to assure that the operator knows and can recall how to perform a particular procedure. We can use the *Walkabout ™* as an operational tool to document the system's procedure so that we can measure our product and process.

The *Walkabout ™* also provides a medium for all management levels to conduct their own audit of the facility's metrics compliance. Management should periodically make an audit of each machine. This would simply require the manager to take the operator and the *Walkabout ™* around each section of the machine. The manager and the operator together can then test the compliance of the machine's metrics. The manager and the operator should discuss why the metric is there. The operator should be able to explain why each metric is important. If he does not understand the metric or its importance, process knowledge base training should then be initiated.

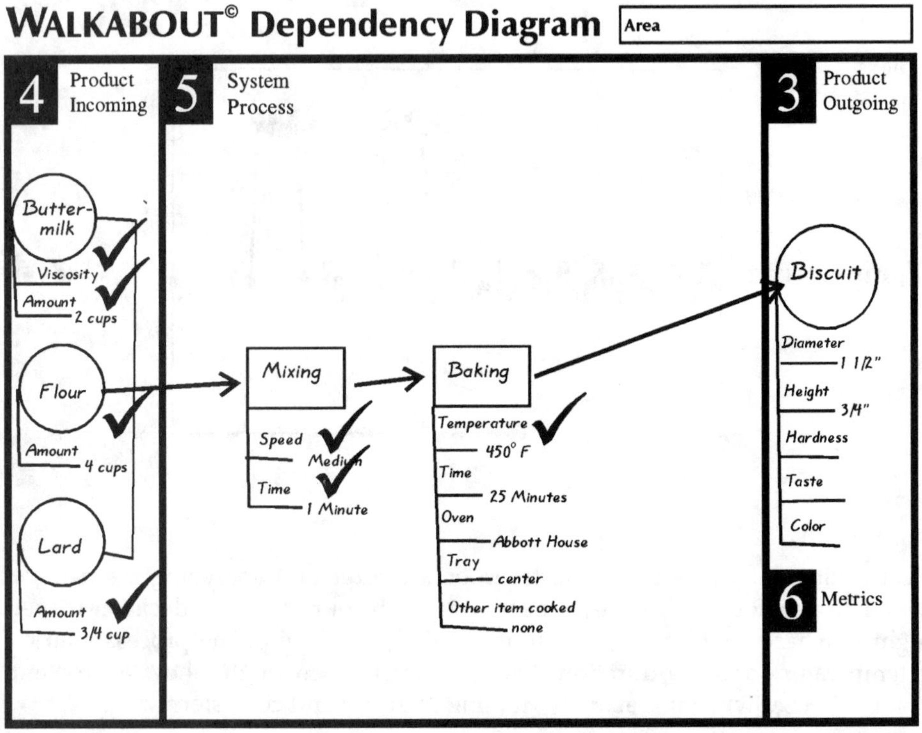

With a process knowledge base, we now have a benchmark to begin an improvement program, Statistical Process Control, and other efforts.

KEEPING THE FACILITY RUNNING CONSISTENTLY

Statistical Process Control charts provide a tool to monitor the consistency of a process. Naturally, then, they also provide a means for an operator to detect any shifts in the consistency of the process or product.

Since this is a tool to assist in the consistent running of a machine, all reporting must be for one particular machine. A machine will have multiple process and product metrics to monitor, but each process and product metric will have its own control chart. For the consistent running of the machine, all process metrics must be in a state of statistical control. The example on the next page shows the temperature process metric with peaks. Even though the product metric is in control, the fact that the temperature is out of control indicates that the machine is not running consistently. When the machine is not run correctly and consistently, then the capability will not be accurate.

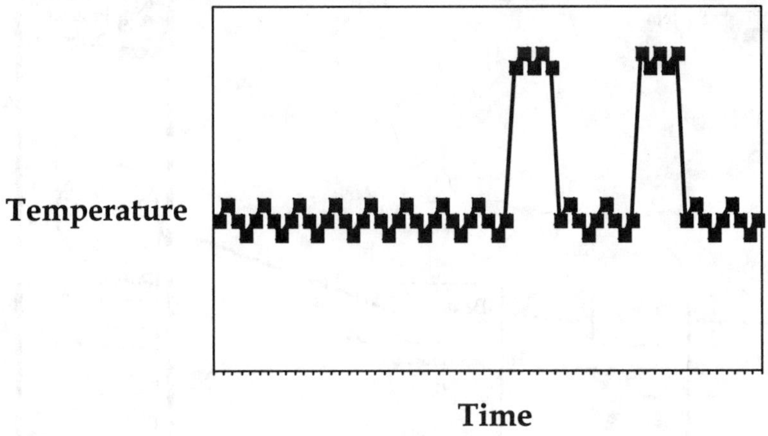

A capability study could be undertaken on a freezer unit analyzing the percent of bad frozen food. If the percentage was high, our strategic decision-maker might purchase a new refrigeration unit. Failing to monitor the process metrics of temperature and the duration that the door is open might show a problem with the freezer when it is actually running correctly and consistently.

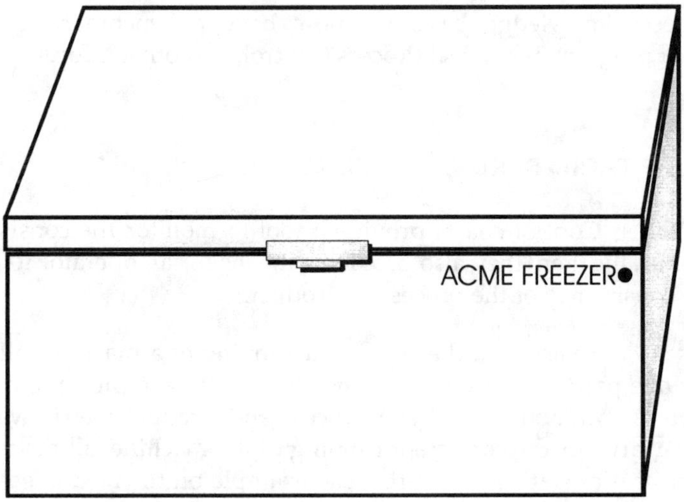

All process metrics must be in control for the machine to be running consistently. We must monitor the process metrics to assure that the machine is running consistently -- only then can we do a completely valid capability study. Control

charts become our tool for assessing whether, over time, we are consistently running the facility. All deviation from the correct and consistent running of the machine must be reported and reviewed for impact on the customer.

In addition to documenting the change, all knowledge of why the change occurred must also be documented and reported. This information may allow our strategic decision-makers to replicate the cause on other machines.

Remember, process metrics must also be in control. They are vital to an accurate capability study. The control of process metrics assures that the process is stable and producing a consistent product. Thus, the capability study requires that all process metrics be run both correctly and consistently. The correctness of the process and product is validated by the *Walkabout™*. The consistency of the process and product is validated by the control chart.

CAPABILITY AND THE SPC MODEL

Just as the members of a baseball team must work together, those of us in manufacturing must work together to make tactical and strategic decisions like a well-oiled team. Control charts provide the proper information to support tactical decisions, and capability studies provide the proper information to support strategic decisions. Each member of a baseball team must play his position well; similarly, each member of a decision-making team must have access to correct and appropriate information.

The overall objective of Statistical Process Control (SPC) methods is to prevent product or performance defects.

If the aim of process control is to prevent defective product, we must predict the percentage of defects from the controlled process. In turn, this requires that we know about the distribution of values from the process itself.

However, our data at this point is the averages of samples drawn from the process for the tactical purpose of running the facility -- not the process values themselves. We can use the same sample data that appears in our control chart to estimate the location and spread of the process distribution and thus the proportion of product that falls outside of the customer's specifications. To this end, we must analyze the values with strategic tools called prediction limits that

use the individual readings. How the individual values are used will be covered later in this chapter.

What does statistical control mean? To define the term statistical control let's look at each word. Statistics means that we are following a prescribed mathematical procedure to summarize and provide a picture of our numbers. For our purposes, we are using past historical information about a product or process to describe the current and future results of the machine. Control means consistent and predictable results are being accomplished. Putting the two words together means that the measurements, numbers, and math from past history are being used to project the future of a consistent and predictable product or process.

We have discussed the idea and use of control limits and control charts. Control limits are the limit of control but they have no relationship to a specification and are three standard error limits around the mean. When a process is in statistical control, this means the process is quantitatively consistent and predictable.

Always remember, a capability study must be done when the process is stable. A process that is statistically in control is stable; we can perform a capability study. What would happen if we attempted to do a capability study on a process that was out of control?

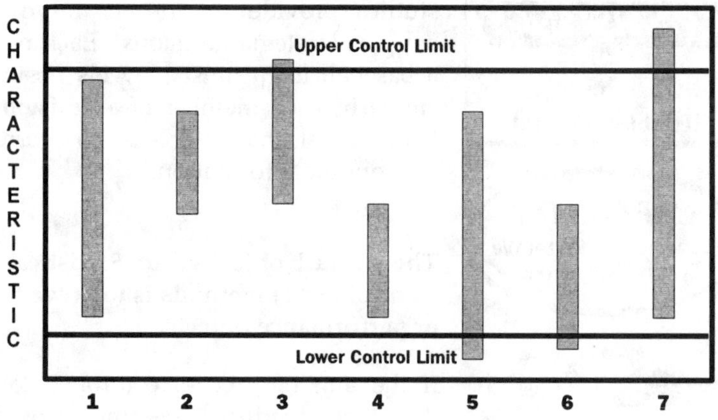

Let's see an example of why control is crucial to a capability study. The chart above shows the results of our product to be very erratic. The results move high and low, and the results are also spread and tight. If this data were plotted on a control chart, the data would be identified as being out of control. These values would make the results of a capability study unpredictable at best and, as we will see later, wrong.

What would happen if a capability study were done on this type of data? To clarify why being in control is so crucial to a capability study, let's analyze a facility and see the control issues and the capability issues.

As a boy growing up in Nashville, Tennessee, my greatest treat was a candy called GooGoo® Clusters. These little bits of heaven were, and still are, made in Nashville by Standard Candy Company. A GooGoo® Cluster contains the finest ingredients known to man. In the center, caramel and the best peanuts grown in southern Alabama and Georgia surround the finest marshmallow. The best chocolate produced in Tennessee, or anywhere else in the world, covers the entire confection. I am a connoisseur of these candies, and being a connoisseur, I know that a GooGoo® Cluster weighs roughly 50 grams because, of course, every time I eat a GooGoo® Cluster, I weigh and inspect the package.

Grand ambition: My grand ambition and most exciting fantasy is to own a candy company. Then, I could make my own chocolate-peanut clusters. I could eat as many as I want, I could give them to my friends, and I could sell them. We will pretend that, because of my boyhood GooGoo® influence, I have purchased a chocolate-peanut cluster candy company.

Meeting my fantasy and the demand: In my fantasy, I purchase a candy company. I decide to build a new state of the art plant in Nashville, Tennessee, and bring in the most competent engineers in the world to design this plant. We hire the best construction company, and we use the best material and equipment in building the plant. Upon completion, the plant will make clusters that weigh about 50 grams.

Customer and management expectations: To assure our customers of quality candy, we have an unconditional guarantee that covers taste, freshness, ingredients, and weight. If there are any deviations, the customer will receive an immediate refund. Our purpose here is to assure that no customer receives a candy that is too light. The guarantee states that no cluster which weighs less than 45 grams will be shipped. We must also protect the investment of the stockholders, for if any candies are manufactured that are too heavy, then we are giving away product and raw material, and this generates no compensation for the company because we are not charging a higher price for the extra ingredients. To protect our shareholders, we have set a specification of no cluster being manufactured that weighs more than 55 grams. Our specifications, therefore, protect both of our customers (shareholder and end consumer).

Operations: Before we proceed, I must explain the operations of the facility. Because the facility is state of the art, the engineers have detailed instructions for its correct running. These detail instructions are spelled out in *Walkabout* ™s provided by the engineers. When the facility is correctly and consistently operated 50 gram clusters (or as close to 50 grams as possible) will be produced. The person in charge of operations will be responsible for the correct and consistent running of the facility, and we will hold him accountable.

WHY WE CANNOT DO A CAPABILITY STUDY IF THE PROCESS IS OUT OF CONTROL

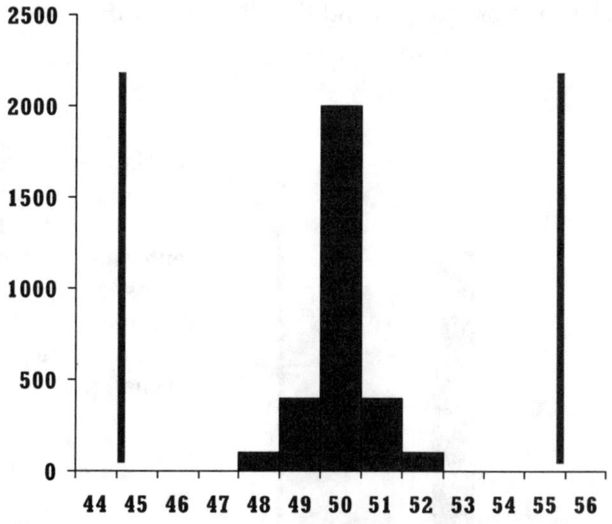

Weight of clusters in grams
Production at 8:00

This chart shows the exact amount of product produced for the varying weights. The weights are not exactly 50 grams but as close as possible for this facility. The chart details the actual production by weight for one of the cluster machines. In an hour, the machine will produce 3000 clusters whose weight will breakdown into the following: 100 clusters that weigh 48 grams each, 400 clusters that weigh 49 grams each, 2000 clusters that weigh 50 grams each, 400 clusters that weigh 51 grams each, and 100 clusters that weigh 52 grams each. This mix of product weight is shown in the above graph. Every candy machine in our facility consistently produces this mixture every hour.

Our process, which is extremely capable, is shown in the graph. We see how the production at 8:00 impacts the customer. No defective product has been produced, for no product depicted in the bars of the chart is above or below our customer specifications.

The quality department issues the revised guidelines that constitute a continuation of the Quality Hell philosophy. The guidelines read, "Whenever a product out of specification is encountered, adjust the machine in the direction that corrects the defects. Five products must be sampled every hour. When any of the five sampled products do not meet the customer's specification, we must adjust the machine. *Only make adjustments when defective* ***products*** *are encountered.*"

Our strategic impact on the tactical running of the machines will be dramatically different. We will only adjust the process when defects are encountered. Any drifts in the process are ignored as long as no defects are detected. No normal adjustments will be made until the process begins to get close to the upper or lower specification.

The graphs below chart the production and the allowable drift created from the new procedure.

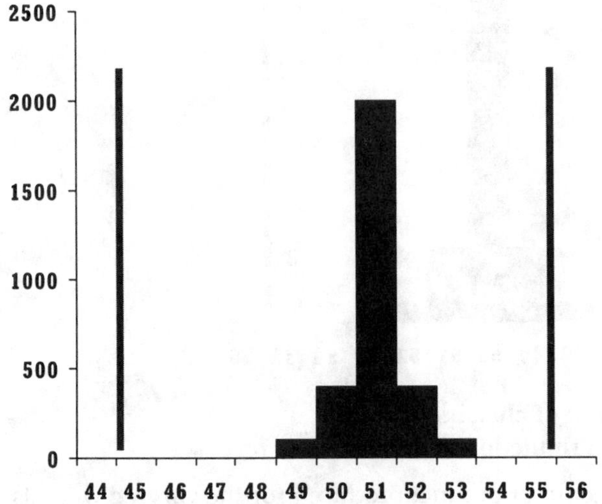

Production at 9:00

At 9:00, the process has begun to drift upward on the heavy side. The center has drifted from 50 grams to 51 grams. Note that due to our inappropriate procedures no change is detected and no adjustments are made.

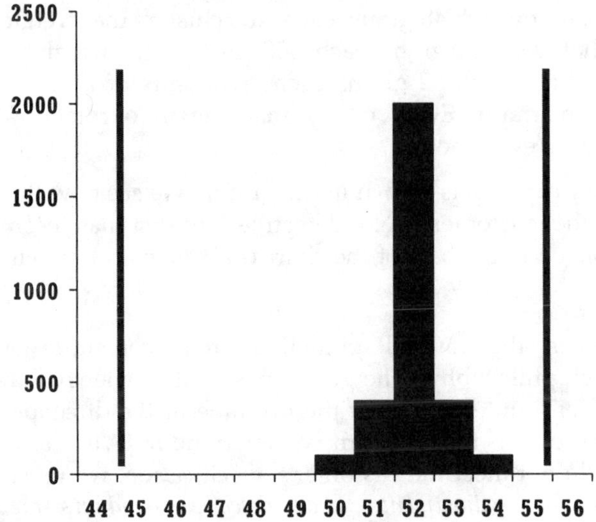

Production at 10:00

At 10:00, the process has continued its upward drift with no correction. Our center is now at 52 grams. Again, no adjustments are made.

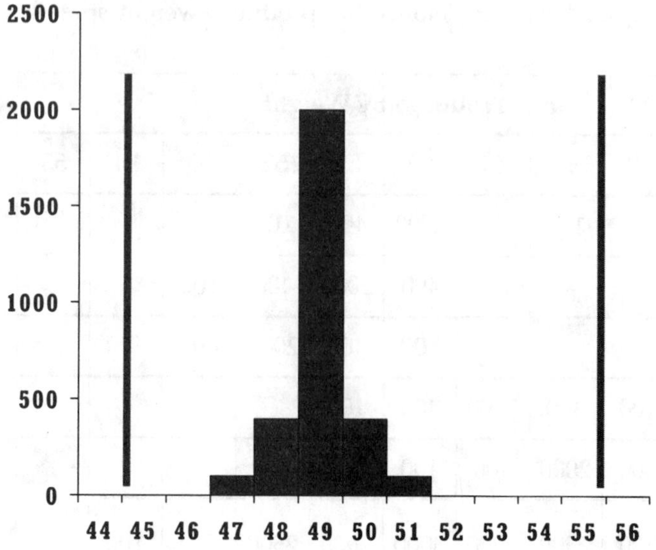

Production at 11:00

At 11:00, the process has slid on a downward drift from a center of 52 grams to a center of 49 grams. Still, no adjustments are made.

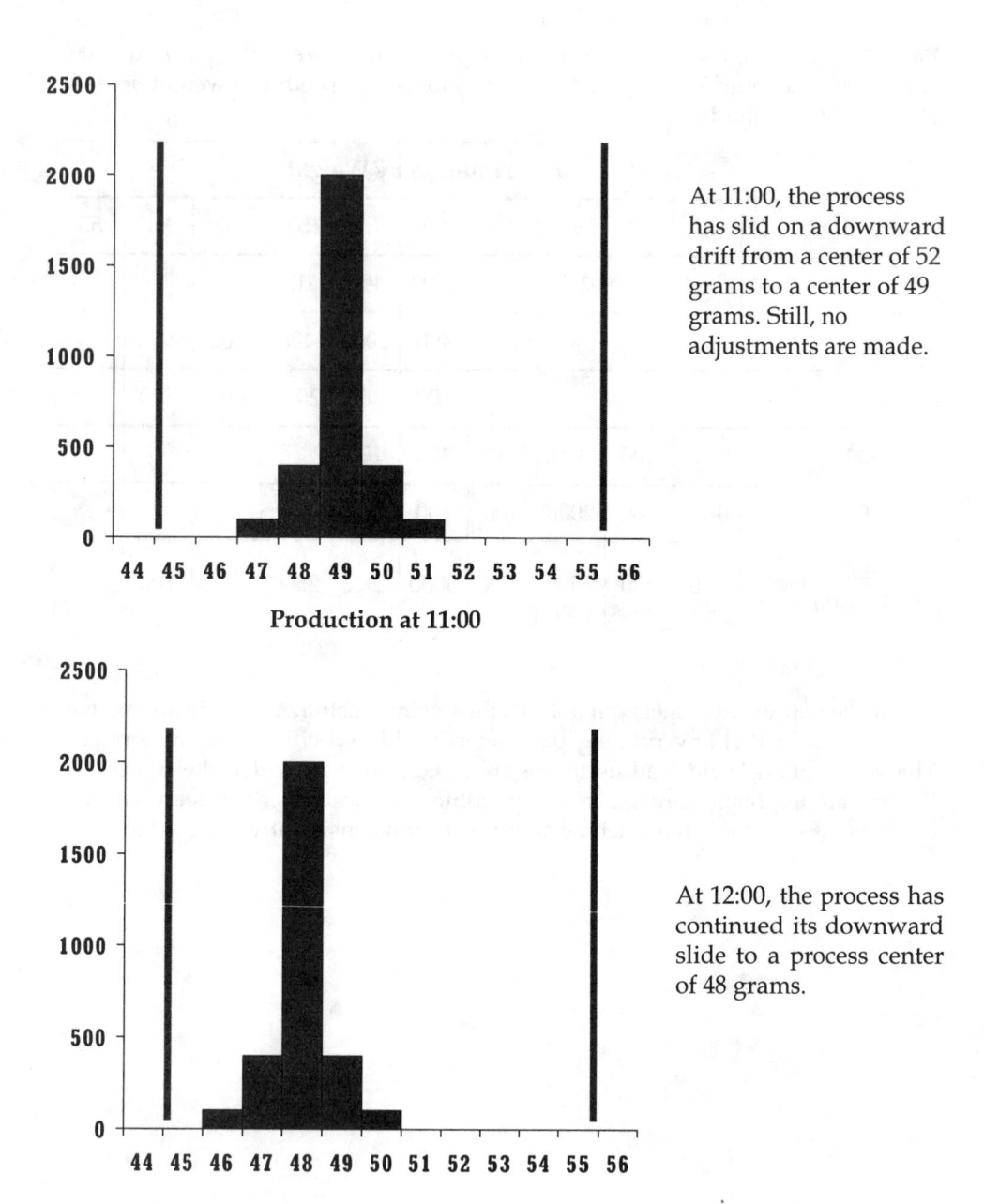

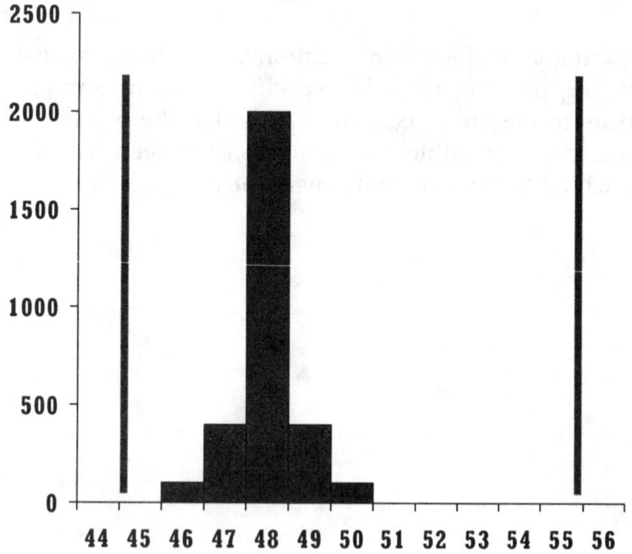

Production at 12:00

At 12:00, the process has continued its downward slide to a process center of 48 grams.

At no time between 8:00 and 12:00 were any defects being produced. Thus our operations staff would have had no reason to make adjustments or to feel they were not running the machine correctly. They would think that they were running the machine correctly because of our incorrect procedures and instructions.

We will record the results of the products produced between the hours of 8:00 and 12:00 in a set of summarized reports. Notice the products' weight spread after we total all products.

	Units Produced by Weight										
Production	45	46	47	48	49	50	51	52	53	54	55
8:00				100	400	2000	400	100			
9:00					100	400	2000	400	100		
10:00						100	400	2000	400	100	
11:00			100	400	2000	400	100				
12:00		100	400	2000	400	100					
Total Production		100	500	2500	2900	3000	2900	2500	500	100	

When we run an extremely capable facility using customer specifications, we simply assume that any running parameters within specifications are correct. This assumption could lead us to the above condition in which the process is floating around haphazardly, oscillating within specifications. This shows a lack of concern for running the machine as correctly and consistently as possible.

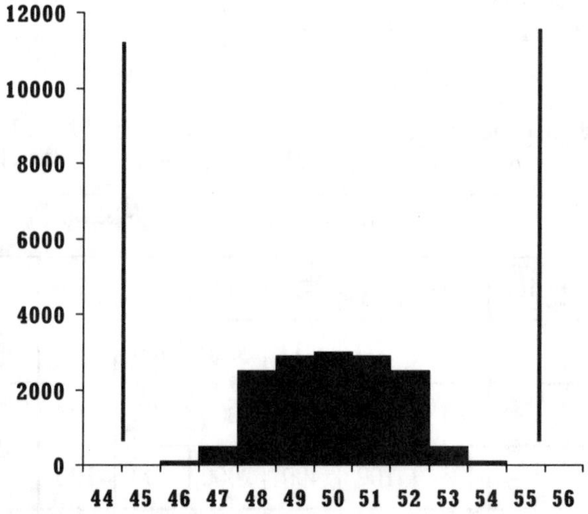

By graphing the summary results of the table above, we see how the customer is impacted. If we used the above graph to review the machine's capability, we would believe, incorrectly, that the machine is only barely capable of producing the product required.

This could lead our strategic decision-makers to begin the purchasing process of a replacement machine. This replacement would be a complete waste of our money and resources. When the new machine came in, our operators using the inappropriate guidelines would make the new machine perform like the old machine.

If we violate the second Principle by making machine adjustments on a capable process based on customer specifications, we will make the process appear less capable than the machine really is. We must conclude that we are not running this machine correctly and consistently.

If our 8:00 to 12:00 production had been run as correctly and consistently as possible, our production of candies would have been as the table below shows:

	Units Produced by Weight										
Production	45	46	47	48	49	50	51	52	53	54	55
8:00				100	400	2000	400	100			
9:00				100	400	2000	400	100			
10:00				100	400	2000	400	100			
11:00				100	400	2000	400	100			
12:00				100	400	2000	400	100			
Total Production				500	2000	10000	2000	500			

The results of the correctly run facility can be graphed. We'll now compare that to the results of the incorrectly run facility from the previous pages.

Poor Productivity

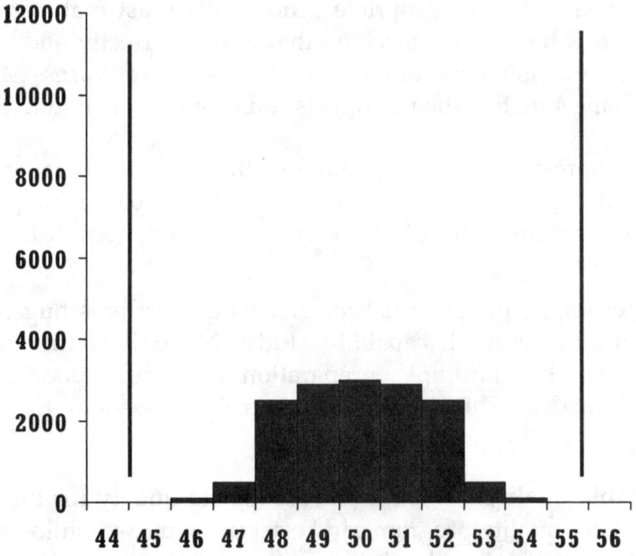

Now compare the poor productivity graph above with the graph below which illustrates a machine that is running correctly and consistently.

Correct and consistent

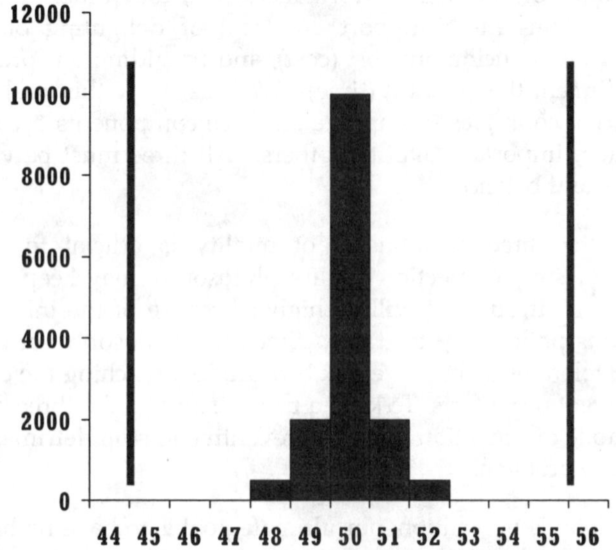

Correct and Consistent Machine

When we note the widely different distributions, we develop two completely different impressions of the same machine. Clearly this could lead to major confusion and potentially inappropriate actions. We must make sure that any decision or action is based on a machine that is run correctly and consistently. Therefore, a clear understanding of the second Principle of Process Management is the key to making sure that the machine is run properly at all times.

Obviously, our impression of the capability of this machine is radically altered depending on which graph we view. We should always base strategic decisions on the validated assumptions of the correct and consistent running of the machine.

For our candy example, the potential for erroneous results is huge. A control chart is essential for an accurate capability study. Not only could our capability study be incorrect, but improper preparation can cause poor and flawed decisions to be made. Thus, statistical control is essential to an accurate capability study.

What is acceptable quality? What is the acceptable quality for the product in our organization? A quality program can be set up with two philosophies. One approach is detection and the other is prevention. Using a detection philosophy our organization tolerates defects and must rework the products that are defective. Using a preventative philosophy, we are working toward controlling and eliminating defects.

In the introduction of this book we have defined quality in a way that is extremely broad and encompassing. According to this definition, quality is comprised of three components: performance, cost, and time. Our research, analysis, and decisions must support our goal of delighting our customer (performance), while reducing our cost (cost), and providing our product to our customers the moment they want it (time). We must view this goal as a never-ending journey that continues to improve all three components because no one component is more important than the others. All three must be viewed with equal importance and balance.

The balance of the three components of quality is crucial to an accurate capability study. Using a detection quality philosophy may keep bad product from the customer, but our cost will be higher because of the inherent rework and scrap that this philosophy tolerates. Since the philosophy of detection or problem solving tolerates defects, we risk bad product reaching the customer no matter how stringent our efforts. To keep a balance among the three components of quality, our mode of operation must be preventive to stop detrimental change before it becomes a problem.

Since our philosophy is prevention, our ultimate goal is to have no bad product, at a minimum cost, and with perfect delivery. Our cost will not be jeopardized by a sole focus on performance. All three components must have a balanced role in continuously improving quality.

Once the capability study is complete, then the control charts become the alarm system to alert us to change in the product or process. Remember, once a change is detected management must be alerted so that a new capability study can be developed. A change can be either an improvement or deterioration, thus SPC forms a powerful team for improvements.

The capability study is the strategic component of SPC. The strategic component of SPC is dependent on the tactical tools to assure that a correct and consistent facility is presented for the capability study. Capability studies allow us to understand how we are meeting our quality objectives.

DETERMINING WHICH DATA POINTS TO INCLUDE IN THE CAPABILITY STUDY

In collecting information for a capability study, many people simply pull all the data readings for the past year. They assume that the more readings we have, the better the capability study must be. In **Chapter One** two analysis flaws were uncovered. Because improper technique is the first analysis flaw, this chapter will focus on assuring that proper techniques are applied to our analysis. For proper numerical analysis, our technique must monitor each of the following:

- Central Tendency
- Variability
- Distribution

Failure to monitor any one of the three will have dire consequences.

Simply having proper analysis technique of a year's worth of data is not enough. Our groups must also form one homogeneous universe based on physical similarity and time of manufacture. We can assure proper physical groups by employing common sense. The time-series groups are formed based on the analytical tool called control charts.

For us to do the detailed analysis that will lead to accurate reporting, a great deal of data gathering will be required. To adequately handle the detailed reporting, all associates must participate in the data gathering effort. To support proper group formation, a bottom up strategy of data reporting is required. This bottom up group formation will test for the time-series groups. The control chart is the tactical tool to assess the time-series groups.

Capability requirements for selecting data points: Each machine's product must be kept separate by time frame so that we can identify homogeneous groups. Correct homogeneous group formation is assured by the following:

- Make sure each individual machine is monitored.
- Use control charts, the SPC tool to identify when the time-series homogenous group has shifted.
- Make sure the monitoring is set at an appropriate time interval for each machine to assure a continuous surveillance. The time interval must be set such that any time-series shift can be detected.
- Make sure a detailed investigation is undertaken when a shift has been noted. This investigation must determine the cause. The effect of the cause can be either an improvement or deterioration.

All our analyses are based on the assumption that both proper technique and groupings have been used. This combination will allow us to provide accurate capability studies and will require a bottom up strategy of data collection and analysis.

The need to create physical groups according to individual machines and differing products should be clear from **Chapter Three**. The time of manufacture or chronological grouping is a little less obvious and requires the special facilities provided by a control chart. The control chart is our means of being certain that the machine is in a state of statistical control.

If we use groups of data that are out of control (non-homogeneous), it would be like mixing apples and oranges. Remember, out of control means inconsistent and improper grouping. For us, the result is very camouflaged and confused. No decision from this kind of analysis would be valid. Let's see an example where the values are improperly grouped.

The table below is the candy weights from one candy machine. Notice that the candy process runs in time zone A consistently for about two days, and then shifts in time zone B. In time zone B the weight has dramatically shifted down for a period of two hours. Finally, in time zone C the candy weight moves back up to its consistent weight. Time zones A and C are very similar. A control chart is the tool designed to make the time of manufacture groups become clear.

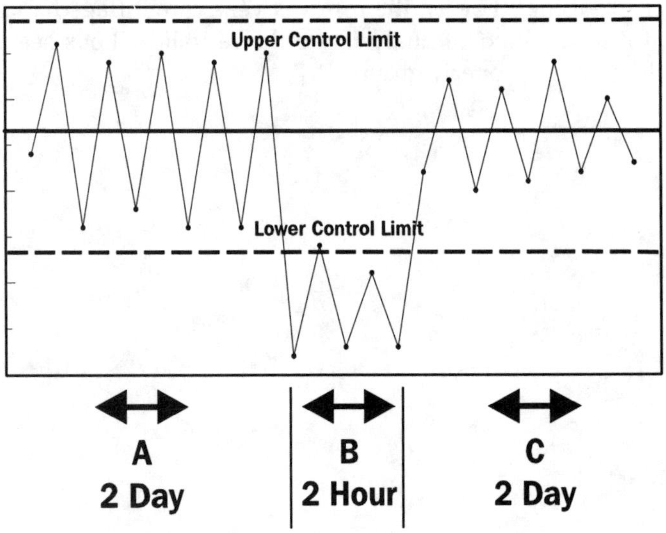

The three zones in this control chart must be understood and analyzed individually. Take particular note of the different statistics from each time zone and then the difference for the lumping of the three zones.

Time Zone	Average	Standard Deviation	Distribution
A	50.00gm	1.0gm	Normal
B	46.55gm	1.0gm	Normal
C	50.00gm	1.0gm	Normal
A+B+C	47.33gm	1.0gm	Normal

From our earlier candy example the candy weight upper specification limit is 55 grams and the lower specification limit is 45 grams.

In **Chapter One** we learned about normal distribution probabilities. These probabilities are computed from the average, the standard deviation, and computing the Z. The formula for Z is:

$$Z = \left| \frac{X_{Ave} - X_i}{Std} \right|$$

The derived Z value is then used to compute the probability of an occurrence. For our candy problem, we have the following statistics and can compute their corresponding Z. Note how the different time zones have different percentage defective rates.

Time Zone	Average	Standard Deviation	Distribution	Z	Percent Defects
A	50.00gm	1.0gm	Normal	5.00	0%
B	46.55gm	1.0gm	Normal	1.55	6%
C	50.00gm	1.0gm	Normal	5.00	0%
A+B+C	47.33gm	1.0gm	Normal	2.33	1%

Time sequence grouping has the potential of presenting our process in very different ways. When the values are simply lumped together with no thought to proper group formation, disaster is on the horizon. Note how different the four possible analyses are.

By viewing A+B+C together we have the impression that, overall, a one percent defect rate is to be expected, even though there are times when (B) the percent defect rate is much higher. This loss of clear knowledge will lead our strategic decision-maker to a very bad conclusion.

Any decision based on improperly grouped (physical, associational, or time-series) data is a prescription for heading straight to Quality Hell.

Now the stage is set for the answer to the first question of "What data points do we include in the capability study?" This first step will use the knowledge that we built in our studies of control charts. For a machine, the process must be in a state of statistical control. Stated another way, the process must be consistent and predictable.

Our control chart labors will now be used to establish what time zones can be grouped together. Those time zones that are in a state of control can be grouped in one capability study.

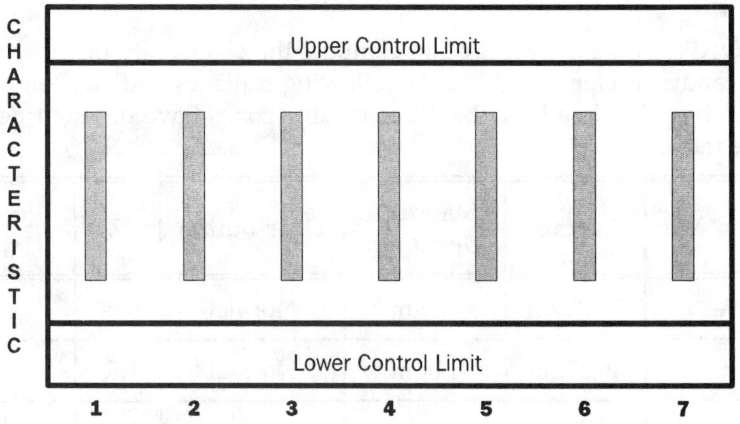

This diagram shows that the results are consistent and in control and thus can be grouped together. A capability study assumes that the process is in control (consistent and predictable). In **Chapter Three**, we studied the flaw of improper groups. The control chart is the means of assuring that a time-series group has been formed.

For the purposes of a capability study, use the data gathered when the process is in control. The in control time zones are shown on the control charts. The following chart shows a process that has shifted and whose values we should include. We will include all values for as long as the process is in control and, for this study, since the shift downward. This large number of data points (in control) increases the accuracy of our projections and thus minimizes the risk that we are making incorrect decisions.

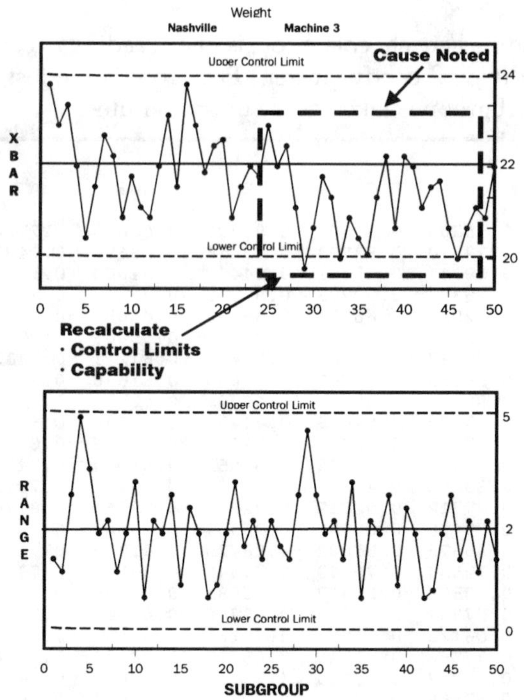

This chart shows that the weight of the clusters produced from machine three has changed. The SPC methodology is to 1) investigate the cause, 2) alert management to the change, and 3) decide what to do. The second step of this methodology alerts the strategic decision-makers to the change and triggers the need for a capability study.

From our candy machine, we can now identify the time zone to include in the capability study. From the control chart, the enclosed area is where the shift has occurred and is the area to include in the capability study.

While the capability study is proceeding, the tactical forces are determining the cause of the shift.

In order to determine which values to include, we must know the process, when changes in process characteristics have taken place, (i.e., temperature, pH, pressure, etc.), if the change is permanent, and if we will be retaining the change.

Finally, a decision as to what to do can be made.

Now that we have a good appreciation for what data to include, let's return to the candy plant and start a study of the consistency of the chocolate machine's product.

A CANDY CAPABILITY STUDY OF CHOCOLATE CONSISTENCY

The following readings are chocolate consistency readings. Each reading is a test result from an individual candy cluster. Each row is the test results taken in a subgroup. Each subgroup is taken every thirty minutes.

TIME	OB1	OB2	OB3	OB4	OB5	$\bar{X}$	RANGE
8:00	0.75655	0.76309	0.79555	0.85799	0.68696	0.77203	0.17103
8:30	0.73337	0.72810	0.83793	0.72416	0.68698	0.74211	0.15095
9:00	0.68130	0.68741	0.72701	0.64468	0.84080	0.71624	0.19612
9:30	0.60811	0.79303	0.90703	0.93568	0.75377	0.79952	0.32756
10:00	0.76692	0.62595	0.60721	0.69480	0.66086	0.67115	0.15971
10:30	0.73468	0.61227	0.66185	0.72843	0.55483	0.65841	0.17985
11:00	0.72128	0.75937	0.79861	0.81424	0.61291	0.74128	0.20133
11:30	0.76573	0.86283	0.66762	0.70669	0.61636	0.72385	0.24647
12:00	0.73689	0.80831	0.80004	0.69097	0.62378	0.73199	0.18453
12:30	0.67940	0.63179	0.64418	0.74433	0.70640	0.68122	0.11254
1:00	0.68170	0.77080	0.62278	0.57358	0.71586	0.67294	0.19722
1:30	0.84709	0.77807	0.59742	0.69553	0.81948	0.74752	0.24967
2:00	0.73915	0.80295	0.49851	0.81626	0.70454	0.71228	0.31775
2:30	0.87418	0.77712	0.92717	0.72820	0.76661	0.81466	0.19897
3:00	0.65501	0.79409	0.68381	0.76357	0.76406	0.73211	0.13908
3:30	0.77542	0.85875	0.54692	0.68720	0.71317	0.71629	0.31182
4:00	0.77416	0.72534	0.70543	0.64646	0.83704	0.73769	0.19058
4:30	0.60286	0.70500	0.68467	0.66985	0.67785	0.66805	0.10214
5:00	0.73883	0.67804	0.72443	0.68760	0.67617	0.70101	0.06267
5:30	0.78914	0.66123	0.62074	0.73161	0.86498	0.73354	0.24424
6:00	0.71017	0.77596	0.61749	0.65637	0.78831	0.70966	0.17082
6:30	0.70909	0.79797	0.72123	0.73636	0.77683	0.74830	0.08888
7:00	0.72207	0.57868	0.67210	0.79768	0.73411	0.70093	0.21900
7:30	0.67223	0.76367	0.65249	0.76464	0.67843	0.70629	0.11214
8:00	0.74534	0.77008	0.71271	0.62285	0.77221	0.72464	0.14936

The readings come from one chocolate machine with the chronological order of manufacture intact. Each time a reading is taken, five consecutive candies are captured and tested. These five test points will be averaged to become our monitors on the control chart.

CONTROL CHART AND CAPABILITY EXAMPLE

Using the data above, compute and prepare the data and control limits from the above chocolate consistency data. The $\bar{\bar{X}}$ value (average of the averages) for our chocolate consistency example is .722548 and the R (range average) is .187377. Once the computations are complete, prepare the control charts and interpret them for a state of statistical control.

Using the chocolate consistency data prepare the data and control limits.

Control limits calculated for the $\overline{X}$ control chart:

$$UCL_{Ave} = \overline{\overline{X}} + A_2 * \overline{R} \qquad LCL_{Ave} = \overline{\overline{X}} - A_2 * \overline{R}$$

$$UCL = .722548 + (.577) * (.187377) = .830665$$

$$LCL = .722548 - (.577) * (.187377) = .614431$$

$$\overline{\overline{X}} = .722548$$

Control limits calculated for the R chart:

$$UCL_R = (D_4) * (\overline{R}) \qquad LCL_R = (D_3) * (\overline{R})$$

$$UCL_R = (2.114) * (.187377) = .396115$$

$$\overline{R} = .187377$$

The following are the $\overline{X}$ chart and the R chart for the data points from the different time zones. The control limits are computed for this chocolate machine. The $\overline{X}$ and R values are now posted on the control chart. The completed control chart will allow us to determine which, if any, points can be included in the capability study.

The above limits were calculated by computer with an A_2 and D_4 of more than three digits of precision. Therefore they vary slightly from the above answers.

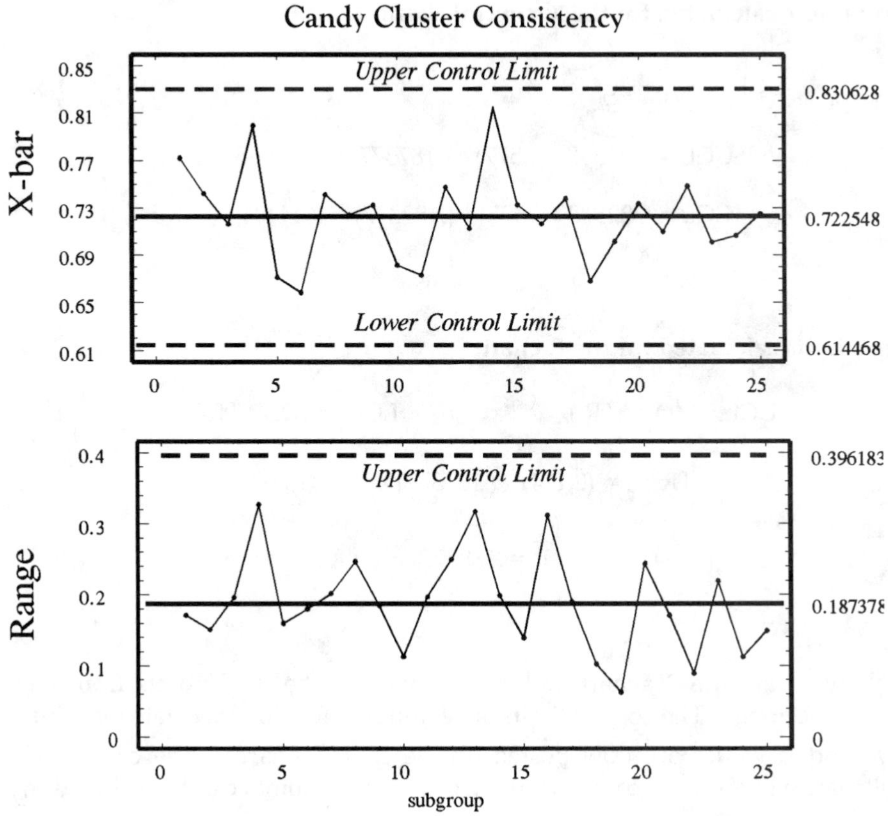

After reviewing the control charts, we can see no out of control points. No $\overline{X}$ or R values outside the control limits, no runs, and no trends are found. The process metric control charts also show no value outside the control limits, no runs, and no trends. We can say that this process is in a state of statistical control. This is a major accomplishment, but is not to be confused with whether we are making good chocolate. We can now move forward to begin the capability study.

THE STEPS FOR THE CAPABILITY STUDY

The following are the steps required for setting up the capability study. These steps can begin once the prerequisites of a correct and consistent facility have been met. Each step in the journey to an accurate capability study will be covered in detail in this chapter. The steps are:

1. Calculate the standard deviation.
2. Determine the specifications.
3. Test for normality.

Now we are ready for the capability study calculation. Since we now know what data points to include, the stage is set for the answer to the question, "How do we calculate standard deviation in the capability study?"

CALCULATING STANDARD DEVIATION

Analysis, decision-making, and goal setting tools are developed to support either strategic or tactical needs. These strategic or tactical tools fill a very precise goal and objective. The monitor for central tendency, the process average (strategic), is the same value as the control chart average (tactical). Remember there is a monitor of variability for strategic purposes and a second monitor for tactical purposes, but these values are different.

The function's strategic monitor of variability, standard deviation, is greater than the function's tactical monitor of variability. The strategic monitor is of individuals and is called standard deviation. The tactical monitor is of averages and is called standard error. The standard deviation is larger by a factor of the square root of the number of samples in the subgroup. These issues were fully covered in **Chapter Two**. The equation for the relationship of standard deviation and standard error is shown below:

$$\frac{Std_{Ind}}{\sqrt{N}} = Std_{Ave}$$

Our capability study is used for many strategic purposes from an initial assessment of the whether the process can perform its mission to determining the impact of a change that is detected by the control charts. First, the clear understanding of the strategic use of this information is critical. Then we are ready to proceed with the mechanics of the capability study.

A capability study is used to assess the possibility of having an individual reading fall outside our specifications. Since we are dealing with individuals, strategic tools are required. Standard deviation is our strategic monitor of

variability and is used in capability studies. The standard deviation of the individuals is used in comparing a process to a specification.

For the purposes of a capability study we must use the standard deviation of the individuals. We have two methods of calculating the standard deviation of the individuals. Note that both methods are estimates of the variability of the process and each will have a certain amount of error associated with it. First we will discuss the capability study's standard deviation formulas when used with an $\overline{X}$ and R chart. Once these are completed, then we will show the differences for both the $\overline{X}$ and S chart and individual charts. Now let's move into the $\overline{X}$ and R chart variability monitors for the capability study.

$\overline{X}$ chart and the R chart: The two equations below are formulas for estimating the variability of the process.

$$Std_{Ind} = \sqrt{\frac{\sum_{i=1}^{N} (\overline{\overline{X}} - X_i)^2}{N-1}}$$

or

$$Std_{Ind} = \frac{\overline{R}}{d_2}$$

The first equation uses the standard sum of squares method. This is the variability monitoring method that was covered in **Chapter One**. We contrast each individual data point with the grand average or $\overline{\overline{X}}$. The equation yields an approximation of standard deviation of the individual. Our alternative equation uses $\overline{R}$. This $\overline{R}$ is divided by a conversion factor to approximate the standard deviation of the individuals. Both methods provide good estimates of the process variability. The more correctly and consistently the process is run, the closer the two estimates will come to each other.

The table below contains all the factors for both $\overline{X}$ and R control charts and capability studies.

Sample Size	A_2	d_2	D_3	D_4
2	1.880	1.128		3.267
3	1.023	1.693		2.574
4	0.729	2.059		2.282
5	0.577	2.326		2.114
6	0.483	2.534		2.004
7	0.419	2.704	0.076	1.924
8	0.373	2.847	0.136	1.864
9	0.337	2.970	0.184	1.816
10	0.308	3.078	0.223	1.777
11	0.285	3.173	0.256	1.744
12	0.266	3.258	0.283	1.717

d_2 is the conversion factor for determining the standard deviation of the individuals for use in our capability studies.

As a general guideline, the sum of squares formula normally results in a larger value than the R estimate. The R estimate technique is smaller because this technique is based on the minimum and part-to-part variability.

The sum of squares, however, encompasses each individual reading independently. The resulting smaller R estimator of variability will result in the percent defective being smaller for the R value estimate.

Since continuous improvement is the normal objective, then I normally use the sum of squares as the estimator of standard deviation in capability studies. This larger standard deviation estimator yields the worst case or most percent defective estimate.

Our candy consistency machine is using $\overline{X}$ and R charts to monitor the consistency of our chocolate candy clusters. Let's compute both the sum of squares and R monitors of the variability for chocolate consistency.

OUR CANDY CAPABILITY STUDY

Let us now begin our capability study. The following readings are chocolate consistency readings. Each reading is a test result from an individual cluster. Each row contains test results for a subgroup. Each subgroup is taken every thirty minutes.

TIME	OB1	OB2	OB3	OB4	OB5	$\bar{X}$	Range
8:00	0.75655	0.76309	0.79555	0.85799	0.68696	0.77203	0.17103
8:30	0.73337	0.72810	0.83793	0.72416	0.68698	0.74211	0.15095
9:00	0.68130	0.68741	0.72701	0.64468	0.84080	0.71624	0.19612
9:30	0.60811	0.79303	0.90703	0.93568	0.75377	0.79952	0.32756
10:00	0.76692	0.62595	0.60721	0.69480	0.66086	0.67115	0.15971
10:30	0.73468	0.61227	0.66185	0.72843	0.55483	0.65841	0.17985
11:00	0.72128	0.75937	0.79861	0.81424	0.61291	0.74128	0.20133
11:30	0.76573	0.86283	0.66762	0.70669	0.61636	0.72385	0.24647
12:00	0.73689	0.80831	0.80004	0.69097	0.62378	0.73199	0.18453
12:30	0.67940	0.63179	0.64418	0.74433	0.70640	0.68122	0.11254
1:00	0.68170	0.77080	0.62278	0.57358	0.71586	0.67294	0.19722
1:30	0.84709	0.77807	0.59742	0.69553	0.81948	0.74752	0.24967
2:00	0.73915	0.80295	0.49851	0.81626	0.70454	0.71228	0.31775
2:30	0.87418	0.77712	0.92717	0.72820	0.76661	0.81466	0.19897
3:00	0.65501	0.79409	0.68381	0.76357	0.76406	0.73211	0.13908
3:30	0.77542	0.85875	0.54692	0.68720	0.71317	0.71629	0.31182
4:00	0.77416	0.72534	0.70543	0.64646	0.83704	0.73769	0.19058
4:30	0.60286	0.70500	0.68467	0.66985	0.67785	0.66805	0.10214
5:00	0.73883	0.67804	0.72443	0.68760	0.67617	0.70101	0.06267
5:30	0.78914	0.66123	0.62074	0.73161	0.86498	0.73354	0.24424
6:00	0.71017	0.77596	0.61749	0.65637	0.78831	0.70966	0.17082
6:30	0.70909	0.79797	0.72123	0.73636	0.77683	0.74830	0.08888
7:00	0.72207	0.57868	0.67210	0.79768	0.73411	0.70093	0.21900
7:30	0.67223	0.76367	0.65249	0.76464	0.67843	0.70629	0.11214
8:00	0.74534	0.77008	0.71271	0.62285	0.77221	0.72464	0.14936

Process Statistical Values
Average = 0.72255
Standard Deviation of Individual = 0.08047
Range Average = 0.1873

Note the average of the individual is .7225, the standard deviation of the individuals (sum of squares method) is .08047, and the range average is .1873. Now let's take these values and compute the two alternative variability values for use in our capability study.

SUM OF SQUARES METHOD

The standard deviation of the individuals using the sum of squares method is .08047. The sum of squares formula and the results are shown below:

$$Std_{Ind} = \sqrt{\frac{\sum_{i=1}^{N}(\bar{\bar{X}} - X_i)^2}{N-1}}$$

$$Std_{Ind} = \sqrt{\frac{\sum_{i=1}^{N}(.7225 - X_i)^2}{N-1}}$$

$$Std_{Ind} = .08047$$

We can also use the range average as the base for standard deviation.

RANGE AVERAGE METHOD

The range average of .1873 is used in our calculation of standard deviation of the individuals. The calculations and the results are shown below.

Sample Size	A_2	d_2	D_3	D_4
2	1.880	1.128		3.267
3	1.023	1.693		2.574
4	0.729	2.059		2.114
5	0.577	2.326		2.114
6	0.483	2.534		2.004
7	0.419	2.704	0.076	1.924
8	0.373	2.847	0.136	1.864

From the table on the left, the d_2 value of 2.326 is selected because the number of samples for the chocolate consistency is five. The d_2 constant is then inserted in the following equation:

$$Std_{Ind} = \frac{\bar{R}}{d_2}$$

$$= \frac{.1873}{2.326}$$

$$= .08052$$

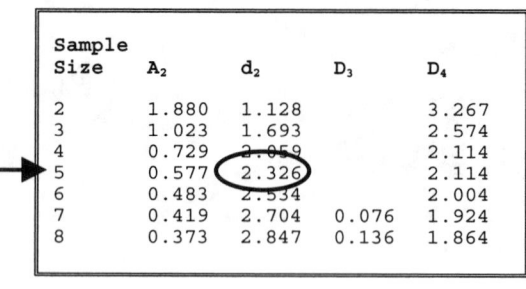

The standard deviation of the individuals using the range average method is .08052.

Notice the difference between the sum of squares method and range average is very small with the actual values of .08047 and .08052 respectively. Since the range average uses the part to part variation then this method should show the best or lowest value if there is group to group movement of the process. For our example, the two values are almost identical but this will not always be the case. Since the process is in control we did expect the two monitors to yield very similar numbers.

My rule of thumb is to always use the bigger of the two variability monitors. This will make the capability reflect the worst case scenario of having the most defects possible.

For our chocolate consistency problem, the rounded standard deviation of 0.0805 will be used.

To complete our variability monitor discussion we must cover our remaining variable control charts: the $\overline{X}$ and S and Individual charts.

OTHER CONTROL CHART METHODS

The following tables and formulas are used to compute the standard deviation of the individuals when $\overline{X}$ and S control chart is being used. The conversion factor changes because of the differing methods of monitoring variability.

$\overline{X}$ chart and the S chart

Subgroup Size	A_3	C_4	B_3	B_4
10	0.975	0.9727	0.284	1.716
11	0.927	0.9754	0.321	1.679
12	0.886	0.9776	0.354	1.646
13	0.850	0.9794	0.382	1.618
14	0.817	0.9810	0.406	1.594
15	0.789	0.9823	0.428	1.572
16	.763	.9835	.448	1.552
17	.739	.9845	.466	1.534
18	.718	.9854	.482	1.518
19	.698	.9862	.497	1.503
20	.680	.9869	.510	1.490
21	.663	.9876	.523	1.477
22	.647	.9882	.534	1.466
23	.633	.9887	.545	1.455
24	.619	.9892	.555	1.445
25	.606	.9896	.565	1.435

$\overline{X}$ & S Conversion Tables

This table is used to compute control limits and standard deviation of the individuals when the $\overline{X}$ and S charts are used.

C_4 is the conversion factor for determining standard deviation of the individuals. This will be used for capability studies and not for control limits.

The two methods of sum of squares or $\overline{S}$ are used to complete the standard deviation for $\overline{X}$ and S charts.

$$Std_{Ind} = \sqrt{\frac{\sum_{i=1}^{N} (\overline{\overline{X}} - X_i)^2}{N-1}}$$

or

$$Std_{Ind} = \frac{\overline{S}}{C_4}$$

The $\overline{X}$ and S chart uses a conversion factor of C_4 to approximate the standard deviation of the individuals.

Individual Charts

For the Individual charts another set of conversion tables is required. The following table uses a d_2 conversion to compute standard deviation of the individuals. The subgroup frequency will be the number of readings included in the moving range.

Subgroup Freq	E_2	d_2	D_3	D_4
2	2.660	1.128	-	3.267
3	1.772	1.693	-	2.574
4	1.457	2.059	-	2.282
5	1.290	2.326	-	2.114
6	1.184	2.534	-	2.004
7	1.109	2.704	0.076	1.924
8	1.054	2.847	0.136	1.864
9	1.010	2.970	0.184	1.816
10	0.975	3.078	0.223	1.777

Individual Chart Conversion Table

This table is used to compute control limits and standard deviation of the individuals when the Individual chart is used.

d_2 is the conversion factor for determining standard deviation of the individuals for use in a capability study. This constant is not used for the control charts.

Once again, two methods of calculation are available for the Individual charts.

$$Std_{Ind} = \sqrt{\frac{\sum_{i=1}^{N} (\bar{\bar{X}} - X_i)^2}{N-1}}$$

or

$$Std_{Ind} = \frac{\bar{R}}{d_2}$$

The d_2 conversion factor from the tables above is used to compute standard deviation.

Again, the required preliminary steps for capability studies are:

1. Calculate the standard deviation.
2. Determine the specifications.
3. Test for normality.

Since we have now covered the first steps, the stage is set to answer the question, "What are the specifications that will be used in the capability study?"

DETERMINING THE SPECIFICATIONS

Before a capability study can be prepared, a clear distinction between the customer's target and the specification must be established. This will allow us to separate what the customer wants from our abilities to achieve their desires.

Airline Example: Since airline travel is part of my regular duties, let's use my last trip from Greenville, South Carolina, to Denver, Colorado, as an example. Imagine sitting on the plane all set to take off when the pilot says that we are going not to Denver International Airport (DIA) but instead to somewhere around Denver. He goes on to explain that enroute he will make a decision as to where to land. He explains that to add a little spice to the flight, we may land at the old airport (Stapleton), or possibly at the Boulder, Colorado airport, or possibly at the original destination of Denver International.

Thankfully, this did not really happen, but think about the consequences of such behavior. Passengers would miss their connecting flights, rental agencies would not know where to leave their cars, and other people meeting the passengers would be at a complete loss as to where to find them. A better way must be developed.

Just as a pilot must file a clear flight plan and stick to it, we, too, must know where we're headed before we begin a capability study. Two issues must be addressed. What does the customer really want? What can and will the customer tolerate today?

What does the customer want? When a customer purchases our product, he normally has a specific purpose or use in mind. Therefore one of our biggest challenges is to assure that we always keep this purpose in mind.

TARGET

When we are traveling on an airline, our objective is to arrive in Denver, Colorado. When we go to the store for milk, we want one gallon of milk. When a half-inch hole is drilled, we want the hole to be exactly a half-inch.

For clarity of purpose, our target must be clearly identified. The target must be explicitly defined, and a value for the target must be established. This target value is a strategic decision. Some refer to the true target as the nominal value. The target simply defined is the value that the customer expects should be perfect.

The knowledge of the target or perfection is key to manufacturing. How can a plant, operation, or service ever achieve perfection if we do not know what perfect is? Worse yet, if we fail to communicate what perfect is, how can we ever expect to achieve perfection?

Most customers do not expect perfection, but for our capability study to be effective, a clear understanding of what perfection would be is important. Remember this is called the target. If this is what the customer wants, then what are specifications and tolerances?

What will the customer tolerate today? Tolerances are what the customer will tolerate today or how much leeway from the target will be tolerated today.

When the customer is describing his product, he communicates through tolerances and specifications. The customer has a specific item in mind. Tolerances are really the amount of **incompetence** that the customer will tolerate today. Using tolerances we can determine our specifications, but first, what are specifications?

SPECIFICATIONS

When we are analyzing a product, we must have a clear, objective way of assessing when the product is totally unacceptable. Generally this is done by specifications that may or may not be from the customer. A common specification misconception is that the customer defines the specification or tolerance. Most of the time, a product designer develops these criteria. We must continually evaluate how well our product is meeting the customer's intended use.

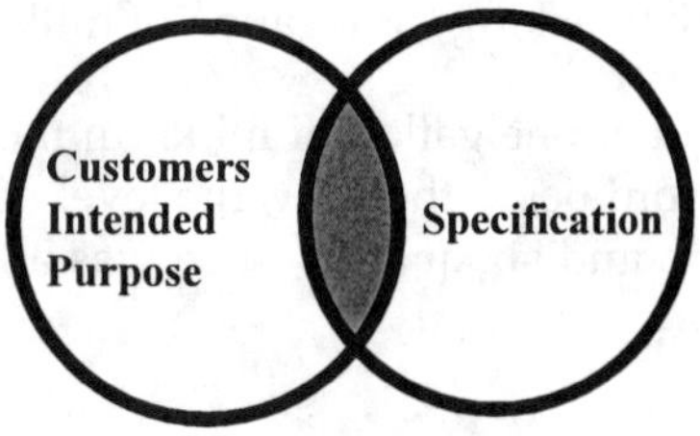

Many times, product specifications are a simulated test of when the product will not perform the customer's intended purpose. Care must be taken to assure a good overlap between the intended purpose and the specification. Frustrating consequences are caused for the customer and the supplier when we encounter the situation shown in the drawing on the left.

The previous drawing depicts the specifications no longer suiting the customer's intended purpose. Over time, we should not be surprised to find our customer's wants and needs changing. Nor should we be surprised that the specification no longer represents the customer's needs. We must always be vigilant to assure that our specifications represent what he needs and wants.

If we use the degree of incompetence to explain specifications, we should not be surprised to see the customer's expectation or target fixed. We should also not be surprised to see the specifications continually changing. The tolerances are continually changing and getting tighter to drive toward the real expectations of the target: perfection. As the tolerances get tighter, so do the specification limits or the spot where the product becomes unacceptable.

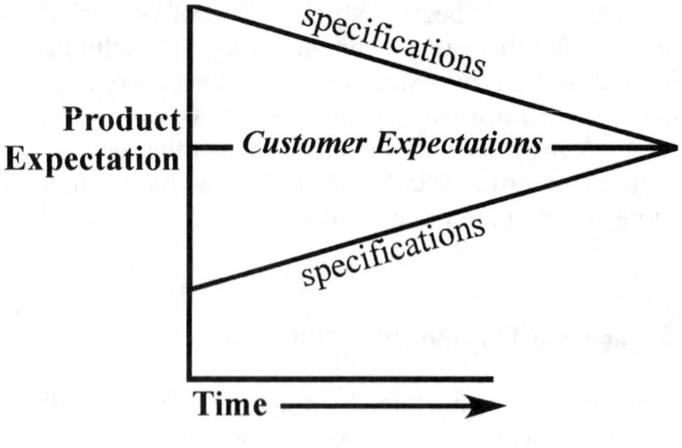

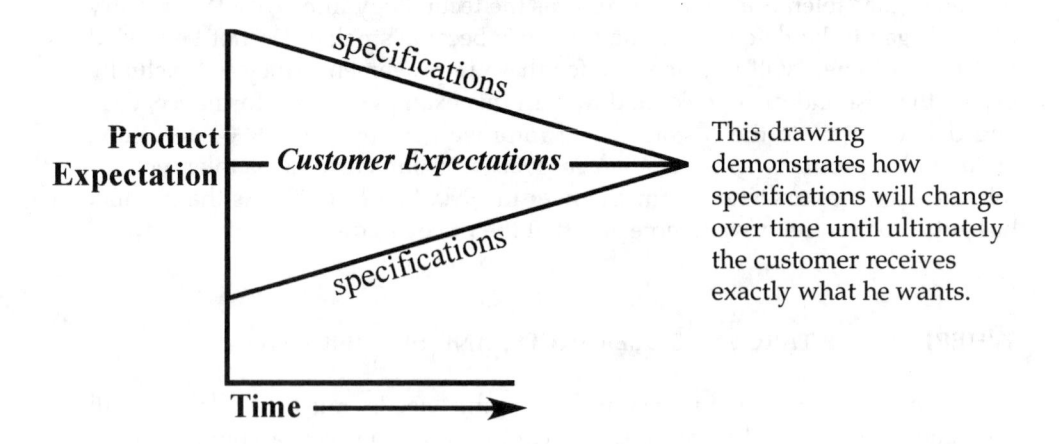

This drawing demonstrates how specifications will change over time until ultimately the customer receives exactly what he wants.

Both the target and the specifications must be defined by the strategic decision-makers. At no time should the tactician attempt to independently change these criteria. Any attempts for the tactician to take on the role of the strategist can lead to disaster.

To clarify the idea that tolerances and specifications will change, let's visit the grocery store to purchase a gallon of milk. Our milk buying

specifications might prompt us to ask for about 2 quarts to 1.5 gallons of something between buttermilk and water, rather than asking for a gallon of milk.

Properly established, the criteria should be a target of one gallon of milk. In the early 1900s when milk was obtained in the barn from Bessy the Cow, the level of incompetence was somewhere between two quarts and six quarts which was all Bessy had.

What Bessy could and would deliver dictated the amount of incompetence that was acceptable in 1900. Over the years the amount of incompetence that is tolerated (the "tolerance") will decrease as the technology improves. When dairy plants began to bottle our milk the tolerance became smaller. Do not be misled that the customers will pay us more for these improvements; they will actually expect the cost and price to come down. In this example, the performance, cost, and delivery time to the customer, will improve over time. In 1990 everything about dairy products is better than in 1900 and our customers' tolerance, or tolerance for incompetence, is much lower in 1990 than in 1900. As the product has gotten better (improved), note also that the price has dropped.

WHERE TO USE TARGETS, TOLERANCES, AND SPECIFICATIONS

How we communicate our requirements and needs must be clear to all associates, vendors, and customers. This communication is best accomplished by stating the true target value. With this number stated the amount of incompetence is expressed through the use of the plus and minus tolerances. Using our candy example, the target weight is 50 grams. The amount of incompetence that we will tolerate is plus or minus 5 grams.

This now leads us to the specification that will be used in our capability study. We add the plus tolerance to the target to compute the upper specification limit. The minus tolerance is subtracted from the target to compute the lower specification limit.

The following equations compute specifications:

Upper Specification Limit = Target + Tolerance

Lower Specification Limit = Target - Tolerance

The target and tolerances are used to communicate our requirements. The specification limits are used in the capability study. These specification limits are defined as the location where the product or process is unusable. The specification limits define where the product or process does not meet the minimum functional requirement. Specification limits must be defined for both product and process metrics. Values outside these limits are totally unacceptable.

OUR INCOMPETENCE DROPS AS THE FACILITY CHANGES

In 1996, with milk in plastic and cardboard containers at the grocery store, our level of incompetence has shrunk. The target is still one gallon, but now the specifications are almost exactly one gallon. Notice that over time, the incompetence index of the specifications will shrink. Also, this must be done without increasing the price.

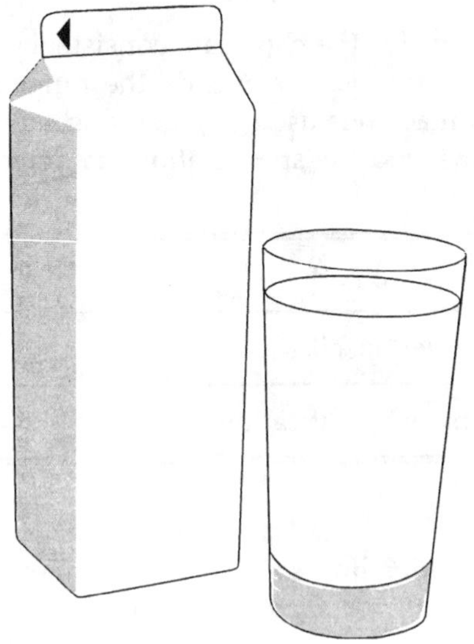

Over time we must move toward the target, or the consequences will be severe. For the grocery store example, we must close in on the one gallon or risk having to always provide more than the customer's expected amount. The option of giving more than a gallon in order to definitely provide a gallon destroys our cost dimension. Remember our definition of quality: performance, cost, and time

are of equal merit. Never allow one dimension to get out of balance with the other two dimensions.

CUSTOMER SPECIFICATIONS AND THE TARGET FOR OUR EXERCISE

Our strategic decision-makers have set the chocolate consistency. For our candy machine, the consistency target is .7. The amount of tolerance that we will tolerate is .2. From our prior specification equation, we can now compute the upper and lower specification limit:

Upper Specification Limit = Target + Tolerance

Upper Specification Limit = .7 + .2

Upper Specification Limit = .9

Lower Specification Limit = Target – Tolerance

Lower Specification Limit = .7-.2

Lower Specification Limit = .5

Our customer specifications for the chocolate consistency are .5 on the low side and .9 on the high side. Any cluster outside the range of .5 to .9 is declared totally unacceptable. All machines used to make this candy must use the target for setting up the machine, and the specifications to determine when the metric is totally unacceptable.

Target	.7
Upper Specification	.9
Lower Specification	.5

The target and the specification limits are set by management to a target of .7, an upper specification limit of .9, and a lower limit of .5.

Specifications are arbitrary requirements by our customers or management. They are a measurement attempting to assess the usability of our product. Specification limits are defined as the points at which the product will not be useable by the customer. Simply having a product that meets the specifications is not a guarantee of a satisfied customer.

Specifications can be expressed as product that is defective only above a certain point, only below a certain point, or outside two measurement points. We may only be concerned with defects on the low side like providing a candy that is too

light. We may also be concerned only with defects on the high side like an overdose of medicine. Finally, we may be concerned with both high and low defects, like the drilling of a hole (a hole that is too big **or** too small will be unusable.)

In summary, the following define capability terminology. The use of clear and precise terms is the key to perfect communication which will lead us to a successful operation.

Target	Perfect!
Tolerances	The amount of incompetence we will tolerate today.
Specification Limit	The calculated limits where the part no longer meets the minimum functional requirement today. Totally unacceptable!

When we are calculating the capability (percent defective), we use the following test based on whether we are testing on one side only or on both sides:

Specification	Capability Test
Product above a certain point	Greater than (upper specification limit)
Product below a certain point	Less than (lower specification limit)
Product outside 2 points	Two tails (outside the specification limits)

A clear understanding of our capability terms of target, tolerance, and specifications is crucial to an accurate capability study.

Product and Process Capability

The typical capability discussion revolves around assessing whether the product will meet the customer's expectations. Many people fail to understand the first Principle of Process Management. The first Principle is stated below:

FIRST PRINCIPLE OF PROCESS MANAGEMENT

A fundamental understanding of BOTH the product and process is essential to improvement. Both the product and the process must be described and understood individually and separately. The underlying component for improving the product is the process.

The last sentence states that to improve the product, we must improve the process. Focusing all of our attention on the product is a recipe for no improvement. Complete capability studies call for all process metrics to be assessed, as well as all product metrics.

Always do capability studies on all product and process metrics for a complete assessment.

Once again, the required preliminary steps for a capability study are:

1. Calculate the standard deviation.
2. Determine the specifications.
3. Test for normality.

Now we must answer the last question, "Is the data normally distributed for the capability study?"

TESTING FOR THE NORMAL DISTRIBUTION

Why is normality important? By having a normal distribution, a predefined set of probabilities can be used to compute the percent of values falling outside our upper and lower specifications. Not having a normal distribution is not disastrous but requires more work to determine the projected distribution. Most times I find that when proper groups are formed and the process is in control, the normal distribution does work well for projections. Many times the normal distribution comes naturally when the machine runs correctly and consistently.

How will we test for normality? Since the normal is not forced for capability studies and strategic decisions, a normality test must be used. There are several means of assessing the fit of our data to a normal distribution. One test, which was covered in **Chapter One,** is the use of a graph of the actual values presented as a bar chart or histogram. This is compared to a perfect normal distribution for our data's average and standard deviation. This test requires some objective decisions and some margin for debate between two individuals.

A second option is to test for the distribution through quantitative means like chi-square or K-S goodness of fit tests. These quantitative means are outside the scope of this book.

The distribution of the individual data must be a normal distribution in order to do a classic capability study. For a complete explanation of the preparation of the histogram, refer to **Chapter One.**

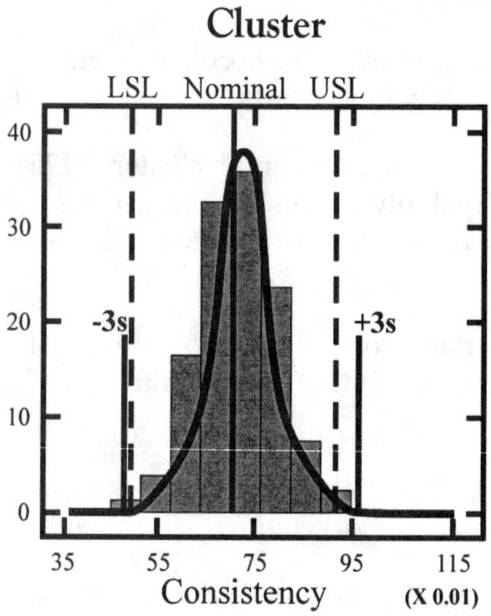

The graph to the left has been prepared so that we can determine if the chocolate consistency meets the criteria of the normal distribution. Passing this test will allow us to make predictions of the percentage defective to be expected from this machine in the future.

The criterion to test for normality was also covered in **Chapter One.** To review, most of the values are clustered around the average; as we move farther from the average, fewer values are observed. Finally the shape of the curve above the average is a mirror image of the curve below the average. Passing this criteria will allow us to use the predictions from the normal distribution table.

We can see that the chocolate candy consistency measurements from this machine are a normal distribution.

Begin analysis of a capability study only after determining normality. If the process tests non-normal, more advanced techniques must be applied to determine the proper fit of its distribution and probabilities. The fitted distribution's probability must then be used for projections.

The normal probabilities were covered in **Chapter One**. The calculation we learned there will be used to compute the Z values and, in turn, obtain the probability for projection. The following equation will now be used for our chocolate consistency example.

$$Z = \left| \frac{X_{Ave} - X_i}{Std} \right|$$

RECAP OF OUR PRELIMINARIES

The preliminary work for the candy exercise capability study is repeated below:

1. *All product and process metrics are run correctly and consistently.* The chocolate machine product and process metrics are run correctly and consistently.

2. *The product and process is in a state of statistical control.* The chocolate machine is in a state of statistical control as shown by its control charts.

3. *Determine which data points to include*: 25 sets of five candy clusters (125 individual clusters) will be used for our capability study. We can use these 25 sets, because the product and process is demonstrating a state of statistical control.

4. *Calculate standard deviation.* The standard deviation of the 125 individual chocolate candy clusters is .0805. This value was computed using the sum of squares method.

5. *Determine the Specifications.* The following define the customer's criteria: upper specification of .9, lower specification of .5, a target of .7.

6. *Test for normality.* From our view of the histogram, the data is declared to be a normal distribution.

7. Since we have now covered all the preliminaries, we are ready to begin the detail work of *computing the capability study* using the information that we have compiled.

We have built the correct and consistent components of our knowledge base-camp. We are now ready to begin our capability study.

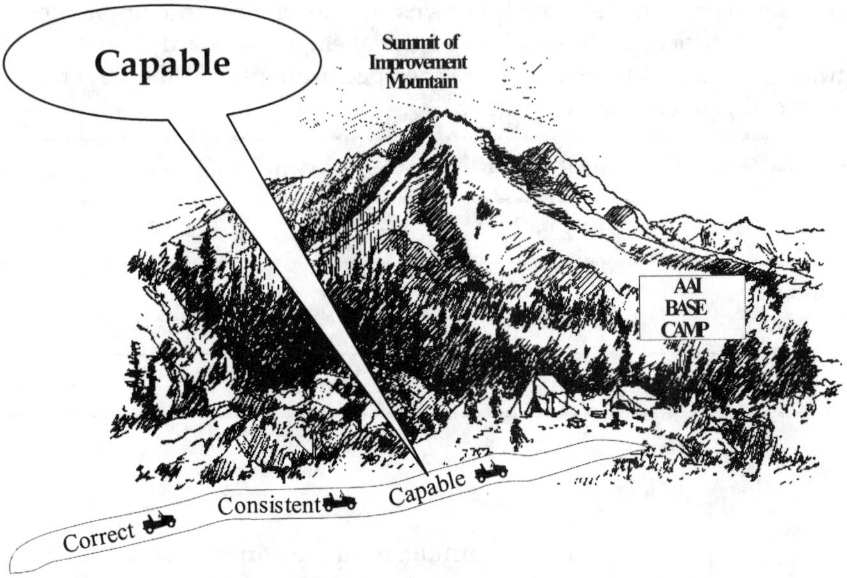

CALCULATION OF DEFECTS

The machine's capability can be calculated. We are then ready to compare the machine's knowns to the customer's knowns. The machine's knowns are defined through our statistical understanding of the average, standard deviation, and histogram. The customer's knowns are the specifications and the target. These values are compared and shown below:

What we know about our Process		What we know about our Customer	
Average	.7225	Lower Specification	.5
Standard Deviation	.0805	Upper Specification	.9
Distribution	Normal	Target	.7

$$Z = \left| \frac{X_{Ave} - X_i}{Std} \right|$$

Our base formula from the normal table is shown to the left. Using standard SPC notation, the mean, X_{Ave}, is now shown as $\bar{\bar{X}}$.

$$Z = \left| \frac{\bar{\bar{X}} - X_i}{Std_{Ind}} \right|$$

Solving the equation algebraically for Z will tell us, in units of standard deviation of the individuals, the distance away from the central point (i.e. three standard deviations). Taking our general formula for Z, we can insert the specification limits to arrive at the capability Z:

$$Z_{USL} = \left| \frac{\bar{\bar{X}} \text{ - Upper Specification Limit}}{Std_{Ind}} \right|$$

Since the Z is the absolute value of the distance (always a positive), then we can reverse the position of the specification limit with no impact on the results. This leaves us with the following equation for the lower specification limit:

$$Z_{LSL} = \left| \frac{\bar{\bar{X}} \text{ - Lower Specification Limit}}{Std_{Ind}} \right|$$

Using our normal distribution table in the **Appendix**, we can determine the percentage of failure or defects above the upper specification and below the lower specification.

To shorten our expressions, the upper specification will be written X_{USL} and the lower specification limit is X_{LSL}. Our final equations will read:

$$Z_{USL} = \left| \frac{\bar{\bar{X}} - X_{USL}}{Std_{Ind}} \right|$$

and

$$Z_{LSL} = \left| \frac{\bar{\bar{X}} - X_{LSL}}{Std_{Ind}} \right|$$

Moving back to our candy machine problem, we can now compute the candy machine's capability.

CAPABILITY ANALYSIS EXAMPLE

The following example provides the candy machine capability study for the upper specification limit. The information to be gleaned from this study is vital to improvement of the process. This provides the base-camp of where we are to make our improvement steps. Improvement requires a clear picture of what a machine's capability is.

What does the upper specification capability mean? Capability is the percent of chocolate clusters that will likely be above the upper specification limit. Those clusters above the limit are then identified as defective; the clusters are not acceptable to our customers. This capability uses our consistent samples (in control) to predict the expected number of future occurrences outside of the specification limits.

UPPER SPECIFICATION CAPABILITY EXAMPLE

Now we can return to our consistent chocolate machine and step through the capability calculations.

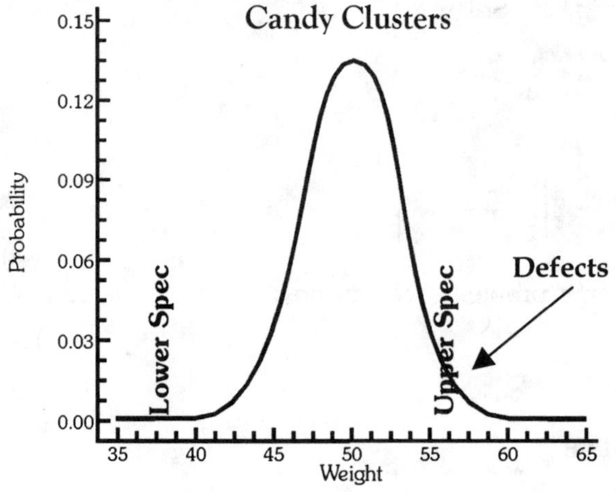

Capability

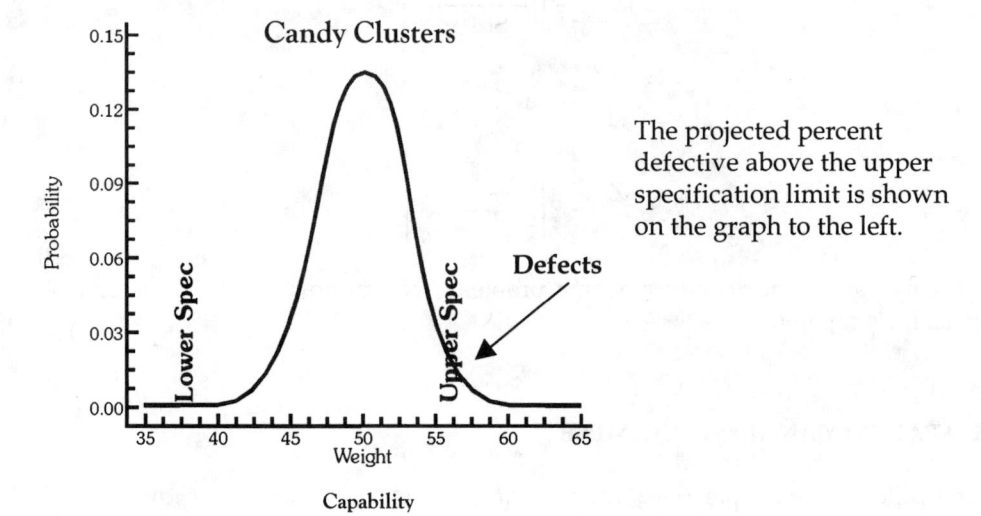

The projected percent defective above the upper specification limit is shown on the graph to the left.

First our formula from the normal table derivation is brought forward. The general formula has been adjusted to include upper specification limits (X_{USL}).

$$Z_{USL} = \left| \frac{\bar{\bar{X}} - X_{USL}}{Std_{Ind}} \right|$$

Next the process values of the average (.7225) and the standard deviation of the individuals (.0805) are inserted in the equation.

$$= \left| \frac{.7225 - X_{USL}}{.0805} \right|$$

Now the customer's upper specification limit (.9) is inserted in the equation.

$$= \left| \frac{.7225 - .9}{.0805} \right|$$

Now the equation is solved to compute our Z value for the upper specification limit.

$$= \left| \frac{.1775}{.0805} \right|$$

$$= 2.20$$

By using the Z table in the **Appendix**, the percent out of specification can be projected. This percent defective above the upper specification limit is 1.39% for the Z_{USL} of 2.20:

$$\% \ OUT_{USL} = 1.39\%$$

The 1.39% is the projected percent defective that we would expect to be above the upper specification limit. When our number of observations is small, the actual percent defective in the sample may be different from the projection. As the sample size increases, the projected and actual percentages will become closer and closer and ultimately reach equality.

LOWER SPECIFICATION CAPABILITY EXAMPLE

Having completed the upper specification for capability, now let's complete our study stepping through our example with the lower specification limits.

The projected percentage defective below the lower specification limit is shown in the graph below:

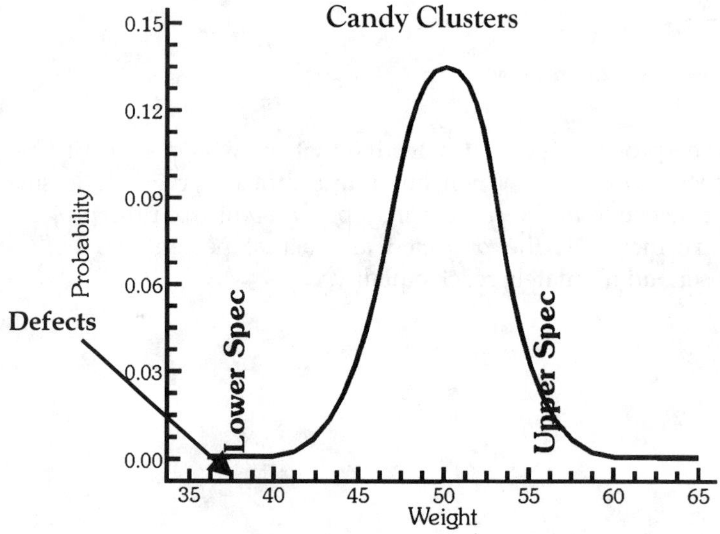

Now repeating the lower specification formula as done with the upper specification limit, our formula from the normal table derivation is brought forward.

$$Z_{LSL} = \left| \frac{\bar{\bar{X}} - X_{LSL}}{Std_{Ind}} \right|$$

Next the process values of the average (.7225) and the standard deviation of the individuals (.0805) are inserted in the equation.

$$= \left| \frac{.7225 - X_{LSL}}{.0805} \right|$$

Now from the customer's requirement the lower specification (.5) is inserted in the equation.

$$= \left| \frac{.7225 - .5}{.0805} \right|$$

Now the equation is solved to compute our Z value for the upper specification limit.

$$= \left| \frac{.2225}{.0805} \right|$$

$$= 2.76$$

By using the Z table in the **Appendix**, the percent out of specification can be calculated.

$$\% \, OUT_{LSL} = .29\%$$

The projected percent defective below the lower specification limits is .29% based on the Z_{LSL} of 2.76. The percentage defective below the lower specification limit and above the upper specification limit must be totaled to arrive at the total percentage defective projected for this machine.

TOTAL OUT OF SPECIFICATION

By adding the upper and lower specification percentages, the total percentage can be calculated. For this candy machine, the total percentage defective is 1.64%.

$$\% \, OUT_{Total} = \% \, OUT_{USL} + \% \, OUT_{LSL}$$

$$= 1.39\% + .29\%$$

$$= 1.68\%$$

CENTERING DISTRIBUTION

In **Chapter One**, the characteristics of a normal distribution were defined. The symmetrical nature of the normal provides an opportunity for improvement. Since the curve's slope is steep, if one of the specification limits is closer to the center than the other, the closer specification limit will have a significantly larger percentage defective. Centering or keeping both specifications equidistant from the average can yield a reduced total percentage defective.

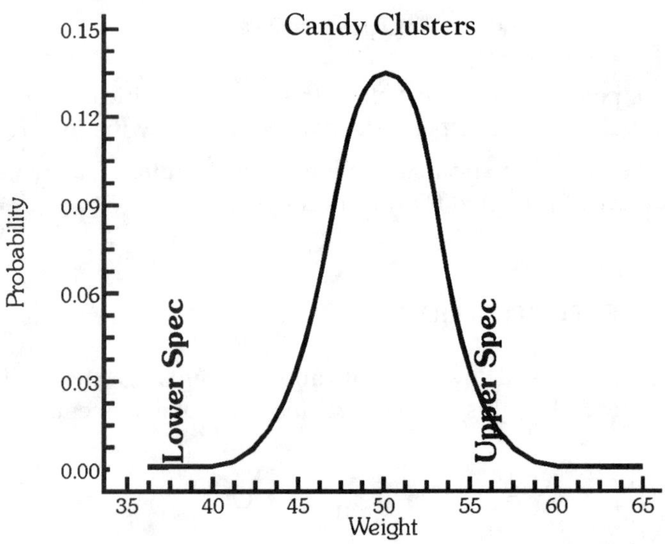

All specification limits are not of equal importance. When drilling a hole, an undersized hole can be reworked and corrected. An oversize hole cannot be reworked and creates scrap. Thus, for some situations we may strategically choose to stay away from the most costly specification and not optimize our process. This is why the knowledge of the target is crucial to the capability study. The target knowledge allows us to always strive for perfection.

Since our candy machine has been identified to be a normal distribution, and the target is in the center of the specification limits, centering can reduce the percent total defective.

By changing the central point of the process in the direction away from the greatest errors, we can reduce the overall percentage error. By increasing the lowest specification defect percentage, a greater reduction of the greater specification defect percentage will be achieved. Not all processes can be

adjusted, but when possible, saving and improvement are possible by centering the metric. When we adjust the metric center, we must be alert that this does not impact variability or any other product or process metric.

Remember, use the target to set the context of the centering effort. The target is always an overriding criteria when a centering effort is undertaken. Strategic decision-makers must assume the responsibility for deviating from the target value.

To calculate the optimum center point (average), the following calculation should be used. This optimum center is where the process average falls in the middle of the upper and lower specification limits. This only applies if the target is in the center of the specification limits. This center point is the spot to attempt to move the process' average if this is possible.

$$Center_{Opt} = \frac{X_{USL} + X_{LSL}}{2}$$

To calculate the percent out of specification when the process is centered, use the following general Z equation and normal tables.

$$Z = \frac{\bar{\bar{X}} - X_{USL}}{Std_{Ind}}$$

Now we insert $\bar{\bar{X}}_{Opt}$ (the optimum average or target designated) into this equation to yield the following:

$$Z_{Opt} = \frac{X_{Opt} - X_{USL}}{Std_{Ind}}$$

Since both of the customer specifications are of equal importance and cost, what would be the optimum average for setting up the process?

CANDY MACHINE CENTERING EXAMPLE

Moving back to our chocolate machine, let's see how centering will improve our performance. The following is an example of how to determine the optimum mean for lowest total out of specification.

$$X_{Opt} = \frac{X_{USL} + X_{LSL}}{2}$$

The customer upper (.9) and lower (.5) specifications are inserted in the equation.

$$\overline{\overline{X}}_{Opt} = \frac{.9 + .5}{2}$$

$$= \frac{1.4}{2}$$

This equation is then solved to yield an optimum process average of .7 chocolate consistency.

$$\overline{\overline{X}}_{Opt} = .7$$

Now with this new optimum process average, our percent defective can be improved. Let's recompute our chocolate candy optimum average percentage defective and see the impact of this optimization.

$$Z_{Opt} = \left| \frac{\overline{\overline{X}}_{Opt} - X_{USL}}{Std_{Ind}} \right|$$

Now we can insert the process optimum average of .7 and the process standard deviation of .0805. The process standard deviation must be tested to assure that a change in the process average will not impact variability. For our example we are assuming that we have not impacted our variability.

$$= \left| \frac{.7 - X_{USL}}{.0805} \right|$$

Next we insert the upper specification limit of .9.

$$= \left| \frac{.7 - .9}{.0805} \right|$$

$$= 2.48$$

By using the Z table in the **Appendix**, the percent out of specification for one of the specification limits can be calculated as follows:

$$\text{Percent out of Specification}_{Optimum} = .66\%$$

The total out of specification can be calculated as follows because the symmetrical characteristics of the normal distribution makes both specifications equally distant from the average and having the same percent defective.

$$\text{Percent out of Specification}_{\text{Optimum}} = \text{USL\%} + \text{LSL\%}$$

$$= .66\% + .66\%$$

$$= 1.32\%$$

If the process can be adjusted to an average of .7, then our total defect rate is 1.32%.

ARE THESE OPTIMIZATION SAVINGS WORTHWHILE

Now we can compare the original defective rate to the new optimum defective rate. The following equation allows us to compute the percent savings.

$$\%\ \text{Savings} = \%\ \text{OUT}_{\text{Total}} - \%\ \text{OUT}_{\text{Total Optimum}}$$

The original percent defective is 1.68% and the optimum percent defective is 1.3%. These percent defectives can be inserted in our equation and the savings can be calculated.

$$\%\ \text{Savings} = \%\ \text{OUT}_{\text{Total}} - \%\ \text{OUT}_{\text{Total Optimum}}$$

$$= 1.68\% - 1.32\%$$

$$= .36\%$$

When the equation is solved a .36% saving can be obtained.

$$\%\ \text{Savings} = .36\%$$

In a high volume manufacturing facility these savings, though small, when spread over time and for all machines, can lead to astronomical savings in the quality of performance, cost, and time.

Let's look at other measures and ways of monitoring the idea of percent defects. These other measures are called capability indices and they are all based on the idea of percent defective.

CAPABILITY INDICES

Capability indices are tools to provide a monitor of capability in one package. These indices, when used correctly, can be an effective strategic tool.

All capability indices assume that the process and product are consistent and in control. No capability index should ever be published on a machine that has not demonstrated it is in control. Capability indices were intended for monitoring the capability of one particular machine. Remember, grouping still applies to capability and capability indices.

THE CONCEPT OF CAPABILITY INDICES

Many times management prefers to see an index that gives an indication of how well things are performing. The CPK is an example of an index that indicates how well our quality is performing. CPK is predicated on the assumption that the process is a normal distribution and that the process and product metrics are in a state of statistical control for the machine under study.

Since the normal distribution is the base for our capability indices, let's review the normal and its associated Z values. A 16% defective can be stated in another way by using a Z of one. A 16% is exactly the same as saying a Z of one. In like manner, a Z of two is the same as saying we have a 2.3% defective. A Z of three is the same as saying we have a .1% defective. The examples can go on and on. The percentage and Z are referring to the same thing. From the normal distribution we can find the Z values and percentage information.

Z	%
1	16%
2	2.3%
3	.1%
4	.003%

As the Z value goes up, the percentage goes down. For a machine, the lower the percentage the better the machine's quality performance. Stating this same idea with Z rather than the percentage, it would read: the higher the Z, the better the machine's performance.

As the Z value goes down, the percentage goes up. For a machine, the higher the percentage the worse the machine's quality performance. Stating this same idea with Z rather than the percentage reads: the lower the Z, the worse the machine's performance.

Most of our capability indices want to reflect the worst case performance for the machine under study. Our first index is called CPK.

How CPK works

The CPK Index is the indicator of the worst case specification and is calculated according to percentage defective. This ratio is the Z for the worst case percentage defective compared to a defined value of three. The worst case between the upper and lower specification limit is the specification limit percentage that is higher. The maximum percent defective of the upper or lower specification is the worst case. This could be stated as the following:

Maximum (percent defective of the lower specification, percent defective of the upper specification)

Whichever specification has the highest percent defect is the "worst case." This worst case is then used in the index calculation.

An alternate way to state the worst case is with Z yielding the lowest specification limit result. Thus, we are trying to determine the specification limit with the smallest Z. This can be converted into the equation that follows:

$$\text{Minimum}(Z_{USL}, Z_{LSL})$$

This formula using Z gives us the same results as the worst case percentage.

This can now be converted into a ratio where the minimum Z is divided by three. This ratio is called CPK.

$$CPK = \frac{\text{Minimum}(Z_{LSL}, Z_{USL})}{3}$$

This equation can then be simplified to reflect the Z_{Min} that is the worst case percentage defective of the two specification limits. Z_{Min} is simply another way of writing (Z_{USL}, Z_{LSL}). This equation is shown below:

$$CPK = \frac{Z_{Min}}{3}$$

A CPK value of one (1) indicates the worst specification equates to the Z score of 3.0, or a .1% defective rate. A CPK value of 1.33 is typically referred to as a world class operation. The CPK of 1.33 equates to a Z of four and a .0032% defective rate. A CPK value of 2.00 is called the six sigma value. The bigger the CPK the better the process is functioning when performance is the only concern. Care must be taken that all indices are kept in context and never used as a standalone.

CANDY MACHINE CPK INDEX EXAMPLE

The machine's capability was calculated and we can compute the machine's CPK from our initial capability study. The initial capability used the following known values for the process and the customer requirements. These are shown below:

What we know about our process		What we know about our customer	
Average	.7225	Lower Specification	.5
Standard Deviation	.0805	Upper Specification	.9
Distribution	Normal	Target	.7

From the capability example we have been using let's analyze the capability of this process. The low specification limit has a capability of .29% defective and a corresponding Z of 2.76. The upper specification limit has a capability of 1.39% defective with a corresponding Z of 2.20. The table below summarizes the capability data from which the CPK will be computed:

	USL	LSL
Z	2.20	2.76
Percent Defective	1.39%	.29%

Note, our efforts are to show the worst case percentage defective for this machine. The worst case is the higher percentage or the lower Z value. The minimum Z value or the highest percentage out of specification is the upper specification limit percentage of 1.39% or Z = 2.20.

To calculate the CPK for our example, we use the following equation:

$$CPK = \frac{\text{Minimum}\,(Z_{USL}, Z_{LSL})}{3}$$

or

$$CPK = \frac{Z_{Min}}{3}$$

The upper specification Z of 2.20 and the lower specification Z of 2.76 are inserted in the equation.

$$CPK = \frac{\text{Minimum}\,(2.20, 2.76)}{3}$$

Now the equation is solved to yield the following results:

$$CPK = \frac{2.20}{3}$$

$$= .73$$

The CPK for this machine is .73. The bigger the CPK, the better the machine's performance. When all other things are equal for two machines, the machine with the larger CPK is the better performer.

In business, CPK values of 1.33 for a machine are defined as a "world class" manufacturing machine. Being able to factually state that a machine is world class has become a major milestone for most companies.

Remember, CPK is the statement of how a machine performs. When the CPK is below our stated goal (i.e. world class CPK=1.33), the strategic decision-makers must get involved. There is no "somehow" or "someway" for the tactician to "wish" the machine better. The strategic decision-makers must come up with the method, tools, and resources to achieve the goal.

Never use a capability study without a clear understanding of all the components of Statistical Process Control (statistical monitors, control charts, and a complete capability study). The simplistic use of one monitor has led many down the slippery slope to the depths of Quality Hell. Remember to keep a balanced perspective of the three components of quality: performance, cost, and time.

MANAGEMENT INDICATORS

The previous capability index requires some knowledge of statistics. A preferable means of noting the capability -- one that everyone can relate to and understand -- follows. First we must revisit our complete definition of quality which includes performance, cost, and time. Then we will build an index around the complete definition.

From our prior tactical and strategic steps, we have a set of known values. The control chart has validated that the process is consistent and predictable. The capability study has projected the percent product out of specification. Any manufacturing facility will know the volume of parts produced per day and the unit cost. Now all these pieces of information can be compiled to compute one cost of quality measure. With this cost of quality, our strategic decision-makers can make informed decisions to take advantage of the opportunities from our quality. This quality cost becomes a quality opportunity cost.

MANAGEMENT QUALITY OPPORTUNITY COST FORMULA

The quality opportunity cost is derived by first computing the percentage of defects, then multiplying by the total units produced per day. This calculation yields a total number of defects for the day. The total defects per day are then multiplied by the cost per unit. The result is the cost of defects per day.

Quality Opportunity Cost = Percent Defect * Units Produced * Cost/unit

We can use the above variables to calculate the total cost of our quality. With this information, management can make strategic decisions as to where to use our limited resources for the most good.

With the quality opportunity cost the strategic decisions of directing our limited resources can be made. The assessment of all machines' quality cost would allow the proper allocation of our resources (time, people, and funds). Next, each machine can be analyzed for maintenance refurbishing, or replacement with a constant view of the return on the investment. The quality opportunity cost provides the factual and logical means of making proper strategic decisions.

MANAGEMENT INDEX EXAMPLE

The following are the results of our prior steps in the SPC process. The candy machine is running consistently or in a state of statistical control. The percentage defective is 1.64% out of 100,000 units produced on this machine every day. The cost of every chocolate candy cluster is $.20 per unit.

Knowns Restated:

Process is in control

Percent Defective...1.64%

Production per day...100,000 units

Cost per Unit...$.20

With this information in hand, let's compute our candy example's production cost and quality opportunity cost.

Production Cost

The product cost for this one candy machine is the unit cost multiplied by the units produced. For our example, the unit cost is $.20 and the units produced are 100,000 per day for this candy machine. This yields a cost of $20,000 per day for this machine to make 100,000 chocolate candy clusters.

Cost of Quality calculations for our candy example:

The formulas for cost of quality are now inserted.

(Percent defective) (Production) (Cost per Unit)

Now the candy machine's percent defect of 1.64%, production of 100,000 units per day, and $.20 per chocolate-peanut cluster are inserted in the formula.

(1.64 %) (100,000 per day) ($.20 per unit)

The formula is then solved to yield a $328 daily quality cost.

$328/day

Opportunity Cost Interpretation

The $328 daily opportunity cost must be weighed against the total cost of $20,000 to keep the opportunity cost in perspective. Now we have a grasp of the magnitude of the potential return from any improvement investments.

These values can be used for strategic decisions as to the potential viability of any project. As an example, if our engineers tell us to eliminate the $328, an enhancement costing $2,000,000 might be strategically rejected. A minor $10 adjustment, saving half of the $328 opportunity cost, might be accepted.

Now our strategic decision-makers can function with clean, sound information and knowledge. Now let's do an exercise.

SAMPLE PROBLEM – CAPABILITY

The chocolate-peanut cluster components' cost per gram is $.005. With this information, we can begin to analyze our strategic options. In our original proposal, the cost is based on a cluster that weighs at least 45 grams.

For this example, we are only concerned with protecting the customer from having light candy. The 45 gram weight thus becomes our only specification. The lower specification limit is 45 grams.

By multiplying the weight of 45 grams times a component cost of $.005/gram, the anticipated cost of a cluster is $.225. For an hour's run, the cost of 3000 candies would be 3000 times $.225/candy equaling $675.

The candy facility is being run correctly and consistently as demonstrated by a control chart.

The following four situations are provided for us to investigate. Imagine that this is your candy company. Compute the capability of each and make a recommendation as to the best situation and why. You will find an analysis in the **Appendix**.

Situations	1	2	3	4
Is the Process In Control?	Yes	Yes	Yes	Yes
Average Weight	50gm	52gm	47gm	50gm
Standard Deviation of Weight	1.0gm	1.0gm	1.0gm	2.0gm
Distribution of Weight?	Normal	Normal	Normal	Normal

CHAPTER SUMMARY

The capability study is the strategic arm of SPC. This tool allows the strategic decision-maker to understand whether the facility is able to produce the customer's product. Once the capability is established for a machine, any changes that are detected by the tactical control chart can be assessed for impact on the customer.

The capability study must be used only in its total context of Statistical Process Control where control is handled by the tactical tool of the control chart. Before we do a capability study, the process must be in a state of statistical control.

As we stated at the beginning of this book, one of the biggest problems facing statistics, analysis, and the quality profession is a poor understanding of the statistical vocabulary. The following terms and their definitions are key to capability. These definitions must be followed religiously.

Target	Perfect!
Tolerances	The amount of incompetence we will tolerate today.
Specification Limit	The calculated limits where the part does not meet the minimum functional requirement today. Totally unacceptable!

We must now keep these terms clear and precise.

THE PROCESS CONTROL METHOD

The overall objective of Statistical Process Control (SPC) methods is to prevent product or performance defects.

How many defects should we tolerate? The aim of process control is to prevent defective product. That requires us to predict the percentage of defects from the controlled process. In turn, this requires that we know about the distribution of values from the process itself. Armed with this knowledge we are prepared to improve to our ultimate objective.

Our data used by the control charts is the averages of samples drawn from the process for the tactical purpose of running the facility - not the process values themselves. We can use the original sample data that was used to compute the averages for our control chart to estimate the location and spread of the process distribution, and thus the proportion of product that falls outside of the customer's specifications. To this end, we must analyze the values with strategic tools called prediction limits that use the individual readings.

The capability study uses the strategic set of calculations called prediction limits. The following summarizes the two complete sets of books available, and which decision-making process will use the appropriate analysis set of books. Strategic decisions use prediction intervals while tactical decisions use confidence intervals.

	Tactical	**Strategic**
	Operation ↓ Detect Change ↓ Averages	Management/Customers/Sales ↓ Assess Capability ↓ Individuals
Central Tendency	$Ave_{Ave} = Ave_{Ind}$	
Variability	Std_{Ave}	Std_{Ind}
	$Std_{Ave} = \frac{Std_{Ind}}{\sqrt{N}}$ Where N = subgroup size	
Distribution	Central Limit Theorem Normalizes Data	Histogram
	Confidence Intervals $X_i = X_{Ave} \pm Z*\frac{Std_{Ind}}{\sqrt{N}}$	**Prediction Intervals** $X_i = X_{Ave} \pm Z*Std_{Ind}$

For this chapter on capability studies, the prediction limits and the standard deviation of the individuals are used.

A capability study provides management with a tool to assess the ability of a machine to make what the customer wants. This same tool is used to assess the impact all changes have on the customer.

Remember, the capability study assumes that all product and process metrics are in a state of statistical control.

Finally, with the steps of correctly and consistently run machines or processes we now have to assess how well the product we make meets the customers' expectations. This is our third base-camp milestone.

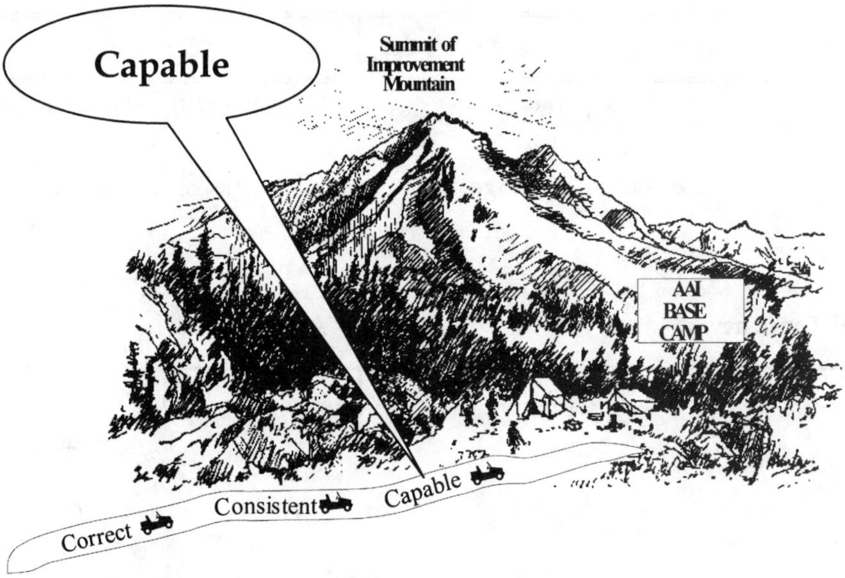

Our strategic and tactical correctness has been established. Each machine's consistency and capability are computed using Statistical Process Control (SPC). Now with all the components of our base-camp built, we must make all three (correct, consistent, and capable) work together. With our base-camp built we are truly ready for continuous improvement.

Concluding Thoughts:

Tactics and Strategy Working Together

Our definition of quality is extremely broad and encompassing. According to that definition, quality is comprised of three components: performance, cost, and time. Our research, analysis, and decisions must support our goal of delighting our customer (performance), while reducing our cost (cost), and providing our product to our customers the moment they want it (time). We must view this goal as a never-ending journey that continues to improve all three components because no one component is more important than the others. All three must be viewed with equal importance and balance. This balance requires the business genius of the manager of the future.

Monitoring a Continuous Process

Conflicting Objectives

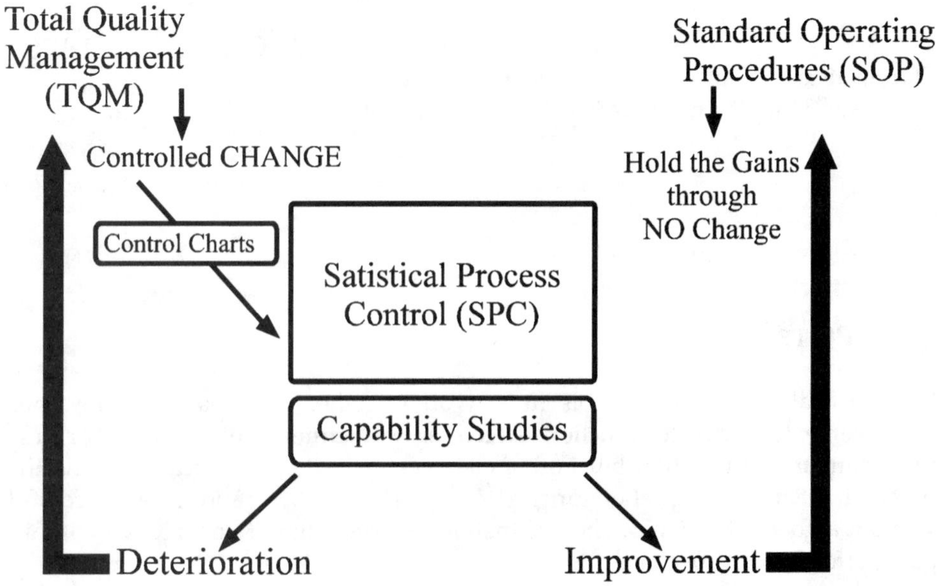

Concluding Thoughts

The improvement model and statistical process control work together to drive improvement. The improvement model that was covered in the **Introduction,** and the SPC tools allow us to improve our continuous operation.

Do you remember Barney Fife in the classic television program *The Andy Griffith Show*? He always told Sheriff Taylor that they had to "nip it, nip it, nip it in the bud" whenever they encountered a problem. SPC and the improvement model teach us that we must nip "it" in the bud! We must find every small problem and correct it before it becomes a big problem. We must also find every improvement and put it into the standard operating procedure.

Control charts and capability studies are the two tools of SPC. When used correctly, they can and will form a team that will keep us on the straight and narrow path to the peak of Improvement Mountain.

Our strategic tool of capability studies will allow the strategic decision-makers to have the information to make effective decisions. These decisions will assure that we provide the best facility to make what the customer wants. The best possible facility means considering performance, cost, and time.

Our tactical tool of control charts will allow us to understand that the machine is running consistently.

THE SPC TEAM

Both tactical and strategic tools must work together as a team to allow our improvement model to function effectively. Neither tool is more or less important than the other, but both must work together as a team just as the baseball pitcher and catcher form a team. The pitcher cannot be successful without a good, effective catcher. Capability studies cannot be effective without good, effective control charts.

PROCESS IMPROVEMENT IS AN ITERATIVE PROCEDURE

Recalculating control limits: Once the process has been determined to be "in control," the control limits should be locked. When a process change has been determined and is desired or permanent, recalculation of the control limits is required. The new control limits must be based on the subgroups that are included in the change.

Once the SPC methodology is in place, a continuous surveillance of the control charts is required. The following is reflective of an alarm having been detected and when an alarm is detected, the following steps are required:

- **Investigate to determine the reason (cause) for the alarm.** This investigation is a tactical duty for the operational staff.

- **Determine the capability.** Prepare a capability study to determine the impact (deterioration or improvement) on the process. The assessment of the change's impact is a strategic effort accomplished by the management staff.

- **Take action**. Develop and implement an action plan to deal with the cause. Remember that we are acting on the cause not the alarm. The action plan will be determined by the reason why the change occurred and the impact of the change on the customer. The action is a joint responsibility of the tactical and strategic team. Both management and operations must work in harmony to develop the best plan of action. This action is a joint decision and not an automatic adjustment.

Please take special note that an out of control condition does not imply bad product. Out of control is intended to draw our attention so that we can investigate for the cause. We may find the alarm has highlighted an improvement.

If the change is permanent, the control limits and capability study must both be recalculated and kept in synchronization. This is true no matter whether the change creates improvement or deterioration. This synchronization keeps the tactical tools of control charts working as a team with the strategic tools of capability studies.

If the change is not permanent, adjustments are made to bring the process back into a state of statistical control. Once again, this keeps both the control charts and capability studies working together as a team.

RECALCULATING CAPABILITY AND CONTROL LIMITS

The control limits and capability studies should only use the data that is reflective of the current status. This can be seen in the area highlighted as "Cause Noted" below:

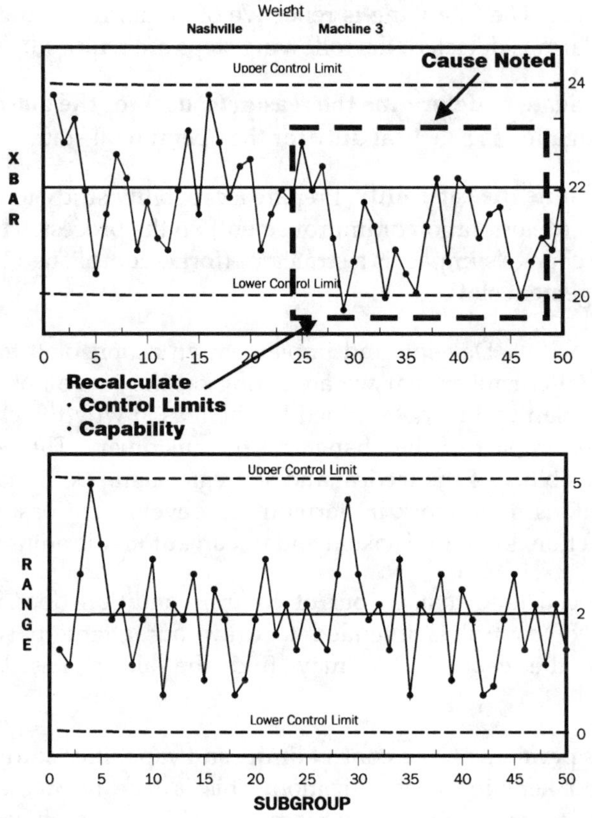

If this current status is based on a relatively small number of data points, the control limits and capability may be made temporary. When more data is gathered, recalibration of the limits can be calculated and then locked into place.

We have discussed at length the monitoring, control, and capability of the product, but this same methodology applies to all product and process characteristics. The timeliness of the data, the analysis of the data, and sound, logical decisions are crucial to the product.

Once the process has been determined to be in control, the control limits should be locked. When a process change has been determined and is desired or permanent, recalculation of the control limits is required. The control chart, control limits, and capability study must all be based on the same time frame. This is required to allow the control chart methodology to function as an alarm system. This alarm system will tell us when the process is either improving or deteriorating.

Note how our control limits have been recalculated to reflect our permanent change.

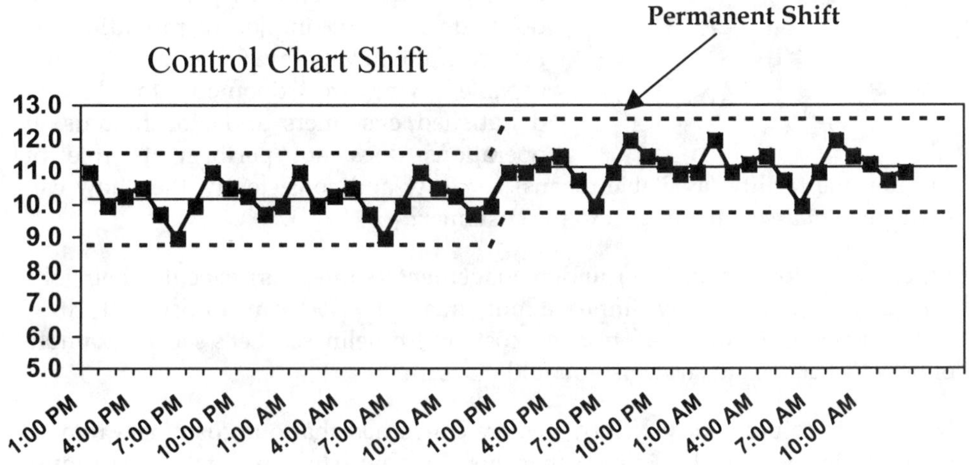

THE DECISION-MAKING TEAM

Tactical execution is required for strategic decisions to be effective. We have already discussed the consequences of incorrectly running the facility. In such cases, no strategy will work. Our strategic decision-makers must count on our tactical decision-makers to do their jobs, for only then can the strategic decisions be effective. Many strategic options are available, but they will work only if the operation can run smoothly, or in a state of control.

To repeat, management can make decisions only when operations is correctly and consistently running the facility. When this is the case, many options are available to management. When the plant is run incorrectly, we have no way of making a strategic decision that is based on sound logic.

When strategic and tactical personnel both do their job, they form a team. Operations is in deep trouble when management does not do its decision-making job of providing the facility. If the facility (available means) is not capable, we are doomed to having dissatisfied customers and stockholders. If operations does not perform its role of running the facility (available means) correctly and consistently, then how can management assess the impact to the customer?

When operations (tacticians) and management (strategists) execute their jobs brilliantly, we can truly improve our quality. We can impact all three components of quality: performance, cost, and timeliness. Let's see an example of how tacticians and strategists should perform.

Let's return to our candy facility. We are concerned that our customers remain satisfied, but we must take care that our company stays profitable. We must investigate a machine for determining our optimum running criteria that will please both our customers and our stockholders.

Let's do a problem to assess several situations for our candy machines. For our examples, we have done complete control charts that show that all products and processes are running in a state of statistical control. Now our strategic decision-maker can begin with the concrete knowledge that the facility is being run consistently.

The clusters' components cost \$.005 per gram. With this information, we can begin to do analysis of our strategic options. In our original proposal, the cost is based on a cluster that weighs 45 grams. By multiplying the weight of 45 grams times a component cost of \$.005/gram, the anticipated cost of a cluster is \$.225. For an hour's run, the cost of 3000 candies would be 3000 multiplied by \$.225/candy equaling \$675. This cost does not take into account the variability of the plant and assumes that all clusters can be made exactly the same. Let's look at the realities of our candy plant.

First, the candy facility is being run correctly and consistently as demonstrated by a control chart on all product and process metrics.

Now let's look at our first strategic option.

Strategic Option 1

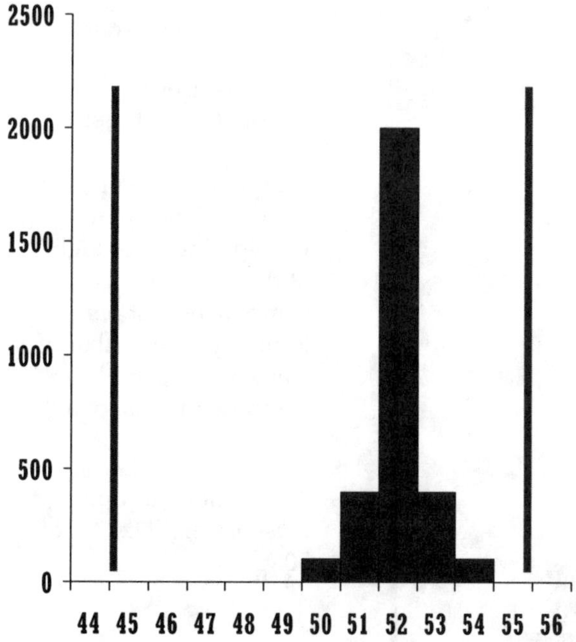

Buying a Delighted Customer

A decision can be made to always give the customer heavy candies. This choice guarantees happy customers but our costs are high. Our package states that no cluster shall weigh less than 45 grams. Since we are selling, advertising, and promoting 45 gram clusters, our customers will give us no additional credit for the additional candy weight. In this option we strategically decide to run our product heavy with a center of 52 grams.

In this option, we will use the same cost base for the component cost of $.005 per candy gram. By multiplying the weight of the clusters, by a component cost per gram, by the number of clusters, we can compute the cost of an hour.

Weight in grams	Cost per Gram	Quantity Produced	Total Cost
50	.005	100	$ 25
51	.005	400	$102
52	.005	2000	$520
53	.005	400	$106
54	.005	100	$ 27
		Total Cost	**$780**

Comparing the original estimate of $675 to our current cost of $780, we are spending an additional $105 per 3000 clusters or 3.5 cents per candy to keep our customers happy.

Concluding Thoughts

In our second option, the candy facility is still being run correctly and consistently as demonstrated by a control chart.

Strategic Option 2

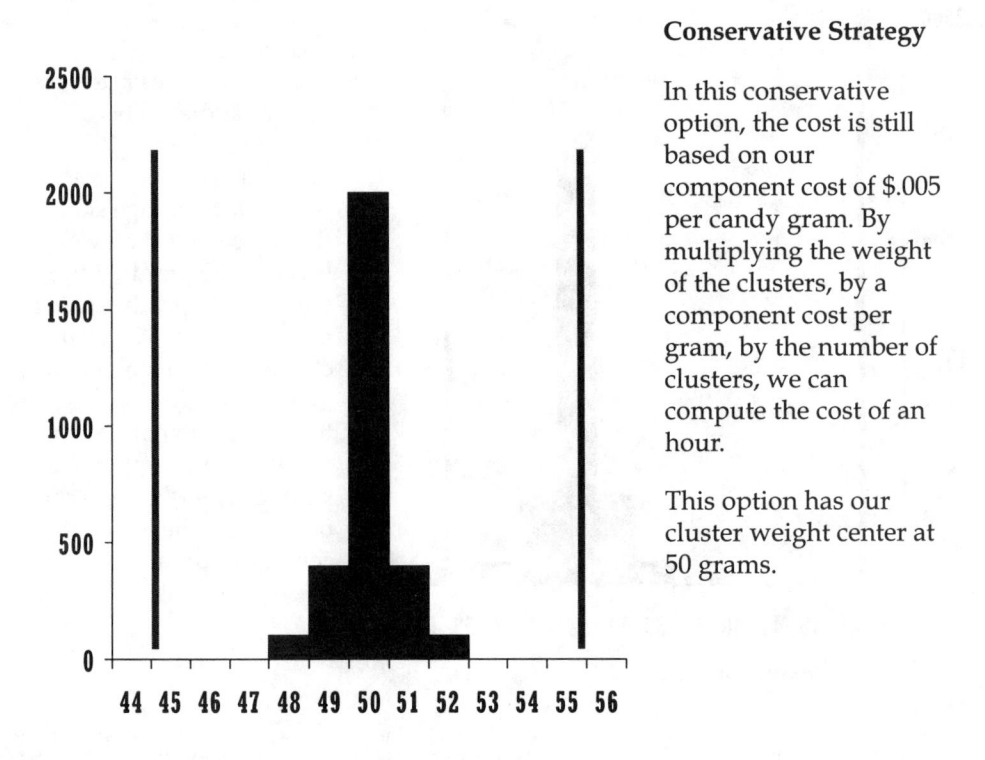

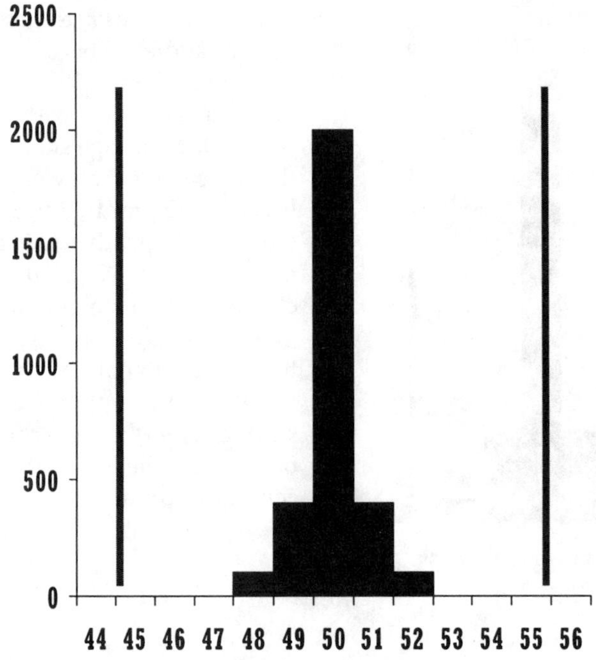

Conservative Strategy

In this conservative option, the cost is still based on our component cost of $.005 per candy gram. By multiplying the weight of the clusters, by a component cost per gram, by the number of clusters, we can compute the cost of an hour.

This option has our cluster weight center at 50 grams.

Weight Cost in grams	Quantity per Gram	Total Produced	Cost
48	.005	100	$ 24
49	.005	400	$ 98
50	.005	2000	$500
51	.005	400	$102
52	.005	100	$ 26
		Total Cost	$750

Comparing the original estimate of $675 to our current cost of $750, we are spending an additional $75 per 3000 clusters or 2.5 cents per candy to keep our customers happy. Again, the candy facility is being run correctly and consistently as demonstrated by a control chart.

Now for strategic option three and here too our tactical workforce is doing their job.

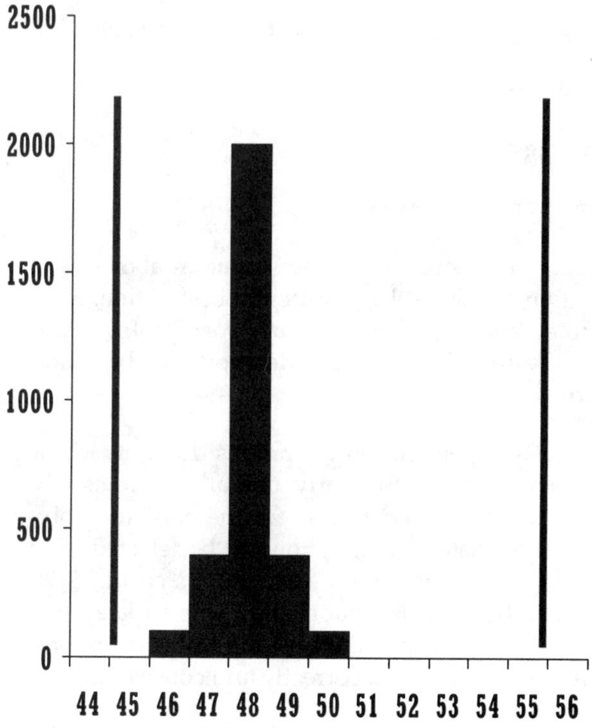

Satisfied Customer and Lower Cost

In the final option of satisfied customer and low cost, the cost is still based on our same component cost of $.005 per cluster gram. By multiplying the weight of the clusters, by a component cost per gram, by the number of candies, we can compute the cost of an hour.

The average cluster weight of strategic option three is 48 grams.

Weight in grams	Cost Quantity per Gram	Total Produced	Cost
46	.005	100	$ 23
47	.005	400	$ 94
48	.005	2000	$480
49	.005	400	$ 98
50	.005	100	$ 25
		Total Cost	$720

Comparing the original estimate of $675 to our current cost of $720, we are spending an additional $45 per 3000 clusters or 1.5 cents per candy to keep our customers happy.

SUMMARY OF THE STRATEGIC OPTIONS

Let's compare our three strategic options.

Strategic Option		Total Cost of Each
1	**Buying Delighted Customers**	$780
2	**Conservative Strategy**	$750
3	**Satisfied Customer and Lower Cost**	$720

No one strategy is correct for every situation. All of the strategies above have merit, and for each different situation, we will select a different best option. Each strategy must be viewed in the total relationship of customer, cost, profit, future potential market, product, and liability. No strategic decision can be made unless operations has done its job.

As can easily be seen, management is dependent on operations doing its job of running the facility correctly and consistently. Similarly, operations are clearly dependent on management to provide the correct facility for the particular job. When the facility runs correctly and consistently, an option can be selected. For our candy company, having satisfied customers and lower cost at a cost of $720 per 3000 clusters would be our selection. This option allows us to keep our customers happy and save $.02 per candy compared to our highest cost option. These savings are only possible if the process is run correctly and consistently.

Never, never, never make the mistake of allowing the tactician to set the target for our product. In many situations our selected strategic option could have been the least attractive option. Only when customer requirements, cost, profit, future market, product, liability, etc. are included can a correct option be selected. The strategic decision-makers must never abdicate their role to tacticians.

SPC TEAMWORK

The SPC team of control charts and capability studies, when functioning together, will allow us to hit the bull's-eye of improvement, customer satisfaction, reduced cost, and timely deliveries.

Remember that the control chart limits are an extension of the capability study. As long as no alarms are detected on the control limits, no change (neither improving nor deterioration) has been detected. Thus, when a change is detected that leads to a long term, permanent, deterioration, then the control limits must be recalibrated to reflect this change to keep the tactical and the strategic efforts in synchronicity. When a change is an improvement that is permanent, then the control limits must be recalculated. When a change is temporary, we fix the problem and no control limit calculations are made.

OBSTACLES TO QUALITY

The statistical process control effort to support our quality is critical. As a final set of thoughts, the following are obstacles that will impede your efforts at improvement if they are not addressed directly.

1. Use of averages as a stand-alone indicator of production, cost, quality, etc.
2. Lack of a clear understanding of consistency and the term "in control."
3. Machines, departments, etc. lumped together for analysis because it is expedient. Using this information to develop production, cost, or quality values without regard to mixing of unlike products or processes.
4. Loss of the traceability of our product. Failure to know when the goods were processed makes any time analysis impossible.
5. Focus on product characteristics only. Failure to monitor and control process characteristics. Failure to understand what is a process and how it works.
6. Unidentified and undocumented assumptions and speculation.
7. Use of opinions as opposed to the correct use of facts.

8. Failure to move SPC to the shop floor, because we assume the operators cannot or will not understand SPC.
9. Failure to understand Division of Labor. Who should be accountable for what is essential to producing a quality product.
10. Customer specification limits appearing on a control chart. This is the most common mistake made in the use of SPC. We must never try to infer whether our product is good or bad from a control chart.
11. Failure to have a metric blueprint.
12. No willingness to make changes.
13. No plan for implementing SPC and the improvement effort.
14. The strategic decision-maker fails to provide adequate and proper resources to assure the successful implementation of the plan.
15. We fail to execute the plan.
16. The plan does not use a focused approach to measure improvements.

Inadequate attention to these obstacles will doom you to remain in that dismal, fiery, awful place called Quality Hell.

BASE-CAMP

Our SPC team of control charts and capability studies form our information team for climbing Improvement Mountain. The tactical tool, control charts, gives us a clear picture that a machine is running consistently. Then the capability study provides the strategic decision-makers with the assessment that the machine can make what the customer wants.

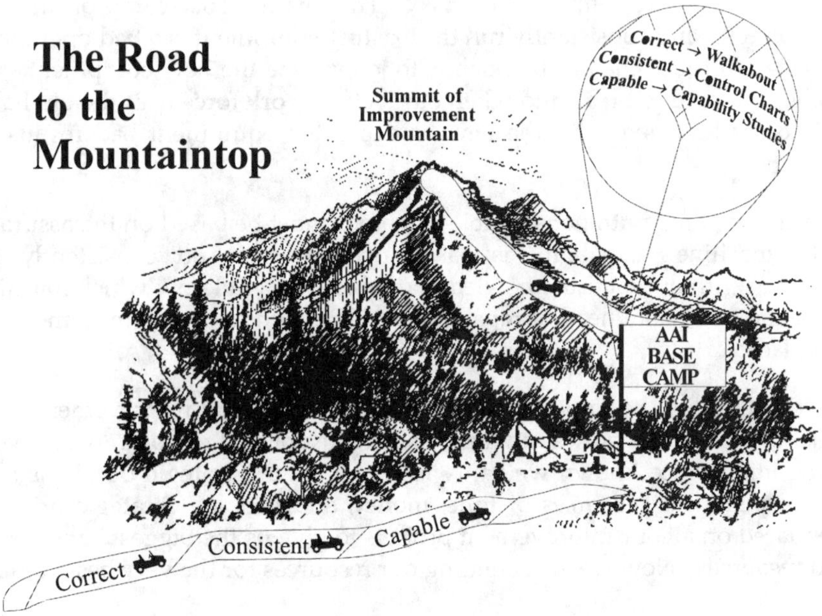

The climbing of a mountain requires a sturdy and strong foundation. This mountain climbing foundation is the base-camp where all ascensions are launched. Our base-camp is the product and process knowledge that Statistical Process Control (SPC) provides.

With this information in hand, our decision-makers are ready to make improvements. This base-camp of our product and process knowledge contains the correct and consistent running of each machine and the capability of each machine to make our product.

Our information is our machine's process and our product knowledge base. This knowledge base is the tactical knowledge that the machine is running correctly and consistently. Supplementing the tactical knowledge is the strategic

knowledge of the capability of this machine. We must use the capability of each machine to then develop a plan for dealing with the results.

First we can use our base-camp of knowledge to launch all our ascensions to the Improvement Mountain summit. With clear knowledge in hand we can make our improvement plans. Each improvement plan is like a mountain-climbing ascension to the summit of a mountain. The improvement project plans must be based on clear facts. Each ascent is a project plan for improvement.

One ascent is a plan for improvement by making informed future expansions and the purchase of new equipment. Any new equipment or expansion that is built without the base-camp will be risky. The missing base-camp of knowing how to correctly and consistently run the existing equipment is a bad operational habit. This can cause the old bad habits to jeopardize the new equipment. The bad habits are hard to break and when our tactical work force uses the old habits of no process knowledge on the new or expanded equipment bad results are sure.

An ascent of dealing with non-capable machines must be based on the assurance that the machine's capability is based on correctly and consistently run equipment. With our tactical knowledge in place we will know which machines to retool and what is in need of repair. We will also know which machines need to be replaced.

Now we will know the importance and magnitude of each improvement. This information will tell us how and where to make major and minor improvements. With the importance known we can wisely make our strategic decisions as to where to spend our resources of time, money, and people. Strategic priorities can be placed on all our improvement projects to give us the biggest bang for our limited resources. Now we are spending our resources for the very best value.

Finally we can use our strategic and tactical information to achieve the original objective of quality. This objective will be achievable since we are sound in the knowledge that each machine is run as correctly and consistently as possible. With our tactical issues clear and validated then the machine's capability is known and accurate. Now our original objective of quality is in sight -- it is the summit of Improvement Mountain.

Quality is comprised of the three components: performance, cost, and time. These can now be achieved. Our research, analysis, and decisions will support our goal of delighting our customer (performance), while reducing our cost (cost), and providing our product to our customers the moment they want it (time). We must view this goal as a never-ending journey that continues to improve all three components because no one component is more important than the others. All three must be viewed with equal importance and balance.

SPC will provide the balance of knowledge that will allow us to achieve this quality objective. Now our quality goal has been reached and we are making regular, frequent ascensions to the summit of Improvement Mountain.

Appendix

Appendix A: Glossary of Terms

Alarm	A signal that warns or alerts.
Analysis of Variance	The comparative study of discrete group data.
ANOVA	See ***Analysis of Variance***
Assignable causes	Those causes which definitely result in a particular effect.
Attribute control chart	A control chart that detects a change in discrete data.
Attribute data	Data that is characterized as counts or percentages.
Average (X_{Ave} or $\overline{X}$)	A point estimate of the measurement of the central tendency of a set of data. The balance point of all data points giving equal weight to each value.
Base-camp	The correct, consistent, and capable running of a facility, along with the information that allows us to achieve these goals.
Benchmark	A standard to compare a value against.
Bimodal distribution	A distribution that is really composed of two centers or distributions.
Binomial	Having two modes or centers.
Binomial distribution	Two or more distributions with different centers lumped together to form another distribution.
C chart	A control chart designed to detect change in counts.
Capability indices	Strategic tools for monitoring capability.
Capability study	The strategic assessment of the facility's ability to make the product the customer wants.
Capable/capability	The strategic ability of a machine , process, or product to meet the customer's expectations.
Categorical data	See ***Attribute Data***
Causes	Why something happened or changed.

Central Limit Theorem	Theorem stating that for any distribution, when samples of values are averaged together, resultant distribution of averages is approximately normal. When normalizing an already normal distribution, subgroup band will be tighter around the center.
Central tendency	The center point around which metric measurements fall.
Common causes	Causes outside one's control.
Confidence limits	The tactical tool used to detect changes in average. This tool is the spot where the average will fall based on the risk that we have selected for our study. These limits are used to define the interval where an average reading will fall.
Confidence interval	The range of the confidence limits. This is a tactical tool for detecting change in averages.
Consistent	A uniform and stable running of our operation.
Continuous data	See ***Variable Data***
Control	A mechanism to guide an operation through the detection of change. Consistency is a synonym for control.
Control chart	The tactical graphing tool used to detect changes in a product or process.
Control limits	A special type of confidence limit designed as an alarm that the product or process has changed from what have been the normal running parameters. Control limits are a special confidence limit that used a Z equal to three.
Correct	The proper running of an operation.
Cost	The amount of time, material, and resources required to make the product.
CPK Index	The strategic performance indicator of the worst case specification. The bigger the CPK, the better the process is functioning.
Confidence interval	The range of the confidence limits. This is a tactical tool for detecting change.
Confidence limits	The tactical tool used to detect changes in average. This tool is the spot where the average will fall based on the risk that we have selected for our study.
Control limits	A tactical tool for an operator to detect change in the usual running of a machine. Control limits are a special confidence limit that uses a Z equal to three.
Degrees of Freedom	The small sample correction formula for standard deviation (N-1).

Discrete data	See *Attribute Data*
Distribution	The shape of the spread of a set of data points.
Effects	The result or consequences of a cause.
Execution/execute	The carrying out of a task.
frequency table	A set of numbers describing the distribution of a metric.
Gaussian Distribution	A synonym for the normal distribution. See also ***Normal distribution.***
Good Intentions	Flawed logic, activities, or instructions that are executed because the user does not grasp the flaw.
Grouping / groups	**Physical:** composed of items that are materially the same. Members of physical groups share characteristics such as type, size, color, same machine or operator. **Associational:** made up of things that are similar but not necessarily exactly the same. Members of associational groups are also of like kind. **Time-series:** composed of material that is similar over time. Members of time-series groups are manufactured at a time when consistency is demonstrated.
Histogram	A bar chart that displays the shape of the data's distribution.
Homogeneous	Things of one, or like, kind.
In control	The condition when a process is consistent and stable in its natural state.
Individual chart	A control chart for detecting change of a single reading.
Interval	The distance between measurements.
Kaizen	The Japanese term for "continuous improvement."
Knowledge base	The product and process information gathered to run an operation.
LCL	The designation for the Lower Control Limits.
LCL_{Ave}	The Lower Control Limit that is three (3) standard errors below the $\overline{X}$ value.
LCL_R	The Lower Control Limit that is three (3) standard errors below the $\overline{R}$ value.
Life cycle	The length of time an entity (i.e. a person, a product, a process, etc.) will live and the phase that it will go through.

Lower Control Limits	The lower control limit is three standard errors below the mean value.
Lower Specification Limits	The low limits where product is deemed defective.
LSL	The designation for the Lower Specification Limits.
Management	The strategic decision-makers for an organization.
Mean	Mean is the monitor of central tendency where the total of all data points is divided by the number of data points. This is also referred to as arithmetic mean, average, $\overline{X}$, or $\overline{\overline{X}}$.
Median	The center value of a set of numbers in ascending sequence. Half the values of the set will be above, the remaining half below. The median is a monitor of central tendency that is not influenced by outliers.
Metric	A study area
Moving Range chart	A control chart that detects a change in variability of an individual set of values.
N	Represents the subgroup size.
Nominal value	The target value for a metric.
Normal distribution	The symmetrical, bell shaped curve.
NP chart	A control chart that detects a change in the attribute data of a nonconforming set of values.
Operations	The tactical decision-makers for an organization.
Out of control	The situation when a change has been detected.
Outliers	Extremes or anomalies in the data. Outliers can be broken into two groups: observable errors and numeric extremes.
P chart	A control chart designed to detect change in percents and proportions.
Pareto	A technique for providing focus to problem areas.
Performance	The product's ability to meet the customer expectations.

Point estimates	The statistical elements of central tendency and variability, as monitored with a value. For example: arithmetic mean is the point estimate of central tendency, and range (or standard deviation) is the point estimate of variability.
Poisson distribution	A special case of the binomial (which is a special case of the normal.) This distribution is used for the basis of assumptions about the C and U charts.
Population (statistics)	Calculations based on measurement of every possible member in a group.
Predictability	The ability to forecast the future. An example is predicting the percent defective from past historical performance of a product, prior to making the product.
Prediction interval	The strategic tool for showing the range of the prediction limits. This tactical tool shows the range where an individual value will fall.
Prediction limits	A strategic tool to assess the impact to the customer of the product that our machine is making. This tool is based on the use of individual readings. These limits are used to define the interval where an individual reading will fall.
Principles of Process Management	The basic truths required to run an operation.
Process	Activities that build the product.
Product	The result that we are trying to manufacture.
Production	Product that has been shipped and paid for.
Quality	Meeting or exceeding the customer's perceived expectations and requirements while reducing cost and providing the product to the customer when he wants it.
Quality Hell	The Good Intentions but flawed efforts at making a quality product.
R	See ***Range***
$\bar{R}$	The central tendency of the variability of a metric.
R chart	The control chart designed to detect movement or changes in the variability of the process.
R value	See ***Range***

Random samples	Method for avoiding bias when attempting to estimate population statistics.
Range	Measure of the variability of a set of number. The smaller the range, the lower the variability and amount of spread.
Repeatability	The variation that one operator has when measuring one metric using one gauge. A measure of the variation in measurement when an operator *repeatedly* measures with the same gauge.
Reproducibility	The measure of the variation when multiple operators measure the same metric all using the same gauge. A measure of the variation in measurement when one operator tries to *reproduce* an operator's measurement results.
Sample (statistics)	Calculations based on selected measurements in a subset of a group.
SOP	See ***Standard Operating Procedure(s)***
Special causes	Causes within one's control.
Specification limits	Points at which customers will consider the product unusable.
Spread	The amount of distance between data points.
Stability	A consistent or steady state, process, or operation.
Standard deviation of the average (Std_{Ave})	Used in monitoring patterns and trends, it is also referred to as standard error. This value is the amount of spread between averages.
Standard deviation of the individuals (Std_{Ind})	The magnitude of the amount of spread between each individual value (variability).
Standard error	See ***Standard deviation of the average***
Standard Operating Procedure(s)	A prescribed method for operating a machine.
Statistical Process Control (SPC)	A Statistical Quality Control tool to monitor a continuous operation. Statistical Process Control is comprised of control charts and capability studies.
Statistical Quality Control (SQC)	The set of numeric tools to monitor and maintain a characteristic of a process or product.

Statistics	Facts or data of a numerical kind, assembled, classified, and tabulated so as to present significant information about a given subject.
Strategy/Strategic	The art of achieving a goal. This term is used in both decision-making and goal setting. For more information on this term, additional reading can be found in *Optimize Your Operation*, by James C. Abbott.
Subgroup	Sample results for a particular timeframe.
Subgroup frequency	The time interval between the sample group readings.
Sum of Squares technique	A statistical method commonly used to analyze data. The basic method compares a data set to a benchmark, squares the distance, and then totals the squares.
Tactics/Tactical	The art of achieving a goal utilizing the *available means.* This term is used in both decision-making and goal setting. For more information on this term, additional reading can be found in *Optimize Your Operation* by James C. Abbott.
Tampering causes	Changes that are caused by too much control. Tampering occurs when we are trying to take action on something that should not be changed.
Target	The amount or point at which the customer considers the product to be perfect. The target should be explicitly defined by the strategic decision-makers.
Time	Making sure the product is delivered to the customer when he wants it.
Tolerances	The amount of incompetence that will be accepted by the customer. The acceptable amount of leeway from the target. The tolerances are used to compute the specification limits.
Total Quality Management	A method for continuous improvement.
TQM	See ***Total Quality Management***

U chart	A C control chart that is offset to take care of varying units of measure.
UCL	The designation for the Upper Control Limit.
UCL_{Ave}	The Upper Control Limit that is three (3) standard errors above the mean value.
UCL_R	The Upper Control Limit that is three (3) standard errors above the $\overline{R}$ value.
Upper Control Limit	Three (3) standard errors above the mean value.
Upper Specification Limit	The upper limits where the product is deemed defective.
USL	The designation for the Upper Specification Limit.
Value	A measurement for a metric.
Variability	The amount of spread in a set of measurements.
Variable data	Data that is characterized by dimensional readings like length, weight, diameter, etc.
Variance (S^2)	The range average.
***Walkabout*™ Dependency Diagram**	A metric blueprint for studying, analyzing, and sharing product and process knowledge between all associates.
***Walkabout*™ Method**	A plan complete with clear roles, tools, techniques, and methods designed to correctly, consistently, and capably run an operation.
X	The measurement of the metric.
$\overline{X}$	The monitor of central tendency of a metric.
$\overline{\overline{X}}$	Designed to detect movement or change in the central tendency of the process.
X axis	The horizontal scale of a graph.
X chart	A control chart that detects a change in central tendency of an individual set of values.

$\overline{X}$ chart	Designed to detect the movement or change in the central tendency of the process.
$\overline{\overline{X}}$ chart	Designed to detect the movement or change in the central tendency of the process.
$\overline{X}$ and R	Two control charts designed to work together to monitor variable data.
$\overline{X}$ and S	Two control charts designed to work together to monitor variable data.
Y axis	The vertical scale of a graph.
Z	The ratio of the distance from the average divided by the standard deviation. The higher the Z value, the better a machine is performing.

Appendix B: Glossary of Constants

A_2 is the conversion factor to arrive at three standard errors for use in determining UCL and LCL of $\overline{X}$ chart for $\overline{X}$ and R and Individual charts.

A_3 is the conversion factor to arrive at three standard errors for use in determining UCL and LSL of $\overline{X}$ and S charts.

B_3 is the conversion factor to arrive at three standard errors for use in determining LCL of S chart.

B_4 is the conversion factor to arrive at three standard errors for use in determining UCL of S chart.

C_4 is the conversion factor for determining standard deviation of the individuals for $\overline{X}$ and S charts.

d_2 is the conversion factor for determining standard deviation of the individuals for the $\overline{X}$ and R charts.

D_3 is the conversion factor to arrive at three standard errors for use in determining LCL of R chart for $\overline{X}$ and R and Individual charts.

D_4 is the conversion factor to arrive at three standard errors for use in determining UCL of R chart for $\overline{X}$ and R and Individual charts.

E_2 is the conversion factor to arrive at three standard errors for use in determining UCL and LSL of Individual charts.

$\overline{R}$ is the benchmark of the central tendency of the process.

R is the range of each subgroup and becomes the statistic of interest for the R chart.

S is the standard deviation of each subgroup and becomes the statistic of interest for the S chart.

X is the individual data point.

$\overline{X}$ is the average of each subgroup and becomes the statistic of interest for the $\overline{X}$ chart.

$\overline{\overline{X}}$ is the benchmark of the central tendency of the process.

Z is the ratio of the distance of a value away from the average as it relates to the monitor of variability standard deviation.

APPENDIX C: GLOSSARY OF FORMULAS

$\overline{X}$ AND R CONTROL CHARTS:

X_N is the data reading for the particular sample where N equals the sample.

$$\overline{X} = \frac{X_1 + X_2 + X_3 + \ldots + X_N}{N}$$

where N equals the number of samples in the subgroup.

$$R = \left| X_{Highest} - X_{Lowest} \right|$$

$$\overline{\overline{X}} = \frac{\overline{X}_1 + \overline{X}_2 + \overline{X}_3 + \ldots + \overline{X}_K}{K}$$

where K equals the number of subgroups.

$$\overline{R} = \frac{R_1 + R_2 + R_3 + \ldots + R_K}{K}$$

$$UCL_{Ave} = \overline{\overline{X}} + A_2 * \overline{R} \qquad LCL_{Ave} = \overline{\overline{X}} - A_2 * \overline{R}$$

$$UCL_R = D_4 * \overline{R} \qquad LCL_R = D_3 * \overline{R}$$

CAPABILITY STUDIES:

$$Std_{Ind} = \sqrt{\frac{\sum_{i=1}^{N} (\overline{\overline{X}} - X_i)^2}{N - 1}} \quad \text{or} \quad Std_{Ind} = \frac{\overline{R}}{d_2}$$

$$\frac{Std_{Ind}}{\sqrt{N}} = Std_{Ave}$$

where N is the number of samples.

$$Z(USL) = \left| \frac{\text{Upper Spec Limit - } X_{Ave}}{Std_{Ind}} \right| \qquad Z(LSL) = \left| \frac{\text{Lower Spec Limit - } X_{Ave}}{Std_{Ind}} \right|$$

$$CPK = \frac{\text{Minimum}\,(Z_{USL}, Z_{LSL})}{3}$$

$\overline{X}$ AND S CONTROL CHARTS:

$$\overline{X} = \frac{X_1 + X_2 + X_3 + \ldots + X_N}{N}$$

where N equals the number of samples in the subgroup.

$$S = \sqrt{\frac{\sum_{i=1}^{N} *(\overline{X} - X_i)^2}{N-1}} \qquad \overline{S} = \frac{S_1 + S_2 + S_3 + \ldots + S_K}{K}$$

where K equals the number of subgroups.

$\overline{X}$ control chart limits:

$$UCL_{Ave} = \overline{\overline{X}} + A_3 * \overline{S} \qquad LCL_{Ave} = \overline{\overline{X}} - A_3 * \overline{S}$$

S control chart limits:

$$UCL_S = B_4 * \overline{S} \qquad LCL_S = B_3 * \overline{S}$$

INDIVIDUAL CONTROL CHARTS:

$$R = \left| X_i - X_j \right| \qquad \overline{R} = \frac{R_1 + R_2 + R_3 + \ldots + R_K}{K}$$

$\overline{X}$ control chart limits:

$$UCL_{Ave} = \overline{X} + E_2 * \overline{R} \qquad LCL_{Ave} = \overline{X} - E_2 * \overline{R}$$

Moving Range control chart limits:

$$UCL_R = D_4 * \overline{R} \qquad LCL_R = D_3 * \overline{R}$$

Appendix D: Control Chart Tables

$\overline{X}$ & R Chart Tables

Subgroup Size	A_2	d_2	D_3	D_4
2	1.880	1.128		3.267
3	1.023	1.693		2.574
4	0.729	2.059		2.282
5	0.577	2.326		2.114
6	0.483	2.534		2.004
7	0.419	2.704	0.076	1.924
8	0.373	2.847	0.136	1.864
9	0.337	2.970	0.184	1.816
10	0.308	3.078	0.223	1.777
11	0.285	3.173	0.256	1.744
12	0.266	3.258	0.283	1.717
13	0.249	3.336	0.307	1.693
14	0.235	3.407	0.328	1.672
15	0.223	3.472	0.347	1.653

Individual Chart Tables

Subgroup Freq	E_2	d_2	D_3	D_4
2	2.660	1.128	-	3.267
3	1.772	1.693	-	2.574
4	1.457	2.059	-	2.282
5	1.290	2.326	-	2.114
6	1.184	2.534	-	2.004
7	1.109	2.704	0.076	1.924
8	1.054	2.847	0.136	1.864
9	1.010	2.970	0.184	1.816
10	0.975	3.078	0.223	1.777

$\overline{X}$ & S Chart Tables

Subgroup Size	A_3	C_4	B_3	B_4
10	0.975	0.9727	0.284	1.716
11	0.927	0.9754	0.321	1.679
12	0.886	0.9776	0.354	1.646
13	0.850	0.9794	0.382	1.618
14	0.817	0.9810	0.406	1.594
15	0.789	0.9823	0.428	1.572
16	.763	.9835	.448	1.552
17	.739	.9845	.466	1.534
18	.718	.9854	.482	1.518
19	.698	.9862	.497	1.503
20	.680	.9869	.510	1.490
21	.663	.9876	.523	1.477
22	.647	.9882	.534	1.466
23	.633	.9887	.545	1.455
24	.619	.9892	.555	1.445
25	.606	.9896	.565	1.435

APPENDIX E: NORMAL DISTRIBUTION TABLE

The table below allows you to look up the area (percent) of the normal distribution based on the ratio of the Z value. This table is a tail oriented probability table.

Known point or X_i

$$Z = \left| \frac{X_{Ave} - X_i}{Std} \right|$$

Known probability or percentage

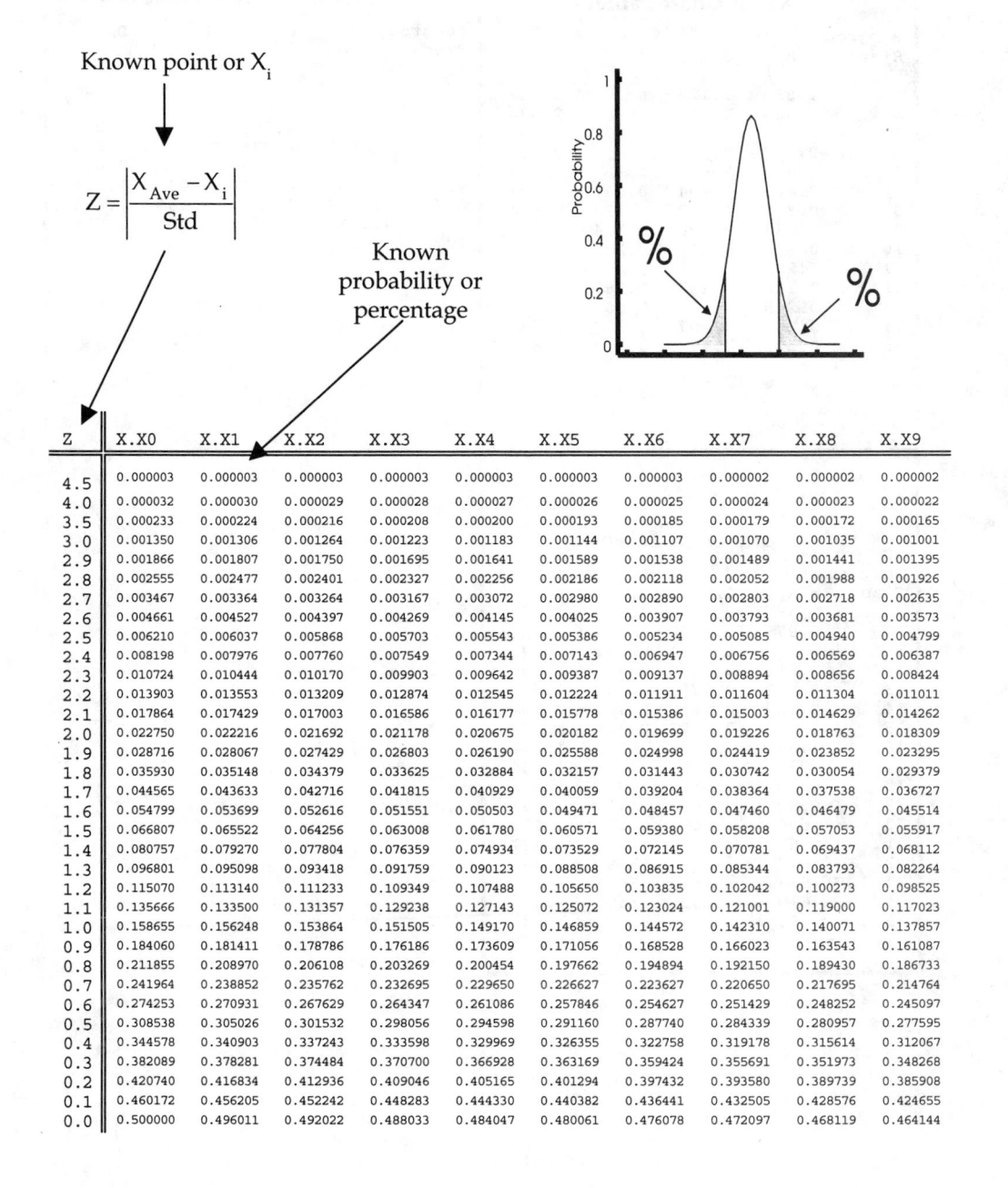

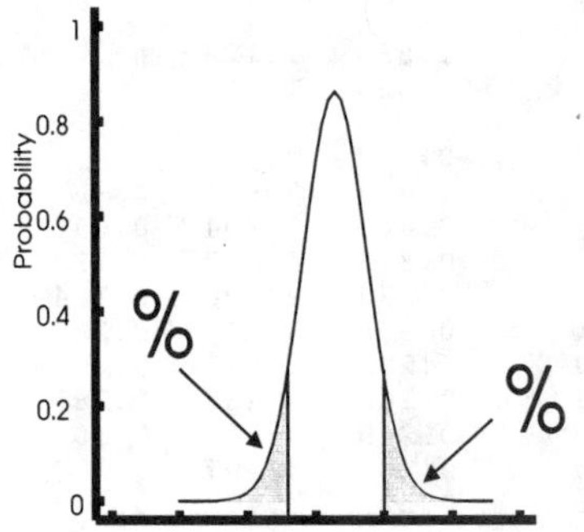

Z	X.X0	X.X1	X.X2	X.X3	X.X4	X.X5	X.X6	X.X7	X.X8	X.X9
4.5	0.000003	0.000003	0.000003	0.000003	0.000003	0.000003	0.000003	0.000002	0.000002	0.000002
4.0	0.000032	0.000030	0.000029	0.000028	0.000027	0.000026	0.000025	0.000024	0.000023	0.000022
3.5	0.000233	0.000224	0.000216	0.000208	0.000200	0.000193	0.000185	0.000179	0.000172	0.000165
3.0	0.001350	0.001306	0.001264	0.001223	0.001183	0.001144	0.001107	0.001070	0.001035	0.001001
2.9	0.001866	0.001807	0.001750	0.001695	0.001641	0.001589	0.001538	0.001489	0.001441	0.001395
2.8	0.002555	0.002477	0.002401	0.002327	0.002256	0.002186	0.002118	0.002052	0.001988	0.001926
2.7	0.003467	0.003364	0.003264	0.003167	0.003072	0.002980	0.002890	0.002803	0.002718	0.002635
2.6	0.004661	0.004527	0.004397	0.004269	0.004145	0.004025	0.003907	0.003793	0.003681	0.003573
2.5	0.006210	0.006037	0.005868	0.005703	0.005543	0.005386	0.005234	0.005085	0.004940	0.004799
2.4	0.008198	0.007976	0.007760	0.007549	0.007344	0.007143	0.006947	0.006756	0.006569	0.006387
2.3	0.010724	0.010444	0.010170	0.009903	0.009642	0.009387	0.009137	0.008894	0.008656	0.008424
2.2	0.013903	0.013553	0.013209	0.012874	0.012545	0.012224	0.011911	0.011604	0.011304	0.011011
2.1	0.017864	0.017429	0.017003	0.016586	0.016177	0.015778	0.015386	0.015003	0.014629	0.014262
2.0	0.022750	0.022216	0.021692	0.021178	0.020675	0.020182	0.019699	0.019226	0.018763	0.018309
1.9	0.028716	0.028067	0.027429	0.026803	0.026190	0.025588	0.024998	0.024419	0.023852	0.023295
1.8	0.035930	0.035148	0.034379	0.033625	0.032884	0.032157	0.031443	0.030742	0.030054	0.029379
1.7	0.044565	0.043633	0.042716	0.041815	0.040929	0.040059	0.039204	0.038364	0.037538	0.036727
1.6	0.054799	0.053699	0.052616	0.051551	0.050503	0.049471	0.048457	0.047460	0.046479	0.045514
1.5	0.066807	0.065522	0.064256	0.063008	0.061780	0.060571	0.059380	0.058208	0.057053	0.055917
1.4	0.080757	0.079270	0.077804	0.076359	0.074934	0.073529	0.072145	0.070781	0.069437	0.068112
1.3	0.096801	0.095098	0.093418	0.091759	0.090123	0.088508	0.086915	0.085344	0.083793	0.082264
1.2	0.115070	0.113140	0.111233	0.109349	0.107488	0.105650	0.103835	0.102042	0.100273	0.098525
1.1	0.135666	0.133500	0.131357	0.129238	0.127143	0.125072	0.123024	0.121001	0.119000	0.117023
1.0	0.158655	0.156248	0.153864	0.151505	0.149170	0.146859	0.144572	0.142310	0.140071	0.137857
0.9	0.184060	0.181411	0.178786	0.176186	0.173609	0.171056	0.168528	0.166023	0.163543	0.161087
0.8	0.211855	0.208970	0.206108	0.203269	0.200454	0.197662	0.194894	0.192150	0.189430	0.186733
0.7	0.241964	0.238852	0.235762	0.232695	0.229650	0.226627	0.223627	0.220650	0.217695	0.214764
0.6	0.274253	0.270931	0.267629	0.264347	0.261086	0.257846	0.254627	0.251429	0.248252	0.245097
0.5	0.308538	0.305026	0.301532	0.298056	0.294598	0.291160	0.287740	0.284339	0.280957	0.277595
0.4	0.344578	0.340903	0.337243	0.333598	0.329969	0.326355	0.322758	0.319178	0.315614	0.312067
0.3	0.382089	0.378281	0.374484	0.370700	0.366928	0.363169	0.359424	0.355691	0.351973	0.348268
0.2	0.420740	0.416834	0.412936	0.409046	0.405165	0.401294	0.397432	0.393580	0.389739	0.385908
0.1	0.460172	0.456205	0.452242	0.448283	0.444330	0.440382	0.436441	0.432505	0.428576	0.424655
0.0	0.500000	0.496011	0.492022	0.488033	0.484047	0.480061	0.476078	0.472097	0.468119	0.464144

Appendix F: PROBLEM SOLUTIONS

CHAPTER ONE, PAGE 30

To compute the average kilowatt consumption for the year 1980, individual consumption for each of the twelve months is added and then divided by the total number of months (twelve). The equation would read:

$$\text{Total KWH consumption} = X_{Jan} + X_{Feb} + X_{Mar} + \ldots + X_{Dec}$$

$$= 2{,}749 + 5{,}405 + 3{,}936 + \ldots + 3{,}439$$

$$= 31{,}387$$

The 1980 total KWH consumed is 31,387 which is then divided by twelve to arrive at the average which is 2,616 KWH.

ELECTRICITY USAGE

	1980	1981	1982	1983
JANUARY	2749	4081	4982	3936
FEBRUARY	5405	5004	4299	5024
MARCH	3936	2708	3793	3239
APRIL	2232	2423	1870	
MAY	1079	1493	1514	
JUNE	1330	2197	1713	
JULY	2616	2918	1890	
AUGUST	2820	2041	1897	
SEPTEMBER	2321	2041	1923	
OCTOBER	1583	1494	1316	
NOVEMBER	1877	1859	1843	
DECEMBER	3439	3936	2919	
Average	**2616**	**2683**	**2497**	**4066**

The average for 1980, 1981, 1982, and 1983 is 2,616; 2,683; 2,497; and 4,066 respectively.

CHAPTER ONE, PAGE 65

From our analysis of the electricity usage, compute the amount of funds that must be on reserve to pay the maximum kilowatt usage for any one month. This study will assume that the distribution of the kilowatts is normal, the cost of a kilowatt is $.10, and that we are prepared to take a five percent risk of not having enough funds available to cover the usage.

From our analysis of the electricity usage, I have computed the maximum kilowatt usage for any one month based on only 1980, 1981, and 1982. My reasoning for not including 1983 is that 1983 included only three months of the highest usage. Using 1983 data will distort the reserve amount for higher than normal usage.

ELECTRICITY USAGE

	1980	1981	1982	1983
JANUARY	2749	4081	4982	3936
FEBRUARY	5405	5004	4299	5024
MARCH	3936	2708	3793	3239
APRIL	2232	2423	1870	
MAY	1079	1493	1514	
JUNE	1330	2197	1713	
JULY	2616	2918	1890	
AUGUST	2820	2041	1897	
SEPTEMBER	2321	2041	1923	
OCTOBER	1583	1494	1316	
NOVEMBER	1877	1859	1843	
DECEMBER	3439	3936	2919	
Average	2616	2683	2497	4066
Range	4326	3511	3666	1785
Std	1211	1112	1211	900

Average of 1980, 1981, 1982: 2598
Standard Deviation: 1147

We are prepared to take a five percent risk of not having enough funds to cover the usage. A five percent risk equates to a Z value of 1.645.

$$X_i = X_{Ave} \pm Z * Std$$

Now we can compute the equation to arrive at the maximum planned budget KWH consumption.

$$X_i = X_{Ave} \pm Z * Std$$

$$= 2,598 + 1.645 * 1,147$$

$$= 2,598 + 1,887$$

$$= 4,485$$

This study will assume that the distribution of the kilowatts is normal, the cost of a kilowatt is $.10. Now the 4,485 KWH is multiplied times $.10 per KWH. This gives us an estimate of $448.50 that must be in reserve to cover our monthly electricity usage.

CHAPTER SIX, PAGE 178

The table below shows the original 1:00 to 10:00 readings for our problem, as well as the calculated average ($\overline{X}$) and range (R) for each subgroup.

	1:00	2:00	3:00	4:00	5:00	6:00	7:00	8:00	9:00	10:00
	50	55	60	45	40	50	55	60	45	40
	51	56	61	46	41	51	56	61	46	41
	52	57	62	47	42	52	57	62	47	42
	49	54	59	44	39	49	54	59	44	39
	48	53	58	43	38	48	53	58	43	38
$\overline{X}$	50	55	60	45	40	50	55	60	45	40
R	4	4	4	4	4	4	4	4	4	4

$$\overline{\overline{X}} = 50.0 \quad \overline{R} = 4$$

The $\overline{X}$ control limits are 52.3 grams and 47.7 grams. The usual mistake in these calculations is the selection of the A_2 constant. The A_2, in this case, is .577 because there are five samples in each subgroup. The total number of subgroups has nothing to do with the selection of the A_2 value. (See the **Chapter Six** summary for a discussion of the constants used in determining UCL and LCL of R and $\overline{X}$ charts.)

$$UCL = \overline{\overline{X}} + A_2 * \overline{R}$$

$$UCL = 50.0 + (.577) * (4) = 52.3$$

$$LCL = \overline{\overline{X}} - A_2 * \overline{R}$$

$$LCL = 50.0 - (.577) * (4) = 47.7$$

The next chart is the graph for the $\overline{X}$ upper and lower control limits.

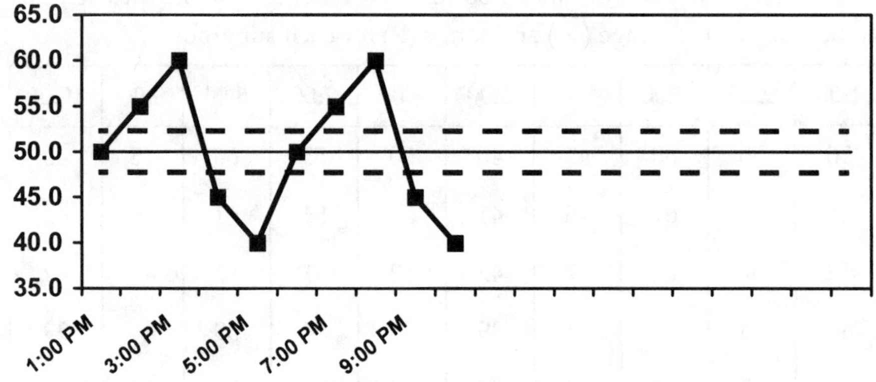

As with the $\overline{X}$, the typical mistake comes in the selection of the constants. We must remember that all constants are based on the number of samples in the subgroup, which allows us to approximate three standard errors. The D_4 value is 2.114 because the subgroup size is five.

The actual individual readings are not used for drawing the chart. They are used in intermediate steps to calculate the data points and compute the control limits.

$$UCL = D_4 * \overline{R}$$

$$UCL = (2.114) * (4) = 8.5$$

The R control limit is 8.5 grams for the upper and zero for the lower because the variability cannot be negative.

The chart below is the graph for the R upper and lower control limits.

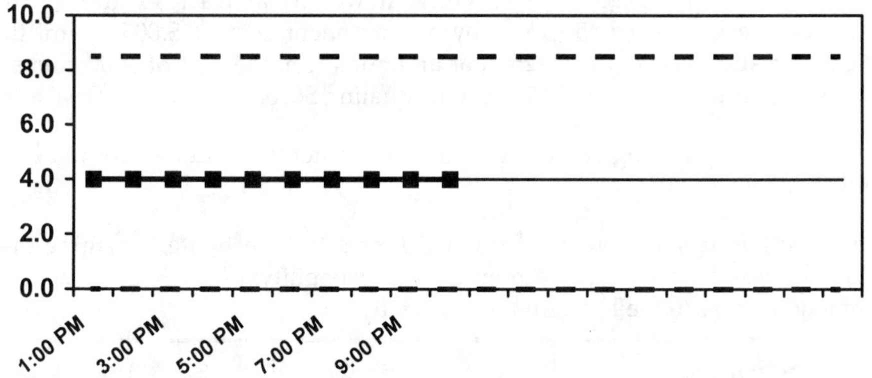

Note the R chart is flat because the control limits are based on part to part variation in the subgroup. Since the values are selected consecutively, it is no surprise that the limits are tight. The tight limits apply for both the $\overline{X}$ & R control charts since both sets are derived from the R values of maximum and minimum for the five consecutive samples.

CHAPTER TEN, PAGE 356

The chocolate-peanut cluster components' cost per gram is $.005. With this information, we can begin to analyze our strategic options. In our original proposal, the cost is based on a cluster that weighs at least 45 grams. By multiplying the weight of 45 grams by a component cost of $.005/gram, the anticipated cost of a cluster is $.225. For an hour's run, the cost of 3000 clusters would be 3000 multiplied by $.225/cluster, equaling $675.

The candy facility is being run correctly and consistently as demonstrated by a control chart.

The following four situations are provided for us to investigate. Imagine that this is your candy company. Compute the capability of each and make a recommendation as to the best situation and why.

Situations	**1**	**2**	**3**	**4**
Is the Process In Control?	Yes	Yes	Yes	Yes
Average Weight	50gm	52gm	47gm	50gm
Standard Deviation of Weight	1.0gm	1.0gm	1.0gm	2.0gm
Distribution of Weight?	Normal	Normal	Normal	Normal
Z	5	7	2	2.5
% defects	.0	.0	2.23	.62
CPK	1.67	2.33	.67	.833

Our strategic recommendation as to the best situation is dependent on our situation, based on the three components of quality. Remember, quality is comprised of performance, cost, and time.

For this situation, balancing performance and cost, I would select option one with an average of 50 grams. This average would become the target for the tactical workforce.

Index

A

B

C

S

W

Z